Directory of UK ELT Research
2005–08

Compiled by Shelagh Rixon
and Richard Smith

TABLE OF CONTENTS

CONSTRUCTION OF
THE DIRECTORY

Rationale

The *British Council Directory of UK ELT Research* was conceived in pursuit of three main aims:

1. *To disseminate and share information generally in the area of UK-based ELT research.* It had become apparent that there was no current, conveniently available source of information about research in the UK relevant to the field of English Language Teaching.

2. *To promote interchange amongst researchers in the UK and other countries.* The directory of research exists both as an online database and in a PDF/paper form. In its online version it will be particularly useful for individuals and institutions in countries outside the UK to use its 'search' facility in order to find institutions or individuals in the UK with research interests close to their own. Typical users envisaged in this category are scholars seeking academic attachments or exchanges, and prospective PhD students looking for academic supervisors in their areas of interest. The PDF/paper version provides a useful annotated bibliography of current research, which also gives information on institutional affiliations of authors.

3. *To publicise and make research available to the broader constituency of ELT professionals worldwide.* An important aim of the directory is to help publicise UK ELT research and thus enable it to have a greater potential impact on practice. An important connected principle underlying construction of the directory is that the research recorded in it should be publicly accessible. This informed a number of decisions with regard to the information that needed to be provided, as outlined under 'Types of entry, and details requested' below.

Background

The idea for a directory of UK ELT research was conceived within the British Council during 2008 as part of an overall strategy to enhance links with research-active UK institutions. An open invitation to tender for the project was sent out in December 2008 and a proposal from the Centre for Applied Linguistics at the University of Warwick was selected from a competitive field. The project team consisted of Dr Richard Smith (co-ordinator) and Shelagh Rixon, assisted by Dr Seongsook Choi and Duncan Hunter. Sian Alsop, Sheila Verrier and Qingqing Xue also assisted in the final editing process. John Knagg of the British Council was also fully involved at all stages. The clarification of parameters, design of research tools, data collection and editing were completed by the end of July 2009. Plans for a second edition were announced to the UK ELT research community at the end of January 2010, and this enabled a number of institutions which had not previously been represented to submit 2005–08 entries, and others to enhance their overall return. Data collection and editing for this phase were carried out by Richard Smith, with the assistance of Seongsook Choi, Niluki Arsacularatne and David Avery, and completed by the end of March 2010.

Methodology

The method for collecting the information for the research directory was to identify key contacts within relevant institutions in the UK and ask them to provide information on their research and that of their colleagues. This made collection of a large body of data feasible within the short time span allotted to the project and meant that institutions were responsible for the selection of entries and the accuracy of returns. To facilitate the collection of data, online database input forms were devised and administered by Seongsook Choi, to which participating institutions had access via a password. Richard Smith and Shelagh Rixon acted as interlocutors with inputting institutions and as editors.

Selection of institutions

A systematic attempt was made to identify and contact all institutions in the UK which had relevant departments or centres or were otherwise likely to have research-active staff members working in the area of ELT. These institutions included accredited language schools and organisations such as CfBT and Cambridge ESOL as well as universities and colleges. Heads of faculty, school, department or centre, as appropriate, were asked to nominate a key contact person, who was then given the necessary log-in details that would provide access to the web-based data collection forms. A total of 57 institutions participated in this initial phase of the project (five of these subsequently submitted a 'zero return'). For the second edition institutions which had not previously replied were again contacted, and invitations to contribute were sent out via various mailing lists, including that of BAAL, the British Association for Applied Linguistics.

Definition of 'UK ELT Research, 2005–2008'

The following definitions of terms were developed by the project team and shared with participating institutions:

Research

For the purposes of this exercise, we adopted a modified version of the 2008 HEFCE RAE (Research Assessment Exercise) definition of 'research'. Thus, we took the primary meaning of 'research' to be *original investigation undertaken in order to gain knowledge and understanding*. However, as for the RAE, the term also includes 'scholarship' – the creation, development and maintenance of the intellectual infrastructure of an activity or area of study, in this case ELT, for example in forms such as dictionaries, research databases and reviews of the 'state of the art' in areas relevant to ELT.

ELT research

'ELT research' was defined as 'any research whose data and/or findings relate directly to the teaching, learning or assessment of English as a Foreign, Second or Additional Language in the UK or any other context'.

UK research

'UK research' refers to research undertaken by a current member of staff or associate of a bona fide educational institution with a base in the UK. The actual research may have taken place anywhere in the world, not necessarily in the UK. 'Current', for the purposes of the 2005–08 directory refers to the census point of 1 May 2009. An exception to the 'current association' rule was made for completed doctoral theses and for externally funded projects: in both these cases, even though the researchers involved may have left the submitting institution (indeed, were likely to have done so in the case of authors of doctoral theses), submission of the theses or projects in question was encouraged, since they were considered to have been 'hosted' by the submitting institution.

The 2005–2008 date range
This refers to date of publication. The earliest publication date for work to be included was 1 January 2005 and the latest was 31 December 2008. In the case of funded projects, the project must have either begun or ended within the date range.

Types of entry, and details requested
Details of the following types of research output were requested:

- journal articles
- chapters in edited books
- papers in conference proceedings
- authored books
- 'unpublished' but electronically accessible items
- doctoral theses supervised within the institution in question
- externally funded research projects.

There was no particular requirement for journal articles to be peer-reviewed – any assessment of their quality was left, as in the case of other types of entry, to the discretion of the submitting institution. With regard to edited books, whereas *editing* – as opposed to *authoring* – a book was not considered to be a research output in its own right, the introduction to such a book could be included in the book chapter category, thus ensuring that editing of the book would be acknowledged in some form. We also wished to give publicity to authored items which had not been 'published' in a formal sense, and thus offered an 'unpublished' category for such items. Doctoral theses and research projects were the only categories where the researchers involved did not need to be *currently* affiliated with the contributing institution: in both cases, it was felt that the institution could legitimately submit details due to their support for the research in question. In the case of doctoral theses, the names of supervisors were requested as a means of acknowledging the important role they have in helping bring theses to completion.

In all cases, we required sufficient bibliographical detail for users to be able to access a particular item for themselves (journal name, volume number and page numbers for journal articles; names of editors, title of book, place of publication, publisher and ISBN number for chapters in edited collections, and so on). For any 'unpublished' items a URL was required, in order to ensure accessibility. The same important principle of accessibility (see 'Rationale' above) was applied to externally funded research projects – for each of these we requested a project website URL, or details of a publicly available project report or associated publication. Some projects originally submitted for consideration had to be excluded when a way could not be found to guide the directory user to further information in the manner just described.

Some optional fields were also provided for each type of item. Most importantly, there was space to enter a summary of up to 60 words. This invitation was taken up in some but by no means in all cases. Selection from the following list of twenty possible descriptors was also encouraged though not required; as many or as few of these descriptors as necessary could be chosen for each item entered:

- Assessment
- Classroom interaction
- Curriculum/syllabus
- English language
- ESP
- ESOL/EAL
- Learner autonomy/strategies
- Learner cognition
- Learning technologies
- Listening
- Management/Innovation
- Materials
- Methodology
- Pronunciation
- Reading

- Cultural issues
- Speaking
- Teacher cognition
- Teacher education
- Writing

This list was derived from a synthesis of different kinds of overview of ELT professional concerns, including names of IATEFL special interest groups, IATEFL annual conference themes, handbooks of ELT methodology, and so on. The list was not intended to be exhaustive or definitive, but it did represent one way to ensure that the online database would be searchable for content, especially in cases where the inputter did not provide a fuller summary.

Inputting of the following details for each item was also encouraged though not required: country of research (selection from a drop-down menu of countries, including 'various'); learners' background (same menu of choices as for 'country of research'); institutional level (selection from pre-primary, primary, secondary, tertiary, adult); and associated funded project (where this had been entered as part of the same institution's submission).

Selection, editing and presentation of entries

Those contributing entries were asked to operate within the parameters described previously in selecting work from their overall research output for inputting into the directory. Responsibility for this selection and for interpretation of the definitions we had provided was therefore placed with the inputting institutions themselves – it was felt that self-monitoring would be effective since it would clearly not be in the best interests of researchers and institutions to enter references to work that was outside the remit or of substandard quality; also, we would be playing a collegial role rather than setting ourselves up as judges of other institutions' input.

We did in fact suggest reconsideration of some entries which seemed to us not to meet the criteria set up and publicised, but did not enforce this except in cases where 'objective criteria' were not met (entries outside the date range, edited collections entered mistakenly under 'authored book', information entered for a researcher not currently affiliated with the institution in question, and so on). The editorial team also undertook small proof-reading changes such as putting in missing commas or changing the case of initial letters, but for larger issues, ranging from the issue of inclusion or exclusion of items to requests for missing or inadequate information, direct contact was made with the institutions to request revisions. All information confirmed by the inputting institution was included, for each item. This meant that in cases of co-authorship or collaboration (in the case of projects) between researchers at different UK institutions the same item sometimes appears twice in the directory with different summaries or other details attached – in these relatively rare cases, respecting the integrity of institutions' own entries meant that duplication resulted, but it meant also that different kinds of useful details were provided.

The contents of the research directory

This second edition of the research directory contains a total of over 1,000 entries from 59 contributing institutions. The distribution of different types of entry is as follows:

- 421 journal articles
- 285 chapters in edited books or papers in conference proceedings
- 65 authored books and project reports
- 18 'unpublished' but electronically accessible items
- 189 supervised doctoral theses
- 61 externally funded projects

The online version
Access to the online version can be gained by following this link:

www.teachingenglish.org.uk/elt-research

The online version is a searchable database with instructions for use incorporated.

The PDF/paper version
This PDF/paper version of the directory contains the same information as the electronic database although it is here expressed in a linear and static form.

The main body of the PDF/paper version consists of an annotated bibliography of research ordered alphabetically by name of first author, which also gives information on the institutional affiliation of the researcher who submitted the entry, or on whose behalf the entry was submitted. The names, URLs and contact e-mail addresses of all contributing institutions can be found at the end of the directory.

For convenience, the list of doctoral theses is presented separately, and is organised according to the institution awarding the degree. In addition, there is a final annotated list of externally funded research projects which are often related to research outputs that are found in the main list.

Future directions

Now that this very substantial body of information on UK-based ELT research has been established, and now that workable procedures have been established for gathering, collating and presenting information, it is hoped that the directory will be supplemented periodically, starting with data for 2009 or 2009–10.

Acknowledgements

The editors would like to thank the many individuals who cheerfully, or less so, spent several hours of their time entering details of their research. We hope that they found this way of proceeding acceptable, both in terms of equity – they themselves and not editors from another institution chose what should be put forward for inclusion – and of feasibility. Without their help we could not have gathered so many items in so short a time (special thanks go to Graham Hall, Huw Jarvis and Pauline Foster for piloting the draft input forms). We hope that all concerned will soon reap benefits in terms of contacts with other scholars and ELT professionals, as well as with prospective students, and that new avenues of co-operation will be the result. We hope that the directory will be found to be a useful and user-friendly way of making links and finding matches – one that will enable researchers, prospective students and other ELT professionals to make contact with the 'right' people in the 'right' places for their own needs and interests.

PERSPECTIVES ON UK ELT RESEARCH

Below are some personal reflections by the directory compilers, Shelagh Rixon and Richard Smith, on some of the issues raised by its creation. Our reflections are intended to initiate debate, and both responses and further comments will be welcomed, within the discussion area associated with the online version of the directory (www.teachingenglish.org.uk/elt-research).

Historical background

In many ways the directory represents a 21st century revival of some of the services that used to be provided in the 1970s and early 1980s by the British Council's ETIC (English Teaching Information Centre), for example the production and distribution of specialised bibliographies on English Language Teaching and the support for international networking within the profession provided by ETIC officers. One of the editors (Shelagh) started her ELT career in ETIC and so found it intriguing to see how these two functions could be mirrored via the present directory, both in its searchable database form and in its PDF/paper form, which has more of the appearance of a conventional annotated bibliography.

In retrospect, the 1970s and early 1980s can be seen to have represented a kind of 'golden age' for links between university-based applied linguists, the British Council and ELT, with the development and worldwide diffusion of communicative language teaching being the most obvious manifestation of this. Although the contributions to the 'communicative movement' of those working within non-university organisations such as International House and the British Council itself should not be underestimated, it is also true that academic applied linguists including Henry Widdowson, David Wilkins, Chris Candlin, Mike Breen, Keith Johnson, Dick Allwright and Chris Brumfit played a particularly influential role.

From a critical perspective, of course, this previous symbiosis between university applied linguists, the British Council and the ELT profession can be viewed as a kind of 'unholy alliance' supporting the spread of inappropriate syllabi, materials and methods and thus maintaining so-called 'recipient' or 'periphery' countries in an unhealthy state of dependence on 'donor' or 'centre' expertise. Indeed, a critical turn in ELT research since the 1990s seems to be reflected in at least some of the work contained in this directory of 2005–2008 research. However, the background phenomenon we would most like to highlight here is the relative lack of interchange between applied linguistics and ELT professional concerns since the 1980s, which, it seems to us, has probably been compounded by the relative absence since the late 1980s of British Council engagement with ELT research in UK universities. From this perspective, the weakening of links between university-based research and initiatives supported by the British Council in the area of ELT can be seen to have been an unfortunate development, since even critical research may have failed to have the impact it might otherwise have had (for example, in relation to the British Council's current 'global products' initiatives).

It is perhaps worth going back to the roots of applied linguistics in British universities to see how far the situation has changed. The term 'applied linguistics' started to be widely used in the UK in the 1960s, largely through the activity of the British Council itself in setting up and supporting specialist courses in this new discipline for its own ELT officers and for sponsored students from overseas in institutions such as the University of Edinburgh. Applied linguistics itself, however, has grown away from this original focus. Whereas in the past many individuals occupying applied linguistics posts in British universities were themselves former ELT practitioners, often with a background in work with the British Council either as career officers or as consultants or contracted specialists to the many ELT-based projects administered by the British Council in other countries, this is not nowadays so commonly the case. Indeed, despite being founded originally (in the UK at least) from a desire to place ELT on a stronger academic and research footing, applied linguistics today has concerns which spread far wider than this original remit (as a glance at the pages of the leading journal in the field, *Applied Linguistics*, or newsletters of the British Association for Applied Linguistics (BAAL) will attest). Even in the 1970s, questions were asked about the relevance of applied linguistics to practical concerns, but the relationship of applied linguistic research with ELT and the degree of interpenetration between them seems to us to have weakened further since then. For this reason, and in the absence of strong links between the British Council and university applied linguistics and ELT departments, there may, understandably, be some scepticism among ELT professionals these days about the relevance of applied linguistic research to their concerns.

As we became aware over the last two to three years that the British Council was beginning to re-engage with universities in order to seek out 'cutting-edge' research with relevance to ELT, we wondered what they would find and whether, given the direction away from ELT that applied linguistics seems to have taken during the last two to three decades, the quest for such research would be fruitful. We were in favour of the idea that the British Council should reassume a mediating role, and that the value specifically of '*ELT* research' should be highlighted in counterbalance to any automatic assumption that applied linguistics is necessarily of value to language teachers. This serves to explain our interest in working to compile this directory of UK ELT research and, we hope, makes sufficiently transparent some assumptions which may have influenced the approach we adopted. Below, we offer further reflections relating to the parameters of the investigation, its methodology and the entries that ended up being included.

The scope of ELT research

As we have indicated, one concern we had before embarking on this venture was whether present-day university-based research would turn out to have relevance to ELT at all. There also seemed to be some scepticism amongst British Council ELT specialists about the value to ELT of much academic research, reflecting concerns within the profession more generally. This pointed to a need, expressed by the British Council to us, specifically to seek out 'ELT research', not simply 'applied linguistic research'.

As compilers of the directory, we therefore found it necessary to come up with our own definition of 'ELT research', because no ready-made definition was at hand. Users of the directory will have their own views, both on the narrowness or otherwise of the definition we adopted, and on what has been included by individual institutions and what excluded on its basis. From our perspective, and going by titles alone, it seems clear that not all entries meet the relatively narrow requirement we set up that they should 'relate directly' to the teaching, learning or assessment of English as a Foreign, Second or Additional Language. However, this does not particularly surprise us, as we felt in advance that the issue of 'direct relationship' to ELT practice would be one of the most problematic and possibly controversial issues we would face.

While we believe that it has proved to be possible to identify a good quantity of what could be termed 'core ELT research' (i.e. research which fully meets the definition we set up), some entries may appear to have only a relatively weak relationship with ELT. This includes, for example, some work carried out primarily in relation to the teaching and learning of languages other than English, and, perhaps, some of the work included from fields including sociolinguistics, intercultural communication, second language acquisition and language description. Thus, while the directory – especially in this, its second edition – has probably captured a very large proportion of the 'core ELT research' carried out in UK institutions between 2005 and 2008, some of the research included could be viewed as having a more indirect or even tangential relationship to ELT. More of this kind of relatively 'non-core' ELT research was doubtless carried out during the period but for various possible reasons was not entered here, for example due to the location of such research in departments not identified with ELT or applied linguistics, or the greater willingness shown by some departments as opposed to others to accept our 'narrow' definition and thereby exclude research of relatively indirect relevance.

We are conscious that our definition of ELT research may seem too narrow, also, for the purposes of some users who might simply wish to find out about interesting recent ELT-related work or ideas in the UK, rather than wanting to know only about research outputs in the way a prospective student seeking an academic supervisor or a scholar seeking partners for a joint research project would want. Thus, although in our invitation to potential contributors we included reference to work such as the creation of databases, corpora and dictionaries – that is, 'scholarship' in the definition we adopted – we requested exclusion both of 'how to' articles and books, and of learning materials that were based on the writer's existing professional experience rather than representing 'original investigation' undertaken in pursuit of new knowledge. This may be an area that needs to be revisited for future editions of the directory, especially given the high output by freelance authors and UK publishers of learning materials. In a similar connection, it should also be noted that much of the ELT research which goes on in the UK is probably 'in-house' and therefore not recordable in the directory in its current form, since accessibility of research outputs was an overriding factor. Such work might include, for example, market research or piloting reports submitted to publishers; consultancy reports for the British Council or other agencies relating to development projects; or much of the research which is undertaken to validate and improve on large-scale language tests. We were very much open, it should be added, to the submission of reports of practitioner research (action research, exploratory practice, etc.), whether published or formally 'unpublished' but nevertheless electronically accessible. However, very few such reports were submitted.

As mentioned above, we initially canvassed a very broad constituency of UK institutions, by no means all of them universities or colleges, but the entries that we actually received are dominated by the higher education sector. One thing that has become clear, then, is that non-university institutions (with the exception, in this directory, of Cambridge ESOL Examinations) do not generally consider themselves to be engaged in research, or at least not research which is publicly accessible. This seems to be a regrettable situation and one which we hope can be improved upon in the future, perhaps with specific British Council encouragement of practitioner research. We welcome views from those outside the university sector who decided not to contribute as to whether the criteria we set up were too restrictive or whether other factors lay behind their current non-representation.

Is UK ELT research distinctive?

Whereas in the past it may have been possible to identify a distinctively 'British' approach or approaches, both to ELT and to related applied linguistic research, we question, on the basis of entries for 2005–2008, whether it makes sense any longer to think in these terms. Although the directory's focus on 'UK' ELT research is valuable as a means for identifying, taking stock of and showcasing the work being carried out within British institutions, it is clear also that many of the individual research outputs in the directory have arisen within international specialist networks (as evidenced, for example, by the publication details for many of the papers in edited collections and conference proceedings). In this connection, another relatively recent phenomenon evidenced in the directory is the internationalisation of British higher education in terms of personnel – a significant number of entries are authored by researchers originally from overseas who have found employment within UK universities. Taken together, these phenomena highlight again the way times have changed since the 'heyday' of the communicative language teaching movement (the 1970s and 1980s) when the last concerted attempts were made by the British Council to 'tap into', showcase and nurture UK academic expertise in the field of ELT. The situation now seems much more complex and more diffuse. One question which arises in our minds, then, is 'To what extent is the UK now a 'centre' for ELT research, as opposed to being one amongst an increased and ever-increasing number of interconnected places around the world where ELT research is based?' 'Decentring' seems to be in evidence, also, in the way a number of what we have termed 'core' ELT research entries explicitly address issues of 'centre–periphery' relations from a critical perspective. At the same time, of course, there is no doubt that the UK does remain an important centre of ELT industry, with UK products ranging from teaching and learning materials to large-scale language tests being marketed worldwide. While extensive links between research and development in the area of large-scale English language assessment are evidenced in the directory, there may appear to be much less engagement by researchers, in either a supportive or a critical role, with some of the other important areas of UK ELT industrial activity, including materials production.

The relevance and impact of ELT research

A peculiarly modern irony might be that of the potential for deskilling, in an ELT sense, of those who enter careers in UK universities and who therefore seem through 'affiliation' to have met the criterion for inclusion in this directory of ELT research. Many academics, even when they are former ELT practitioners, may find themselves increasingly cut off from ELT practice by the nature of the daily work they undertake. The modern twist in this tale is the current pressure put upon them by their institutions to carry out the sort of research that wins the greatest accolades in the periodic HEFCE Research Assessment Exercise (RAE, renamed for the next such exercise the Research Excellence Framework, or REF for short) and within the 'academy' more generally. This could lead to the possibility that they are deterred from work that would contribute more directly and usefully to the ELT field, and this, we feel, is an area where the British Council can help by finding further means to support such research. For our part, by deliberately casting the net wide in encouraging the submission of items which might not have been 'RAE-able', for example those not written for international journals or publishers but instead for local journals, publishers or conference proceedings around the world, or indeed those not published at all in a formal sense, we wished to acknowledge research work which might be relatively appropriate to particular contexts of practice. The directory provides access, then, to a number of lesser-known but thereby potentially more valuable and relevant documents than some of those submitted recently to the RAE. Another factor we would like to highlight in this connection is the way the directory includes a substantial body of research carried out into ESOL and EAL within the British adult education and school sectors, representing work which has perhaps not traditionally been associated with ELT but which does meet the quality criterion we have been arguing for, that is, of connecting well with issues in contexts of 'local' – in this case, UK – practice.

A recent trend that the editors have become aware of as doctoral supervisors in their own institution and as external examiners elsewhere is that higher degree students seem to be getting younger (and this is not just a matter of us getting older!), with a number aiming to start a PhD or even EdD directly after, or within one or two years of, completing an MA. This is likely to have an impact on the types of ELT-related research that are undertaken for such theses. There might have been a decrease in the proportion of research topics emerging directly from very substantial classroom or other career-based experience, although the overall number of doctoral theses submitted seem to have been on the increase. The separate list of PhD and EdD projects supervised in different institutions will allow readers to make up their own minds on this issue.

While both established academics and doctoral students may feel a pressure to work towards abstraction and generalisation rather than the particular and the contextually relevant in their work, research that is of most direct impact in the ELT field is often very particular – directed at local needs within a small geographical area, a particular school or other institution, or even the researcher's own practice. As suggested above, we were keen to include such work due to its relevance to practice, even though it might not currently enjoy high status in the academic world. In fact it appears to us that relatively little work of this nature seems to have been submitted to the directory, and this may reflect the danger within those sectors of tertiary education which at the same time claim a connection with the ELT profession, of according more esteem to work that aims at universality and abstraction than at practical applicability. However, a development that may suggest a reversal of such a trend in research assessment – and that may accordingly have some effect on research production – is the HEFCE announcement made in July 2009 that, in future, assessments of the worth of university departments' research output may include up to 25 per cent for 'impact'. This is, of course, a controversial area, and we invite comments from users of the directory on their own conceptions of relevance, quality and impact in *ELT research* and how the contents entered for 2005–2008 seem to measure up against them.

The limitations and importance of ELT research

Aside from issues of appropriateness or relevance of research to local contexts, there is the fundamental question of why ELT *research* should be particularly highlighted. The directory's focus on research-based contributions is a necessary one in that one of its major functions is to support networking between UK institutions or individual scholars and potential research students, research visitors and/or research collaborators from outside the UK. However, ELT practitioners – or would-be practitioners – seeking MA-level qualifications still form the majority of the student body in many departments where applied linguistic research is carried out. This brings in an important facet of ELT-related work – that of training teachers and its relationship with the development of ELT methodology. As we have already noted above, many of the most respected figures of the 1970s and 1980s followed the career route from ELT teacher to ELT teacher trainer to a university post in applied linguistics, but this may not be so much the case nowadays as it was in the past. At the same time, a significant number of the most influential people in ELT teacher training, materials creation or syllabus design have never occupied academic posts in the strict sense. It remains the case that many of the best-known UK-based ELT writers and teacher trainers are not 'in the academy'.

Research work by such figures was in fact eligible for inclusion in the directory but it was also necessary for them to be currently affiliated with an organisation such as a university, language school or testing agency. This has meant that any research by authors who work in an entirely freelance capacity and/or who have retired and no longer retain an institutional affiliation has not been included.

In this regard, we should not forget the important contribution to the ELT field of networks like the IATEFL Research Special Interest Group, which does not confine its membership to university staff or to UK-based professionals. It would be good to hear from users of the present directory whether the low number of entries from outside the higher education sector has resulted, from their point of view, in an excessively limited record of relevant ELT inquiry over the last few years.

Despite the possible limitations referred to in these reflections, we would like to end with a positive justification of the focus on ELT research which has been adopted in the present directory. In this connection, we find the following quotation from the recently developed (2005) TESOL 'Position statement on research and policy' particularly apposite:

> Research-based knowledge provides a principled basis for understanding language teaching and learning, and making decisions about policies, plans, and actions. Research has the potential to help English language teaching professionals improve the processes, outcomes and conditions for language teaching, learning and assessment. It also can help the profession address urgent social and political issues around the world, improve the materials used for second language teaching in schools, institutions and workplaces, as well as clarify debates and debunk myths regarding second language acquisition. A strong commitment to research as a means of improving professional knowledge is vital to the field of teaching of English to speakers of other languages (TESOL).

www.tesol.org/s_tesol/seccss.asp?CID=236&DID=1708
(accessed 1/10/09)

If this kind of argument is found to be plausible, then the increasing awareness within the British Council that links with and support for UK ELT research need to be re-established is a welcome development, and one which we hope this directory will help to carry forward.

Final note

Without wishing to claim too much for our work, we would like to think that in working on this new British Council initiative we have contributed to the consolidation, if not the establishment, of ELT research as a field in its own right. Once again, we encourage users of the directory to join in the debate which we hope will ensue, via the directory website (www.teachingenglish.org.uk/elt-research), about the nature of ELT research, its relevance to practitioners and policy-makers, and the emphasis and impact of work currently being carried out. We very much welcome such debate, both for its own sake – as a means to further consolidate the field of ELT research – and, more specifically, as a way to influence possible changes in the parameters and procedures for future versions of the directory.

ARTICLES, CHAPTERS, AUTHORED BOOKS AND UNPUBLISHED ITEMS

A

Aboshiha, P. 2007. 'Changing perceptions of reading' in A. Jendli, S. Troudi and C. Coombe (eds.) *The Power of Language*. Dubai: TESOL Arabia.

ISBN: 978-9948-03-366-0

Pages: 154–163

Descriptor(s): Reading

Entered by: Canterbury Christ Church University (Department of English and Language Studies)

Adolphs, S. 2005. "I don't think I should learn all this" – A longitudinal view of attitudes towards "native speaker" English' in C. Gnutzmann and F. Intemann (eds.) *The Globalisation of English and the English Language Classroom*. Tuebingen: Gunter Narr.

ISBN: 9783823361367

Pages: 115–127

Descriptor(s): Cultural issues, Learner cognition, Learner autonomy/strategies

Entered by: University of Nottingham (School of English Studies)

Adolphs, S. 2005. 'Multi-word units and second language speech fluency' in C. Cosme, C. Gouverneur and F. Meunier (eds.) *Phraseology 2005. The Many Faces of Phraseology. Louvain-la-Neuve*. Amsterdam: John Benjamins.

ISBN: 978-9027232441

Pages: 27–30

Principal format: Printed

Descriptor(s): Speaking, Learner cognition

Entered by: University of Nottingham (School of English Studies)

Alderson, J.C. 2005. *Diagnosing Foreign Language Proficiency: The Interface between Learning and Assessment*. London: Continuum.

ISBN: 0826485030

Descriptor(s): Assessment

Entered by: Lancaster University (Linguistics and English Language)

Alderson, J.C. 2007. 'The CEFR and the need for more research'. *Modern Language Journal* 91/ix: 658-662.

Descriptor(s): Assessment

Entered by: Lancaster University (Linguistics and English Language)

Alderson, J.C. 2007. 'The challenge of diagnostic testing: Do we know what we are measuring?' in J.M. Fox, M. Wesche, D. Bayliss, L. Cheng, C. Turner and C. Doe (eds.) *Language Testing Reconsidered*. Ottawa: University of Ottawa Press.

ISBN: 9780776606576

Pages: 21–39

Descriptor(s): Assessment

Entered by: Lancaster University (Linguistics and English Language)

Alderson, J.C. 2007. 'Judging the frequency of English words'. *Applied Linguistics* 28: 383-409.

Summary: The present paper reports on three investigations of word frequency judgements. Using different methodologies and with varying sizes of word samples, it is shown that judgements by professional linguists do not correlate highly with corpus-based frequency counts.

Descriptor(s): Assessment

Entered by: Lancaster University (Linguistics and English Language)

Alderson, J.C. and A. Huhta. 2005. 'The development of a suite of computer-based dianostic tests based on the Common European Framework'. *Language Testing* 22/3: 301–320.

Descriptor(s): Learning technologies, Assessment

A

Entered by: Lancaster University (Linguistics and English Language)

Alderson, J.C. and D. McIntyre. 2006. 'Implementing and evaluating a self-assessment mechanism for the web-based Language and Style course'. *Language and Literature* 15/3: 291-306.

Descriptor(s): Materials, Learning technologies, Curriculum/syllabus, Assessment

Entered by: Lancaster University (Linguistics and English Language)

Alderson, J.C., N. Figueras, H. Kuiper and G. Nold. 2006. 'Analysing tests of reading and listening in relation to the Common European Framework of Reference: The Experience of the Dutch CEFR Construct Project'. *Language Assessment Quarterly* 3: 3-30.

Summary: The project methodology involved gathering expert judgments on the usability of the CEFR for test construction, identifying what might be missing from the CEFR, developing a frame for analysis of tests and specifications, and examining a range of existing test specifications and guidelines to item writers and sample test tasks.

Descriptor(s): Assessment

Entered by: Lancaster University (Linguistics and English Language)

Alexander, O. 2007. 'Introduction' in O. Alexander (ed.) *New Approaches to Materials Development for Language Learning.* Oxford: Peter Lang.

ISBN: 978-3-03910-909-8

Principal format: Printed

Summary: Introduction to proceedings of the BALEAP/SATEFL conference in 2005 highlighting current issues in EAP. Key themes include the diversity of the student population, socialization within disciplines, research in genre analysis and corpus

linguistics to design targeted teaching materials, the importance of critical thinking and academic literacy for learner autonomy.

Descriptor(s): Writing, Cultural issues, Reading, Methodology, Materials, Learning technologies, Learner autonomy/strategies, ESP, Curriculum/syllabus, Assessment

Entered by: Heriot-Watt University (School of Management and Languages)

Al Kamil, I. and S. Troudi. 2008. 'Can theory help us understand the nature of writing challenges?' in C. Coombe, A. Jendli and P. Davidson (eds.) *Teaching Writing Skills in EFL: Theory, Research and Pedagogy.* Dubai: TESOL Arabia.

Pages: 3–15

Descriptor(s): Writing, ESOL/EAL

Entered by: University of Exeter (School of Education and Lifelong Learning)

Angouri, J. and N. Harwood. 2008. 'This is too formal for us... A case study of variation in the written products of a multinational consortium'. *Journal of Business and Technical Communication* 22/1: 38–64.

Descriptor(s): Writing, ESP, English language

Country of research: various

Entered by: University of Essex (Department of Language and Linguistics)

Arizpe, E. 2006. 'Young interpreters: Affective dimensions of bilingual children's response to pictures' in J. Enever and G. Schmid-Schönbein (eds.) *Picturebooks and Primary EFL Learners.* Munich: Langenscheidt.

ISBN: ISBN-13: 978-3-526-50836-6

Pages: 35–48

Summary: This article focuses on the responses of bilingual children, particularly on their affective, intellectual and aesthetic responses to picturebooks based on the 'Reading Pictures' project based at the Faculty of Education, University of Cambridge. It shows how visual art in picturebooks can encourage the use of language of EAL pupils in primary schools.

Descriptor(s): Reading, Materials, Learner cognition, English language, Classroom interaction

Country of research: United Kingdom

Learners' background: various

Institutional level: primary

Entered by: University of Glasgow (Language and Literature, Faculty of Education)

Arnold, W. and S. Rixon. 2008. 'Materials for teaching English to young learners' in B. Tomlinson (ed.) *English Language Learning Materials: A Critical Review.* London: Continuum.

ISBN: 978-0-8264-9350-7

Pages: 38–58

Summary: A review of the state of the art in Young Learners materials design worldwide, taking in nearly 100 different sets of course materials. Current trends such as the move towards cross-curricular content are highlighted, as is the continuing need for systematic development of literacy in English.

Descriptor(s): Writing, Speaking, Reading, Methodology, Materials, Listening, English language, Curriculum/syllabus

Learners' background: various

Institutional level: primary

Entered by: University of Warwick (Centre for Applied Linguistics)

Ashton, K. 2006. 'Can do self-assessment: Investigating cross-language comparability in reading'. *Cambridge ESOL: Research Notes* 24: 10–14.

Summary: Karen Ashton reports on the development of a Can Do self-assessment tool for learners of German, Japanese and Urdu which aims to ensure that the difficulty of tasks and ability of learners taking tests in different languages are comparable.

www.cambridgeesol.org/rs_notes/rs_nts24. PDF

Entered by: University of Cambridge ESOL Examinations

A

Ashton, K. 2008. 'The languages ladder and asset languages: A new assessment framework for languages in England' in C. Kenner and T. Hickey (eds.) *Multilingual Europe: Diversity and Learning.* Oakhill, Stoke-on-Trent: Trentham Books.

ISBN: 9781858564234

Pages: 175–177

Descriptor(s): Cultural issues, Learner cognition, Learner autonomy/strategies, Assessment

Country of research: United Kingdom

Learners' background: various

Institutional level: secondary

Entered by: University of Cambridge ESOL Examinations

Ashton, M. and E. Galaczi. 2008. 'Assessment for teaching: Cambridge ESOL's CLIL exam'. *Cambridge ESOL: Research Notes* 34: 15–21.

Summary: Mick Ashton and Evelina Galaczi describe the background to the new CLIL module for Cambridge ESOL's Teaching Knowledge Test, a flexible way to assess teachers' knowledge about teaching a non-language subject (e.g. history or science) through a second or foreign language such as English.

www.cambridgeesol.org/rs_notes/rs_nts34. PDF

Entered by: University of Cambridge ESOL Examinations

Ashton, M. and H. Khalifa. 2005. 'Assessing teachers' knowledge: Cambridge ESOL teaching knowledge test'. *Modern English Teacher* 14/1: 65–68.

Descriptor(s): Teacher education, Assessment

Country of research: various

B

Learners' background: various

Institutional level: adult

Entered by: University of Cambridge ESOL Examinations

Ashton, M. and H. Khalifa. 2005. 'Opening a new door for teachers of English: Cambridge ESOL teaching Knowledge Test'. *Cambridge ESOL: Research Notes* 19: 5–7.

Summary: Mick Ashton and Hanan Khalifa outline the Teaching Knowledge Test (TKT), an award for teachers of English at any stage in their career, which was developed in response to stakeholder needs.

www.cambridgeesol.org/rs_notes/rs_nts19. PDF

Entered by: University of Cambridge ESOL Examinations

Ashton, M. and H. Khalifa. 2007. 'Opening a new door for teachers: Cambridge ESOL teaching knowledge test' in *TESOL Arabia: Teacher Education and Continuing Professional Development: Insights from the Arabian Gulf.* Dubai: TESOL Arabia.

Principal format: Printed

Descriptor(s): Assessment

Country of research: various

Learners' background: various

Institutional level: adult

Entered by: University of Cambridge ESOL Examinations

B

Badger, R. and M. Macdonald. 2008. 'Cultural awareness and teacher education'. *Pedagogy, Culture and Society* 15/2: 215–228.

Descriptor(s): Teacher education, Cultural issues

Entered by: University of Exeter (School of Education and Lifelong Learning)

Badger, R.G. 2006. 'Investigating agonism in linguistics'. *Journal of Pragmatics* 38/9: 1442–1456.

Entered by: University of Leeds (School of Education)

Baker, W. 2008. 'A critical examination of ELT in Thailand: The role of cultural awareness'. *RELC Journal* 39/1: 131–146.

Summary: An essential element in fostering successful intercultural communication is developing cultural awareness as part of ELT pedagogy. To illustrate this, a case study of Thailand is presented. This leads to suggestions on how locally relevant intercultural communicative practices can form part of ELT classroom pedagogy with the aim of developing learners' cultural awareness.

Descriptor(s): Cultural issues, Methodology, ESOL/EAL, English language

Country of research: Thailand

Learners' background: Thailand

Institutional level: tertiary

Entered by: University of Southampton (Modern Languages, School of Humanities)

Banerjee, J. and D. Wall. 2006. 'Assessing achievement on pre-sessional English for Academic Purposes courses'. *Journal of English for Academic Purposes* 5/1: 50–69.

Summary: A discussion of the challenges of assessing progress in pre-sessional EAP courses, and a discussion of the challenges facing the developers of an instrument and set of procedures for determining whether learners on an EAP course were ready to enter mainstream university departments.

Descriptor(s): Management/Innovation, ESP, English language, Assessment

Country of research: United Kingdom

Learners' background: various

Institutional level: tertiary

Entered by: Lancaster University (Linguistics and English Language)

B

Barker, F. 2006. 'Corpora and language assessment: Trends and prospects'. *Cambridge ESOL: Research Notes* 26: 2–4.

Summary: Fiona Barker outlines the growth in the existence and use of corpora for language assessment and describes a range of current corpus-related activities before looking to future applications of this field for language testers, both within Cambridge ESOL and more widely.

www.cambridgeesol.org/rs_notes/rs_nts26.PDF

Entered by: University of Cambridge ESOL Examinations

Barker, F. and S. Shaw. 2007. 'Linking language assessments for younger learners across proficiency levels (Phase 1)'. *Cambridge ESOL: Research Notes* 28: 14–18.

Summary: Fiona Barker and Stuart Shaw's article reports on an ongoing and long-term study to locate the three levels of YLE on to a common scale, thereby providing empirical validation for the vertical equating of levels.

www.cambridgeesol.org/rs_notes/rs_nts28.PDF

Entered by: University of Cambridge ESOL Examinations

Barker, F., S. McKenna, S. Murray and I. Vidakovic. 2007. 'Overview of FCE and CAE review project research'. *Cambridge ESOL: Research Notes* 30: 31–34.

Summary: Fiona Barker, Steve Murray, Stephen McKenna and Ivana Vidakovic outline a range of other research and stakeholder projects undertaken within the FCE and CAE Review project.

www.cambridgeesol.org/rs_notes/rs_nts30.PDF

Entered by: University of Cambridge ESOL Examinations

Bartlett, T. and E. Erling. 2007. 'Local voices in global English: The authenticity and legitimisation of non-standard ways of speaking' in L. Barbara and T. Berber Sardinha (eds.) *Proceedings of the 33rd International Systemic Functional Congress* (PUCSP, São Paulo, Brazil). São Paulo, Brazil: International Systemic Functional Congress.

ISBN: ISBN 85-283-0342-X

www.pucsp.br/isfc/proceedings

Entered by: Cardiff University (School of English, Communication and Philosophy)

Bax, S. 2006. 'Making CALL work: Towards normalisation'. *System* 34: 465–479.

Descriptor(s): Learning technologies

Entered by: Canterbury Christ Church University (Department of English and Language Studies)

Bax, S. 2006. 'The role of genre in language syllabus design: The case of Bahrain'. *International Journal of Educational Development* 26: 315–328.

Descriptor(s): English language, Curriculum/syllabus

Entered by: Canterbury Christ Church University (Department of English and Language Studies)

Baynham, M. 2005. 'Network and agency in the migration stories of Moroccan women' in M. Baynham and A. De Fina (eds.) *Dislocations/Relocations: Narratives of Displacement.* Manchester: St Jerome Publishing.

ISBN: 978-1900650793

Entered by: University of Leeds (School of Education)

Baynham, M. 2006. 'Agency and contingency in the language learning of refugees and asylum seekers'. *Linguistics and Education* 17/1: 24–39.

Entered by: University of Leeds (School of Education)

B

Baynham, M. 2006. 'Performing self, family and community in Moroccan narratives of migration and settlement' in A. De Fina, D. Schiffrin and M. Bamberg (eds.) *Discourse and Identity*. Cambridge: Cambridge University Press.

ISBN: 9780521541916

Pages: 87–95

Entered by: University of Leeds (School of Education)

Baynham, M. 2006. 'Power of numbers: Research agendas in a number-saturated world' in L. Tett, M. Hamilton and Y. Hillier (eds.) *Adult Literacy, Numeracy and Language*. Maidenhead and New York: Open University Press.

ISBN: 978-0335219377

Pages: 87–95

Entered by: University of Leeds (School of Education)

Baynham, M., C. Roberts, M. Cooke, J. Simpson and K. Ananiadou. 2007. *Effective Teaching and Learning ESOL*. London: NRDC.

ISBN: 1-905188-27-7

Summary: Available online: www.nrdc.org.uk/content.asp?CategoryID=422&ArticleID=786

Descriptor(s): ESOL/EAL

Associated project: ESOL Effective Practice project

Entered by: University of Leeds (School of Education)

Benson, C., J. Gollin and H. Trappes-Lomax. 2007. 'Reporting strategies in academic writing: from corpus to materials' in O. Alexander (ed.) *Proceedings of BALEAP Conference 2005*. Stuttgart: Peter Lang.

Principal format: Printed

Descriptor(s): Writing, Reading

Entered by: University of Edinburgh (Institute for Applied Language Studies/Office of Lifelong Learning)

Benson, C., J. Pavitt and M. Jenkins. 2005. 'The use of dictogloss to encourage discussion of language use'. *Edinburgh Working Papers in Applied Linguistics* 14: 1–17.

Descriptor(s): Methodology, Learner cognition, English language, Classroom interaction

Entered by: University of Edinburgh (Institute for Applied Language Studies/Office of Lifelong Learning)

Blackhurst, A. 2005. 'Listening, reading and writing on computer-based and paper-based versions of IELTS'. *Cambridge ESOL: Research Notes* 21: 14–17.

Summary: Andrew Blackhurst reports on the latest trial of the computer-based IELTS test, looking at candidates' familiarity with computers and how examiner attitudes affected marking of writing scripts. Statistical analysis revealed no significant intergroup differences by gender, age or first language, which suggests that the relationship between CB and PB scores is not affected by these differences between candidates.

www.cambridgeesol.org/rs_notes/rs_nts21.PDF

Entered by: University of Cambridge ESOL Examinations

Blackhurst, A. 2007. 'Computer-based and Paper-based versions of IELTS' in O. Alexander (ed.) *New Approaches to Materials Development for Language Learning*. Bern: Peter Lang AG.

ISBN: 978-3-03910-909-8

Descriptor(s): Learning technologies, Assessment

Country of research: various

Learners' background: various

Institutional level: tertiary

Entered by: University of Cambridge ESOL Examinations

Blackledge, A.J. 2006. 'The magical frontier between the dominant and dominated: Sociolinguistics and social justice in a multilingual world'. *Journal of Multilingual & Multicultural Development* 27/1: 22–41.

Country of research: United Kingdom

Learners' background: United Kingdom

Institutional level: adult

Entered by: University of Birmingham (School of Education)

Blackledge, A.J. 2006. 'The men say "They don't need it": Gender and the extension of language testing for British citizenship'. *Studies in Language and Capitalism* 1: 143–162.

Country of research: United Kingdom

Learners' background: United Kingdom

Institutional level: adult

Entered by: University of Birmingham (School of Education)

Blackledge, A.J. 2008. 'Liberalism, discrimination and the Law: Language testing for citizenship in Britain' in G. Rings and A. Ife (eds.) *Neo-colonial Mentalities in Contemporary Europe? Language and Discourse in the Construction of Identities.* Newcastle upon Tyne: Cambridge Scholars Publishing.

ISBN: 9781847185129

Descriptor(s): Cultural issues, ESOL/EAL, Assessment

Country of research: United Kingdom

Learners' background: various

Institutional level: adult

Entered by: University of Birmingham (School of Education)

Blackledge, A.J. and A. Creese. 2008. 'Contesting "language" as "heritage":

Negotiation of identities in late modernity'. *Applied Linguistics* 29/4: 533–554.

Entered by: University of Birmingham (School of Education)

B

Block, D. 2005. 'Convergence and resistance in the construction of personal and professional identities: Four French modern language teachers in London' in S. Canagarajah (ed.) *Reclaiming the Local in Language Policy and Practice.* Mahwah, NJ: Lawrence Erlbaum.

ISBN: 0805845925

Pages: 167–196

Summary: This paper focuses how, via their talk about their lives, four French nationals working as French teachers in London schools construct nationality-influenced (though not determined) hybrid professional and personal identities, lying in a metaphorical third place between home and London.

Descriptor(s): Teacher education, Cultural issues

Entered by: Institute of Education, London (Department of Learning, Curriculum and Communication)

Block, D. 2006. 'Identity in applied linguistics: Where are we?' in T. Omoniyi and G. White (eds.) *The Sociolinguistics of Identity.* London: Continuum.

ISBN: 1847063322

Pages: 34–49

Summary: This paper is a short reflection on how language and identity researchers need to seek not only confirmation for their views, but also to engage with critiques of the rise of identity in the social sciences.

Descriptor(s): Cultural issues, ESOL/EAL

Entered by: Institute of Education, London (Department of Learning, Curriculum and Communication)

Block, D. 2006. *Multilingual Identities in a Global City: London Stories.*

B

London: Palgrave.

ISBN: 1–4039–3964–0

Summary: This book begins with a discussion of globalization, migration, multiculturalism, identity, the global city and the history of migration to Britain and London. It then examines the language/cultural identities of four groups in London: East Asian graduate students, French foreign language teachers, Spanish-speaking Latinos and second-generation British Asian university students.

Country of research: United Kingdom

Institutional level: adult

Entered by: Institute of Education, London (Department of Learning, Curriculum and Communication)

Block, D. 2007. '"Socialising" second language acquisition' in H. Zhu, P. Seedhouse, W. Li and V. Cook (eds.) *Language Learning and Teaching as Social Interaction*. London: Palgrave Macmillan.

ISBN: 0230517005

Pages: 89–102

Summary: The call for the socialisation of SLA in The Social Turn in Second Language Acquisition (2003) paralleled Rampton's (1997) call for a 'retuned' applied linguistics, with a bigger and better 'toolkit'. This paper considers what bringing an entire hardware store to bear on language learning research might mean.

Descriptor(s): Cultural issues, ESOL/EAL

Entered by: Institute of Education, London (Department of Learning, Curriculum and Communication)

Block, D. 2007. 'Bilingualism: Four assumptions and four responses'. *Innovation in Language Teaching* 1/1: 66–82.

Summary: Embedded in ongoing debates about multiculturalism are frequent references to bilingualism, which range from negative assessments to more positive views. This paper presents and critiques four assumptions often made about bilinguals and bilingualism. It concludes with some thoughts on how this discussion is relevant to the readers of this journal.

Descriptor(s): Cultural issues, ESOL/EAL

Country of research: United Kingdom

Institutional level: adult

Entered by: Institute of Education, London (Department of Learning, Curriculum and Communication)

Block, D. 2007. *Second Language Identities*. London: Continuum.

ISBN: 0-8264-7406-3

Summary: This book begins with a presentation of a poststructuralist approach to identity and then considers early SLA research on affective variables, examining how identity was an issue. It then considers research focussing on identity in three distinct contexts: (1) adult migration, (2) foreign language classrooms and (3) study abroad programmes.

Descriptor(s): Cultural issues, ESOL/EAL

Entered by: Institute of Education, London (Department of Learning, Curriculum and Communication)

Block, D. 2007. 'The rise of identity in SLA research, post Firth and Wagner (1997)'. *Modern Language Journal* 91/5: 861–874.

Summary: This article focuses on empirical research linking L2 learning and identity which has been published since Firth and Wagner (1997). It begins with a discussion of the broadly poststructuralist approach to identity and then critically reviews key publications carried out in naturalistic, foreign language and study abroad contexts.

Descriptor(s): ESOL/EAL

Entered by: Institute of Education, London (Department of Learning, Curriculum and Communication)

B

Block, D. 2008. 'Language education and globalization' in S. May and N. Hornberger (eds.) *Encyclopedia of Language and Education: Language Policy and Political Issues in Education.* New York: Springer.

ISBN: 0387328750

Pages: 31–43

Summary: This chapter examines globalisation theory before considering its relevance and applications to language education research. The latter discussion is organised in terms of: (1) early developments, (2) work in progress, problems and difficulties and (3) future directions.

Descriptor(s): Cultural issues, ESOL/EAL

Entered by: Institute of Education, London (Department of Learning, Curriculum and Communication)

Block, D. 2008. 'On the appropriateness of the metaphor of LOSS' in R. Rubdy and P. Tan (eds.) *Language as Commodity: Global Structures, Local Marketplaces.* London: Continuum.

ISBN: 184706423X

Pages: 187–203

Summary: This chapter explores the extent to which the metaphor of LOSS (MoL) is always appropriate as a way of framing discussions of language maintenance and shift in the lives of individuals. It concludes with a call for a more nuanced approach to this area of research.

Descriptor(s): Cultural issues, ESOL/EAL

Country of research: United Kingdom

Institutional level: primary

Entered by: Institute of Education, London (Department of Learning, Curriculum and Communication)

Block, D. 2008. 'Spanish-speaking Latinos in London: Community and language practices'. *Journal of Language, Identity and Education* 7/1: 5–21.

Summary: This paper focuses on Spanish-speaking Latinos in London, an under-researched ethnolinguistic group. It first establishes that there is a substantial number of Spanish-speaking Latinos in London and then moves to explore the extent to which one can say that there is a Spanish-speaking Latino community in the city.

Descriptor(s): Cultural issues, ESOL/EAL

Country of research: United Kingdom

Learners' background: Colombia

Institutional level: adult

Entered by: Institute of Education, London (Department of Learning, Curriculum and Communication)

Boonmoh, A. and H. Nesi. 2008. 'A survey of dictionary use by Thai university staff and students, with special reference to pocket electronic dictionaries'. *Horizontes de Lingüística Aplicada* 6/2: 79–90.

Summary: This study identifies some basic characteristics of pocket electronic dictionaries on sale in Thailand, and explores the dictionary using habits and preferences of staff and students at a Thai university.

Descriptor(s): Materials, Learning technologies, Learner autonomy/strategies, English language

Country of research: Thailand

Learners' background: Thailand

Institutional level: tertiary

Entered by: Coventry University

Borg, S. 2005. 'Experience, knowledge about language and classroom experience in teaching grammar' in N. Bartels (ed.) *Applied Linguistics and Language Teacher Education.* New York: Springer.

ISBN: 0-380-387-23451-97-23451-9

Pages: 325–340

Entered by: University of Leeds (School of Education)

B

Borg, S. 2005. 'Teacher cognition in language teaching' in K. Johnson (ed.) *Expertise in Second Language Learning and Teaching.* Basingstoke: Palgrave Macmillan.

ISBN: 10: 1-4039-2096-6

Pages: 190–209

Descriptor(s): Teacher cognition

Entered by: University of Leeds (School of Education)

Borg, S. 2006. 'Classroom research as professional development' in S. Borg (ed.) *Classroom Research in ELT in Oman.* Muscat: Ministry of Education, Oman.

ISBN: No ISBN

Pages: ix–xii

Entered by: University of Leeds (School of Education)

Borg, S. 2006. 'Conditions for teacher research'. *English Teaching Forum* 44/4: 22–27.

Entered by: University of Leeds (School of Education)

Borg, S. 2006. 'Language teacher research in Europe' in S. Borg (ed.) *Language Teacher Research in Europe.* Alexandria, VA: TESOL.

ISBN: 9781931185370

Pages: 1–6

Entered by: University of Leeds (School of Education)

Borg, S. 2006. *Teacher Cognition and Language Education: Research and Practice.* London: Continuum.

ISBN: 0826477283

Descriptor(s): Teacher cognition

Entered by: University of Leeds (School of Education)

Borg, S. 2006. 'The distinctive characteristics of foreign language teachers'. *Language Teaching Research* 10/1: 1–29.

www.education.leeds.ac.uk/research/uploads/40.PDF

Entered by: University of Leeds (School of Education)

Borg, S. 2007. 'English language teachers' views of research: Some insights from Switzerland'. *ETAS Newsletter* 24: 15–18.

www.education.leeds.ac.uk/research/uploads/56.PDF

Entered by: University of Leeds (School of Education)

Borg, S. 2007. 'Research engagement in English language teaching'. *Teaching and Teacher Education* 23: 731–747.

Entered by: University of Leeds (School of Education)

Borg, S. 2007. 'Understanding what teachers think about research'. *The Teacher Trainer* 21: 2–4.

Summary: This paper illustrates ways of studying what research means to teachers in an in-service teacher education context.

Entered by: University of Leeds (School of Education)

Borg, S. 2008. 'English language teachers' beliefs about research: Perspectives from the Netherlands'. *Levende Talen Tijdschrift [Journal of the Dutch Association of Modern Language Teachers]* 9/3: 3–13.

Entered by: University of Leeds (School of Education)

Borg, S. 2008. 'Teacher research in English language teaching' in S. Borg (ed.) *Investigating English Language Teaching and Learning in Oman.* Muscat: Ministry of Education, Oman.

ISBN: 9789948037699

Pages: ix–xiii

Entered by: University of Leeds (School of Education)

B

Borg, S. and A. Burns. 2008. 'Integrating grammar in adult TESOL classrooms'. *Applied Linguistics* 29/3: 456–482.

Entered by: University of Leeds (School of Education)

Borg, S. and S. Ioannou-Georgiou. 2008. 'IATEFL research publications'. *Language Teaching* 41/3: 431–443.

Entered by: University of Leeds (School of Education)

Bowles, H. and P. Seedhouse. 2007. 'Introduction' in H. Bowles and P. Seedhouse (eds.) *Conversation Analysis and Languages for Specific Purposes.* Bern: Peter Lang.

ISBN: 9783039114696

Summary: Introduction to a ground-breaking volume which shows how conversation analysis can make a significant contribution to the teaching of spoken language for specific purposes (LSP) and provides a firm foundation for future research and practice in this area.

Descriptor(s): Classroom interaction, Speaking, Methodology, ESP, Curriculum/syllabus

Country of research: various

Learners' background: various

Entered by: Newcastle University (School of Education, Communication and Language Sciences)

Bowles, H. and P. Seedhouse. 2007. 'Interactional competence and the LSP classroom' in H. Bowles and P. Seedhouse (eds.) *Conversation Analysis and Languages for Specific Purposes.* Bern: Peter Lang.

ISBN: 9783039114696

Pages: 305–330

Summary: This chapter attempts a brief overview of the implications of CA-based approaches to interaction for the teaching of speaking in the LSP classroom.

Descriptor(s): Speaking, Methodology, ESP, Classroom interaction

Entered by: Newcastle University (School of Education, Communication and Language Sciences)

Bressan, E. and V.M. Cribb. 2007. 'Group project work in higher education: What it is and what it is not' in M. Conrick and M. Howard (eds.) *From Applied Linguistics to Linguistics Applied.* Birmingham: British Association of Applied Linguistics/Irish Association for Applied Linguistics.

ISBN: 0-7044-2627-7

Pages: 180–194

Summary: Looks at how home and international students interact in group project work in higher education.

Descriptor(s): Cultural issues, ESOL/EAL, Assessment

Country of research: United Kingdom

Learners' background: various

Institutional level: tertiary

Entered by: Coventry University

Brick, B. and J. Holmes. 2008. 'Using screen capture software for student feedback' in D. Klinshuk, G. Sampson, J.M. Spector, P. Saias and D. Ifenthaler (eds.) Freiburg, Germany: IADIS CELDA.

Pages: 339–342

Principal format: CD-ROM

Summary: In the wake of negative responses by students regarding the quality and helpfulness of feedback, tutors have begun to explore ways in which new technologies can improve feedback. This paper reviews the literature in the area of student feedback and provides some initial results into trials conducted using screen capture software for student feedback. The final part of the paper discusses some of the procedural and practical issues which need to be addressed in developing a clear methodology for this type of feedback.

Descriptor(s): Writing, Teacher education,

B

Methodology, Learning technologies, English language, Classroom interaction, Assessment

Country of research: United Kingdom

Learners' background: various

Institutional level: tertiary

Entered by: Coventry University

Brown, A. and L. Taylor. 2006. 'A worldwide survey of examiners' views and experience of the revised IELTS speaking test'. *Cambridge ESOL: Research Notes* 26: 14–18.

Summary: Annie Brown and Lynda Taylor report on a project commissioned by Cambridge ESOL to survey examiners' views and experience of the IELTS Speaking Test following its revision in 2001. This survey explored both the Speaking Test's format and tasks and how raters assessed candidates taking the test.

www.cambridgeesol.org/rs_notes/rs_nts26. PDF

Entered by: University of Cambridge ESOL Examinations

Brown, P., R.C. Smith and E. Ushioda. 2007. 'Responding to resistance' in A. Barfield and S.H. Brown (eds.) *Reconstructing Autonomy in Language Education: Inquiry and Innovation.* Basingstoke: Palgrave Macmillan.

ISBN: 978-0-230-00173-2

Pages: 71–83

Summary: Report on an action research project involving development of teacher-learner autonomy within initial teacher education, including consideration of how resistance to the course design was responded to through investigation and changes which safeguarded the innovation.

Descriptor(s): Teacher education, Teacher cognition, Learner cognition, Learner autonomy/strategies

Country of research: United Kingdom

Learners' background: various

Institutional level: tertiary

Entered by: University of Warwick (Centre for Applied Linguistics)

Burden, P. and S. Troudi. 2007. 'An evaluation of student ratings of teaching in a Japanese university context' in C. Coombe, M. Al-Hamly, P. Davidson and S. Troudi (eds.) *Evaluating Teacher Effectiveness in ESL/EFL Contexts.* Ann Arbor: University of Michigan Press.

Pages: 152–166

Descriptor(s): Teacher education, ESOL/EAL

Entered by: University of Exeter (School of Education and Lifelong Learning)

Bygate, M. 2005. 'Applied linguistics: A pragmatic discipline, a generic discipline?'. *Applied linguistics:* 26/4: 568–581.

Descriptor(s): Cultural issues, ESOL/EAL, ESP, Curriculum/syllabus

Entered by: Lancaster University (Linguistics and English Language)

Bygate, M. 2005. 'Oral second language abilities as expertise' in K. Johnson (ed.) *Expertise in Second Language Teaching.* Basingstoke: Palgrave Macmillan.

ISBN: 978-1-4039-2096-6

Descriptor(s): Speaking, Methodology, Materials, ESOL/EAL, Curriculum/syllabus

Entered by: Lancaster University (Linguistics and English Language)

Bygate, M. 2006. 'Areas of research that influence L2 speaking instruction' in E. Uso-Juan and A. Martinez-Flor (eds.) *Current Trends in the Development and Teaching of the Four Language Skills.* The Hague: Mouton De Gruyter.

ISBN: 978-3-11-01896-1

Pages: 159–186

Descriptor(s): Speaking, Methodology, Materials, ESOL/EAL, Curriculum/syllabus

Entered by: Lancaster University (Linguistics and English Language)

C

Cajkler, W. and J. Hislam. 2005. 'Teacher trainees' explicit knowledge of grammar and primary curriculum requirements in England in N Bartels (ed.) *Applied Linguistics in Language Teacher Education*. New York: Springer.

ISBN: 0-387-23451-9

Descriptor(s): Teacher education, English language

Country of research: United Kingdom; Learners' background: United Kingdom; Institutional level: secondary

Entered by: University of Leicester (English Language Teaching and Applied Linguistics, School of Education)

Cameron, L. and A. Deignan. 2006. 'The emergence of metaphor in discourse'. *Applied Linguistics* 27/4: 671–690.

Entered by: University of Leeds (School of Education)

Cameron, L., A. Cienki, P. Crisp, A. Deignan, R. Gibbs, J. Grady, Z. Kovecses, G. Low, E. Semino and G. Steen. 2007. 'MIP: A method for identifying metaphorically used words in discourse'. *Metaphor and Symbol* 22/1: 1–40.

Entered by: University of Leeds (School of Education)

Carter, R.A. and L. Fung. 2007. 'Discourse markers and spoken English: Native and non-native use in pedagogic settings'. *Applied Linguistics* 28/3: 410–439.

Descriptor(s): Speaking, Listening, English language

Entered by: University of Nottingham (School of English Studies)

Carter, R.A. and M.J. McCarthy. 2006. *Cambridge Grammar of English: A Comprehensive Guide to Spoken and Written Grammar and Usage.* Cambridge: Cambridge University Press.

ISBN: 978-0521674393

Summary: Book and CD-ROM versions

Descriptor(s): Speaking, Listening, Learning technologies, English language, Curriculum/syllabus

Entered by: University of Nottingham (School of English Studies)

Chambers, L. 2008. 'Computer-based and paper-based writing assessment: A comparative text analysis'. *Cambridge ESOL: Research Notes* 34: 9–15.

Summary: Lucy Chambers explores the impact of computer-based formats on writing performance by comparing the paper-based and computer-based writing from the PET exam.

www.cambridgeesol.org/rs_notes/rs_nts34.PDF

Entered by: University of Cambridge ESOL Examinations

Charles, M. 2006. 'The construction of stance in reporting clauses: A cross-disciplinary study of theses'. *Applied Linguistics* 27/3: 492–518.

Summary: This corpus-based study compares reporting clauses in theses in politics and materials science. Reporting clauses are used to comment on the writer's own work and they enable writers to emphasize or hide responsibility for their own propositions. The findings have implications for teaching learners to construct an appropriate disciplinary stance.

Descriptor(s): Writing, ESP, English language

Country of research: United Kingdom;

Institutional level: tertiary

Entered by: University of Oxford (Language Centre)

C

C

Charles, M. 2006. 'Phraseological patterns in reporting clauses used in citation: A corpus-based study of theses in two disciplines'. *English for Specific Purposes* 25/3: 310–331.

Summary: This study investigates the phraseology of reporting verbs in citations. In politics the predominant pattern is a verb of verbal communication in present tense, while in materials science, research action verbs in past tense are frequent. It is argued that working with patterns is beneficial in raising students' language awareness.

Descriptor(s): Writing, ESP, English language

Country of research: United Kingdom;

Institutional level: tertiary

Entered by: University of Oxford (Language Centre)

Charles, M. 2006. 'Revealing and obscuring the writer's identity: Evidence from a corpus of theses' in R. Kiely, P. Rea-Dickins, H. Woodfield and G. Clibbon (eds.) *Language, Culture and Identity in Applied Linguistics.* London: BAAL and Equinox.

ISBN: 978-1-84553-219-2

Pages: 147–161

Summary: This chapter shows how five grammatical patterns are used in two corpora of theses to reveal or obscure the writer's identity. It is argued that learners need to use different levels of visibility to construct an appropriate academic identity, depending on disciplinary characteristics, professional status and rhetorical purpose.

Descriptor(s): Writing, ESP, English language

Country of research: United Kingdom

Institutional level: tertiary

Entered by: University of Oxford (Language Centre)

Charles, M. 2007. 'Argument or evidence? Disciplinary variation in the use of the noun "that" pattern in stance construction'. *English for Specific Purposes* 26/2: 203–218.

Summary: This paper examines disciplinary differences in the use of nouns followed by a that-clause. Politics writers use nouns of communication to take a stance towards others' research, while materials science writers use evidential nouns to evaluate their own research. This study has pedagogical implications for teaching disciplinary research practices.

Descriptor(s): Writing, ESP, English language

Country of research: United Kingdom;

Institutional level: tertiary

Entered by: University of Oxford (Language Centre)

Charles, M. 2007. 'Reconciling top-down and bottom-up approaches to graduate writing: Using a corpus to teach rhetorical functions'. *Journal of English for Academic Purposes* 6/4: 289–302.

Summary: This paper describes an approach to teaching academic writing which combines awareness-raising work on rhetorical functions with hands-on concordancing. The discourse tasks focus primarily on function and the corpus tasks on form. It is argued that the combination of approaches helps students link general rhetorical purposes to specific lexico-grammatical choices.

Descriptor(s): Writing, Methodology, Learning technologies, ESP

Country of research: United Kingdom

Learners' background: various;

Institutional level: tertiary

Entered by: University of Oxford (Language Centre)

Charles, M. 2008. 'Using a corpus to teach rhetorical functions: Students' evaluation of a hands-on concordancing approach' in A. Frankenberg-Garcia, T. Rkibi, M. Braga da Cruz, R. Carvalho, C. Direito and D. Santos-Rosa (eds.) *8th Teaching and Language Corpora Conference.* Lisbon, Portugal: ISLA.

ISBN: 978-989-95523-1-9

Pages: 60–64

Principal format: Printed

Summary: In this study, 49 international graduates evaluated a hands-on concordancing course for academic writing. Attitudes towards corpus work were generally favourable: percentages of students who agreed with positive statements about corpus work ranged from 73% to 96%. However lower ratings were recorded concerning the practicalities of the corpus tasks.

Descriptor(s): Methodology, Learning technologies, ESP

Country of research: United Kingdom;

Learners' background: various;

Institutional level: tertiary

Entered by: University of Oxford (Language Centre)

Cheng, H-F. and Z. Dörnyei. 2007. 'The use of motivational strategies in language instruction: The case of EFL teaching in Taiwan'. *Innovation in Language Learning and Teaching* 1/1: 153–174.

Descriptor(s): Teacher education, Cultural issues, Learner cognition, Learner autonomy/strategies

Country of research: Taiwan

Entered by: University of Nottingham (School of English Studies)

Chuang, F-Y. and H. Nesi. 2006. 'An analysis of formal errors in a corpus of Chinese student writing'. *Corpora* 1/2: 251–271.

Summary: This paper describes the investigation of a small corpus of writing of English for academic purposes produced by L1 speakers of Mandarin.

Descriptor(s): Writing, Methodology

Country of research: United Kingdom

Learners' background: China

Institutional level: tertiary

Entered by: University of Warwick (Centre for Applied Linguistics)

Chuang, F-Y. and H. Nesi. 2006. 'An analysis of formal errors in a corpus of L2 English produced by Chinese students'. *Corpora* 1/2: 251–271.

Summary: This paper describes the analysis of a small corpus of writing in English for academic purposes produced by L1 speakers of Mandarin. A tagset was developed for the identification of formal errors in the corpus, and these errors were subsequently analysed with a view to creating remedial grammar materials.

Descriptor(s): Writing, Methodology, Materials, ESP

Country of research: United Kingdom

Learners' background: China

Institutional level: tertiary

Entered by: Coventry University

Chuang, F-Y. and H. Nesi. 2007. 'GrammarTalk: Developing computer-based materials for Chinese EAP students' in O. Alexander (ed.) *New Approaches to Materials Development for Language Learning.* Oxford: Peter Lang.

ISBN: ISBN 978-3-03910-909-8

Pages: 315–330

Summary: This paper describes the design of corpus-based online materials to address students' most common grammatical mistakes, to improve proofreading skills, and to provide international EAP students with flexible and independent learning support. The materials were particularly targeted at Chinese and East Asian learners.

Descriptor(s): Writing, Materials, Learning technologies, ESP

Country of research: United Kingdom

Learners' background: China

Institutional level: tertiary

Entered by: Coventry University

Chuang, F-Y. and H. Nesi. 2007. 'GrammarTalk: Developing computer-based materials for the Chinese EAP student' in

C

C

O. Alexander (ed.) *Proceedings of the Joint Conference of BALEAP (British Association of Lecturers in English for Academic Purposes) and SATEFL on New Approaches to Materials Development for Language Learning*. Bern: Peter Lang.

Pages: 315–330

Principal format: Printed

Summary: This paper describes the process of developing GrammarTalk, a set of interactive grammar materials designed to help Chinese EAP students improve their formal accuracy.

Descriptor(s): Writing, Materials, Learning technologies, ESOL/EAL

Country of research: United Kingdom

Learners' background: China

Institutional level: tertiary

Entered by: University of Warwick (Centre for Applied Linguistics)

Chuang, F-Y. and H. Nesi. 2008. 'GrammarTalk: International students' responses to an online grammar resource' in M. Edwardes (ed.) *Proceedings of the BAAL annual conference on Technology, Ideology and Practice in Applied Linguistics.* London: Scitsiugnil Press.

Principal format: CD-ROM

Summary: This paper investigates international students' responses to GrammarTalk, a set of interactive grammar materials designed to help Chinese EAP students improve their formal accuracy.

Descriptor(s): Writing, Materials

Country of research: United Kingdom

Learners' background: various

Institutional level: tertiary

Entered by: University of Warwick (Centre for Applied Linguistics)

Clark, E.L. and A. Paran. 2007. 'The employability of non-native-speaker teachers of EFL: A UK survey'. *System* 35/4: 407–430.

Summary: This study surveyed 90 UK ELT institutions to investigate the extent to which the Native Speaker criterion played a part in employing EFL teachers. This was found to be a pre-interview criterion which often excludes competent EFL teachers from consideration in the recruitment process. This was true of the sample as a whole as well as of subsamples.

Descriptor(s): Management/Innovation

Country of research: United Kingdom

Entered by: Institute of Education, London (Department of Learning, Curriculum and Communication)

Clark, R. and S. Gieve. 2005. 'On the discursive construction of the Chinese learner'. *Language, Culture and Curriculum* 19/1: 54–73.

Descriptor(s): Cultural issues

Country of research: United Kingdom

Learners' background: China

Institutional level: tertiary

Entered by: University of Leicester (English Language Teaching and Applied Linguistics, School of Education)

Cogo, A. 2008. 'English as a lingua franca: Form follows function'. *English Today* 95: 41–44.

Descriptor(s): Cultural issues, English language

Country of research: United Kingdom

Entered by: University of Southampton (Modern Languages, School of Humanities)

Cogo, A. and M. Dewey. 2006. 'Efficiency in ELF communication: From pragmatic motives to lexico-grammatical innovation'. *Nordic Journal of English Studies* 5/2: 59–93.

Summary: This article provides a detailed investigation into pragmatic and interactive aspects of lingua franca talk, and considers the impact these have on the lexicogrammar of speakers engaged in ELF communication.

Descriptor(s): Teacher education, Speaking, Cultural issues, English language

Country of research: United Kingdom

Institutional level: tertiary

Entered by: King's College London (Department of Education and Professional Studies)

Cogo, A. and M. Dewey. 2006. 'Efficiency in ELF communication: From pragmatic motives to lexico-grammatical innovation'. *Nordic Journal of English Studies* 5/2: 59–93.

http://ojs.ub.gu.se/ojs/index.php/njes/article/view/65/69

Descriptor(s): Speaking, Cultural issues, Methodology, ESOL/EAL, ESP, English language

Country of research: United Kingdom

Entered by: University of Southampton (Modern Languages, School of Humanities)

Conklin, K. and G. Mauner. 2005. 'Bilingual semantic access of homographs' in J. Cohen, K.T. McAlister, K. Rolstad and J. Macswan (eds.) *ISB4: Proceedings of the 4th International Symposium on Bilingualism.* Somerville, MA: Cascadilla Press.

ISBN: 978-1-57473-107

Pages: 552–569

Principal format: Printed

Descriptor(s): Learner cognition

Entered by: University of Nottingham (School of English Studies)

Conklin, K. and N. Schmitt. 2008. 'Formulaic sequences: Are they processed more quickly than nonformulaic language by native and non-native speakers?'. *Applied Linguistics* 29/1: 72–89.

Descriptor(s): Learner cognition

Entered by: University of Nottingham (School of English Studies)

C

Conteh, J. 2007. 'Bilingualism in mainstream primary classrooms in England' in Z. Hua, P. Seedhouse, L. Wei and V. Cook (eds.) *Language Learning and Teaching as Social Interaction.* Basingstoke: Palgrave Macmillan.

ISBN: 9780230517004

Pages: 185–198

Entered by: University of Leeds (School of Education)

Conteh, J. 2007. 'Opening doors to success in multilingual classrooms: Bilingualism, codeswitching and the professional identities of 'ethnic minority' primary teachers'. *Language and Education* 21/6: 457–472.

Entered by: University of Leeds (School of Education)

Conteh, J. and Y. Kawashima. 2008. 'Diversity in family involvement in children's learning in English primary schools'. *Teaching Practice and Critique* 7/2: 113–125.

http://education.waikato.ac.nz/research/files/etpc/files/2008v7n2art7.PDF

Entered by: University of Leeds (School of Education)

Conteh, J., D. Beddow and R. Kumar. 2008. 'Investigating pupil talk in multilingual contexts: Sociocultural learning, teaching and researching'. *Education* 36/3: 223–235.

Entered by: University of Leeds (School of Education)

Cook, G. 2005. 'Calm seas or troubled waters? Transitions, definitions and disagreements in applied linguistics'. *International Journal of Applied Linguistics* 15/3: 282–302.

Descriptor(s): Cultural issues, Methodology, ESOL/EAL, English language

C

Institutional level: adult

Entered by: The Open University (Faculty of Education and Languages)

Cook, G. 2005. 'The best teacher. The Francesca Target Memorial Lecture 2005'. *Language Issues* 17/1: 2–6.

Descriptor(s): Teacher education, Teacher cognition, English language, Curriculum/syllabus, Classroom interaction

Institutional level: adult

Entered by: The Open University (Faculty of Education and Languages)

Cook, G. 2007. 'A thing of the future: translation in language learning'. *International Journal of Applied Linguistics* 17/3: 396–401.

Descriptor(s): Cultural issues, Methodology, Materials, Learner cognition, English language, Curriculum/syllabus, Classroom interaction

Institutional level: adult

Entered by: The Open University (Faculty of Education and Languages)

Cook, G. 2008. 'Plenary: An unmarked improvement: Using translation in ELT' in B. Beaven (ed.) *IATEFL 2007 Aberdeen Conference Selections*. Kent: University of Kent.

ISBN: 1 901095142

Pages: 76–86

Descriptor(s): Cultural issues, Methodology, Learner cognition, English language, Curriculum/syllabus

Institutional level: adult

Entered by: The Open University (Faculty of Education and Languages)

Cooke, M. 2008. '"What we might become": The lives, aspirations and education of young migrants in the London area'. *Journal of Language, Identity and Education* 7/1: 22–40.

Descriptor(s): ESOL/EAL

Country of research: United Kingdom

Learners' background: various

Institutional level: secondary

Entered by: King's College London (Department of Education and Professional Studies)

Cooke, M. 2008. 'When I wake up I dream of electricity: The lives, aspirations and 'needs' of adult ESOL learners'. *Linguistics and Education* 17/1: 56–73.

Descriptor(s): ESOL/EAL

Country of research: United Kingdom

Learners' background: various

Institutional level: adult

Entered by: King's College London (Department of Education and Professional Studies)

Cooke, M. and J. Simpson. 2008. *ESOL: A Critical Guide.* Oxford: Oxford University Press.

ISBN: 978-0-19-442267-3

Summary: Part of the Oxford Handbooks for Language Teachers series, the book examines the teaching and learning of English in migrant contexts. The authors draw on their extensive research in ESOL in the UK.

Descriptor(s): Teacher education, ESOL/EAL

Country of research: United Kingdom

Learners' background: various

Institutional level: adult

Entered by: King's College London (Department of Education and Professional Studies)

Cooke, M. and J. Simpson. 2008. *ESOL: A Critical Guide.* Oxford: Oxford University Press.

ISBN: 978-0194422673

Entered by: University of Leeds
(School of Education)

Coombe, C., M. Al-Hamly, P. Davidson and S. Troudi. 2007. *Evaluating Teacher Effectiveness in ESL/EFL Contexts.* Ann Arbor: University of Michigan Press.

Descriptor(s): Teacher education, ESOL/EAL

Entered by: University of Exeter
(School of Education and Lifelong Learning)

Cooze, M. and S. Shaw. 2007. 'Establishing the impact of reduced input and output length in FCE and CAE writing'. *Cambridge ESOL: Research Notes* 30: 15–19.

Summary: Margaret Cooze and Stuart Shaw report on research to establish the impact of reduced input and output length in FCE and CAE Writing papers using a series of multiple rating exercises where groups of examiners rated common sets of writing performances for the updated specifications.

www.cambridgeesol.org/rs_notes/rs_nts30.PDF

Entered by: University of Cambridge ESOL Examinations

Copland, F. 2008. 'Deconstructing the discourse: Understanding the feedback event' in S. Garton and K. Richards (eds.) *Professional Encounters in TESOL.* Basingstoke: Palgrave Macmillan.

ISBN: 9780230553514

Pages: 5–23

Summary: Explores what happens in the post-observation feedback conference in initial teacher training for EFL teachers.

Descriptor(s): Teacher education

Country of research: United Kingdom

Learners' background: United Kingdom

Institutional level: adult

Entered by: Aston University
(School of Languages and Social Sciences)

Corkill, D. and M. Robinson. 2006. 'Using the global legal community in the development of ILEC'. *Cambridge ESOL: Research Notes* 25: 10–11.

Summary: David Corkill and Martin Robinson report on how Cambridge ESOL designs tasks for LSP tests, describing how the International Legal English Certificate (ILEC), an exam for the global legal community, is being developed with the assistance of legal expertise.

www.cambridgeesol.org/rs_notes/rs_nts25.PDF

Entered by: University of Cambridge ESOL Examinations

Coverdale-Jones, T. 2008. 'Afterword: Responses to internationalisation in the UK and a survey on responses to intercultural communication teaching' in T. Rastall Coverdale-Jones (ed.) *Internationalising the University: The Chinese Context.* Houndmills, Basingstoke: Palgrave Macmillan.

ISBN: 978-0-230-20351-8/0-230-20351-5

Pages: 223–238

Summary: This volume brings together contributions from experts in this diverse and complex field and presents an up-to-date picture of thinking on internationalisation and its impact on Chinese and Western institutions, their regulatory framework, motivations, aspirations and quality assurance considerations.

Descriptor(s): Cultural issues, Curriculum/syllabus

Country of research: United Kingdom

Entered by: University of Portsmouth
(School of Languages and Area Studies)

Creese, A. 2005. 'Is this content-based language teaching?'. *Linguistics and Education* 16/2: 188–204.

Entered by: University of Birmingham
(School of Education)

C

C

Creese, A. 2005. 'Mediating allegations of racism in a multi-ethnic London school: What speech communities and communities of practice can tell us about discourse and power' in D. Barton and K. Tusting (eds.) *Beyond Communities of Practice.* Cambridge: Cambridge Press.

ISBN: 13:9780521544924

Entered by: University of Birmingham (School of Education)

Creese, A. 2005. *Teacher Collaboration and Talk in Multilingual Classrooms.* Clevedon: Multilingual Matters.

ISBN: 1853598224

Descriptor(s): Cultural issues, ESOL/EAL, Classroom interaction

Country of research: United Kingdom

Learners' background: various

Institutional level: secondary

Entered by: University of Birmingham (School of Education)

Creese, A. 2006. 'Supporting talk? Partnership teachers in classroom interaction'. *International Journal of Bilingual Education and Bilingualism* 9/4: 434–453.

Entered by: University of Birmingham (School of Education)

Cribb, V.M. 2005. 'Language as a cueing system: Pragmatic and semantic miscues in non-native spoken discourse' in CamLing (ed.) *CamLing 2005 Conference Proceedings.* Cambridge: Cambridge University.

Principal format: Printed

Summary: Looks at extended non-native spoken discourse to see how coherence breaks down. Considers miscues in semantic consistency (specificity) and pragmatic relevance and how these accumulate leading to a loss in coherence.

Descriptor(s): Speaking, ESOL/EAL, English language

Country of research: United Kingdom

Learners' background: various

Institutional level: tertiary

Entered by: Coventry University

Cribb, V.M. 2007. 'A systems approach: Teachers and learners as both guests and hosts to the learning context' in Canterbury Christ Church University Department of English and Language Studies (ed.) *Cutting Edges Conference Proceedings: Classrooms, People and Cultures.* Canterbury: Canterbury Christ Church University.

Principal format: Printed

Summary: Looks at how international students are both guests and host to the learning context, based on a systems approach to intercultural communication.

Descriptor(s): Teacher education, Cultural issues, Classroom interaction

Country of research: United Kingdom

Learners' background: various

Institutional level: tertiary

Entered by: Coventry University

Cross, J. 2006. 'Understanding and improving Chinese learners' pronunciation of English'. *Speak Out!* Issue 35b: 16–21.

Entered by: University of Portsmouth (School of Languages and Area Studies)

Cross, J. and R. Hitchcock. 2007. 'Chinese students' (or students from China's) views of UK HE: differences, difficulties and benefits, and suggestions for facilitating transition'. *The East Asian Learner* 3/2: 1–31.

Summary: The research shows Chinese learners are clearly aware of differences and difficulties in the British university system, particularly in teacher/student expectations, lesson purposes and assessment methods, but that they also find benefits. It concludes that learning styles are contextual, not cultural and gives practical advice to facilitate adaptation.

SCT theory

- Concepts - everyday-/scientific
- Mediation
- ZPD
- Joint Productive Activity
- Dialogic interaction

- Alexander's description of 'Dialogic talk'
  - Mercer 3 types of talk.
  - Co-quective development (eddy)
  Copland + Mann.

Practicum
  - Problems
    Copland + Mann - much
    'Directed'
    Suslaw — Lottie / Assess/Devels
Kinds of feedback
    Kurleglo - Hooter

www.brookes.ac.uk/schools/education/eal/eal-3-2/Cross%20and%20Hitchcock%202007.pdf

Descriptor(s): Teacher cognition, Cultural issues, Methodology, Learner cognition, Learner autonomy/strategies, ESOL/EAL, Classroom interaction

Country of research: United Kingdom

Learners' background: China

Entered by: University of Portsmouth (School of Languages and Area Studies)

Cross, J. and S. Papp. 2008. 'Creativity in the use of verb + noun combinations by Chinese learners of English' in G. Gilquin, S. Papp and M.B. Díez-Bedmar (eds.) *Linking Up Contrastive and Learner Corpus Research.* Amsterdam and New York: Rodopi.

ISBN: 9789042024465

Pages: 57–81

Summary: Research into verb and noun combinations shows Chinese learners of English use memorized chunks in written interlanguage and have a higher error rate in verb and noun combinations compared with Greek and German learners; it is argued this behaviour relates to input and education, as well as L1 influence and produces a form of linguistic creativity.

Descriptor(s): Writing, Learner cognition

Country of research: United Kingdom

Learners' background: China

Institutional level: adult

Entered by: University of Portsmouth (School of Languages and Area Studies)

Cross, J. and S. Papp. 2008. 'Creativity in the use of verb + noun combinations by Chinese learners of English' in G. Gilquin, S. Papp and M. Díez-Bedmar (eds.) *Linking up Contrastive and Learner Corpus Research.* Amsterdam, New York: Rodopi.

ISBN: 978-90-420-2446-5

Pages: 57–81

Summary: In this paper we examine verb + noun combinations as used by Chinese learners of English and compare them with Greek and German learners as investigated by Giovi (2006) and Nesselhauf (2003), respectively.

Descriptor(s): Writing, Learner cognition, Learner autonomy/strategies, English language

Country of research: United Kingdom

Learners' background: various

Institutional level: tertiary

Entered by: University of Cambridge ESOL Examinations

Crow, C.M. and C. Harrison. 2006. 'Developing the Cambridge ESOL Teacher Portfolio'. *Cambridge ESOL: Research Notes* 25: 12–13.

Summary: Clare Mitchell Crow and Clare Harrison describe the Teacher Portfolio, a web-based professional development tool for teachers to document various aspects of their teaching career. This new provision sits alongside existing portfolios available for other groups, for example the EAQUALS/ALTE European Language Portfolio (ELP) for language learners.

www.cambridgeesol.org/rs_notes/rs_nts25.PDF

Entered by: University of Cambridge ESOL Examinations

Crow, C.M. and C. Hubbard. 2006. 'ESOL professional support network extranet'. *Cambridge ESOL: Research Notes* 23: 6–7.

Summary: Clare Mitchell Crow and Chris Hubbard describe how Cambridge ESOL is developing a web-based resource to support and communicate directly with all of our Professional Support Network (the worldwide community of examiners, item writers, presenters, inspectors and other external resources who provide professional support to Cambridge ESOL activity).

C

C

www.cambridgeesol.org/rs_notes/rs_nts23.PDF

Entered by: University of Cambridge ESOL Examinations

Csizér, K. and Z. Dörnyei. 2005. 'Language learners' motivational profiles and their motivated learning behaviour'. *Language Learning* 55/4: 613–659.

Descriptor(s): Learner cognition, Learner autonomy/strategies

Country of research: Hungary

Institutional level: secondary

Entered by: University of Nottingham (School of English Studies)

Csizér, K. and Z. Dörnyei. 2005. 'The internal structure of language learning motivation and its relationship with language choice and learning effort'. *Modern Language Journal* 89/1: 19–36.

Descriptor(s): Cultural issues

Country of research: Hungary

Institutional level: secondary

Entered by: University of Nottingham (School of English Studies)

Csizér, K. and J. Kormos. 2008. 'The relationship of inter-cultural contact and language learning motivation among Hungarian students of English and German'. *Journal of Multilingual and Multicultural Development* 29: 30–48.

Summary: In this paper we report the results of a questionnaire survey conducted with 1777 Hungarian primary school children aged between 13 and 14 studying English and German. In our research we investigated the differences in the motivational and intercultural contact measures as well as determinants of motivated behaviour between learners of English and German.

Descriptor(s): Cultural issues

Country of research: Hungary

Learners' background: Hungary

Institutional level: primary

Entered by: Lancaster University (Linguistics and English Language)

Cullen, R. 2008. 'Teaching grammar as a liberating force'. *ELT Journal* 62/3: 221–230.

Descriptor(s): Methodology, English language

Entered by: Canterbury Christ Church University (Department of English and Language Studies)

Cullen, R. and V. Kuo. 2007. 'Spoken grammar and ELT materials'. *TESOL Quarterly* 41/2: 361–386.

Descriptor(s): Speaking, Materials, Classroom interaction

Entered by: Canterbury Christ Church University (Department of English and Language Studies)

Cummins, J., V. Bismilla, P. Chow, S. Cohen, F. Giampapa, L. Leoni, P. Sandhu and P. Sastri. 2005. 'Affirming identity in multilingual classrooms'. *Educational Leadership* 63/1: 38–43.

Summary: English language learners' cultural knowledge and home language skills are important resources in enabling academic engagement. English language learners tend to engage academically to the extent that instruction affirms their identities and enables them to invest their identities in learning. One effective approach to identity affirmation is the identity text, in which a student creates an expressive written, oral, dramatic, or artistic product. Encouraging students to write dual language books in the classroom is another way to show that schools value both the student's culture and home language. Acknowledging and actively promoting students' linguistic and cultural capital creates a pedagogy of respect and encourages English language learners to engage in literacy.

Descriptor(s): Writing, Cultural issues

Country of research: Canada

Institutional level: primary

Entered by: University of Bristol (Graduate School of Education)

Cummins, J., V. Bismilla, S. Cohen, F. Giampapa and L. Leoni. 2005. 'Timelines and lifelines: Rethinking literacy instruction in multilingual classrooms'. *Orbit* 36/1: 22–26.

Summary: In this article, we argue that given the timelines required for bilingual ESL students to catch up to their peers in English literacy skills, instruction that builds on students' home language (L1) proficiency represents a potential lifeline that enables students to participate academically and express their intelligence and identities within the classroom.

www.oise.utoronto.ca/orbit/documents/cummins_etal_002.PDF

Descriptor(s): Writing, Cultural issues, English language, Classroom interaction

Country of research: Canada

Learners' background: Canada

Institutional level: primary

Entered by: University of Bristol (Graduate School of Education)

Cutting, J. 2005. 'Spoken grammar: Vague language and EAP' in R. Hughes (ed.) *Spoken English, TESOL and Applied Linguistics: Challenges for Theory and Practice.* Basingstoke, England: Palgrave Macmillan.

ISBN: 9780230217041

Summary: This chapter argues that implicitness is an essential feature of spoken grammar, lexis and discourse structure, that it demands a systematic study of its inter-related parts, and that it should be a central part of the model taught to students of English as a Foreign Language, so that they can be helped to communicate on all levels with their interlocutors.

Descriptor(s): Teacher education, Speaking, Cultural issues, Materials, Listening, English language, Curriculum/syllabus, Classroom interaction

Country of research: United Kingdom

Entered by: University of Edinburgh (School of Education)

Cutting, J. 2007. 'Doing more stuff – Where's it going? Exploring vague language further' in J. Cutting (ed.) *Vague Language Explored.* Basingstoke: Palgrave Macmillan.

ISBN: 9781403988171

Summary: I describe my model of Vague Language (VL) and discuss studies on the influence of social factors, such as function, depth of relationship and gender. The chapter also explores applications of findings to TEFL and describes an experiment on the teachability of VL.

Descriptor(s): Writing, Speaking, Cultural issues, Reading, Methodology, Materials, Listening, English language, Curriculum/syllabus, Classroom interaction

Entered by: University of Edinburgh (School of Education)

Cutting, J. 2007. 'Introduction' in J. Cutting (ed.) *Vague Language Explored.* Basingstoke, England: Palgrave Macmillan.

ISBN: 9781403988171

Summary: Vague Language (VL) is a central feature of daily language, spoken and written. Gathering descriptions from a variety of specialisms, this book examines the function of VL in a range of social contexts. It then suggests applications to language teaching, and directions that research could take next.

Descriptor(s): Writing, Speaking, Cultural issues, Reading, Methodology, Materials, Listening, English language, Classroom interaction

C

D

Entered by: University of Edinburgh (School of Education)

Cutting, J. 2007. *Pragmatics and Discourse: a Resource Book for Students* (2nd edition). London: Routledge.

ISBN: 9780415446679

Summary: This book covers the core areas of the subject and suggests applications to ELT: Context and Co-text, Speech Act Theory, Conversation Analysis, Exchange Structure, Interactional Sociolinguistics, the Co-operative Principle, Politeness Theory, Corpus Linguistics, Communities of Practice, Intercultural Pragmatics, Interlanguage Pragmatics and Language Learning.

Descriptor(s): Teacher education, Teacher cognition, Cultural issues, Materials, English language, Curriculum/syllabus, Classroom interaction

Entered by: University of Edinburgh (School of Education)

Daller, H., J. Milton and J. Treffers-Daller. 2007. 'Editors' introduction: Conventions, terminology and overview of the book' in H. Daller, J. Milton and J. Treffers-Daller (eds.) *Testing and Modelling Lexical Knowledge.* Cambridge: Cambridge University Press.

ISBN: 978-0-521-70327-7

Pages: 1–32

Summary: Introduction to a volume which presents and evaluates cutting-edge research into the way vocabulary knowledge is stored, learned and tested.

Descriptor(s): Assessment

Entered by: Swansea University (Department of Applied Linguistics)

Daller, M.H. and D. Phelan. 2006. 'The C-test and TOEIC® as measures of students' progress in intensive short courses in EFL' in R. Grotjahn (ed.) *The C-test. Theoretical Basis and*

Practical Applications (Vol. 4). Frankfurt/New York: Lang Verlag.

ISBN: 3-631-55304-8

Pages: 101–119

Summary: This paper investigates whether the C-test can partially replace the Test of English for International Communication (TOEIC). It is argued that the C-test is the more suitable test for large numbers when measuring students' progress.

Descriptor(s): ESOL/EAL, ESP, English language, Assessment

Country of research: United Kingdom

Institutional level: tertiary

Entered by: University of West of England (School of Humanities, Languages and Social Sciences)

Daller, M.H. and D. Phelan. 2007. 'What is in a teacher's mind? The relation between teacher ratings of EFL essays and different aspects of lexical richness' in M.H. Daller, J. Milton and J. Treffers-Daller (eds.) *Testing and Modelling Lexical Knowledge.* Cambridge: Cambridge University Press.

ISBN: 978-0-521-87851-7

Pages: 234–245

Summary: The present study investigates to what extent teacher judgement of EFL essays can be predicted by measuring the lexical richness of these texts. Although the teachers did have different individual preferences in the detailed analysis of the essays, there was a highly significant correlation between them, which is an indication for reliable rating.

Descriptor(s): Assessment, English language, ESP

Country of research: United Kingdom

Institutional level: tertiary

Entered by: University of West of England (School of Humanities, Languages and Social Sciences)

Daller, M.H. and H-J. Xue. 2007. 'Lexical richness and the oral proficiency of Chinese EFL students' in M.H. Daller, J. Milton and J. Treffers-Daller (eds.) *Testing and Modelling Lexical Knowledge.* Cambridge: Cambridge University Press.

ISBN: 978-0-521-87851-7

Pages: 150–164

Summary: In this chapter we intend to investigate which measurement of lexical richness appears the most suitable for measuring oral proficiency of Chinese EFL learners. This is a specific task and one where the vocabulary knowledge that a learner can bring to bear should play an important role in their success in carrying out the task.

Descriptor(s): Cultural issues, ESP, English language, Curriculum/syllabus, Assessment

Country of research: United Kingdom

Learners' background: China

Institutional level: tertiary

Entered by: University of West of England (School of Humanities, Languages and Social Sciences)

Daller, M.H., J. Milton and J. Treffers-Daller. 2007. 'Editors' introduction: Conventions, terminology and overview of the book' in M.H. Daller, J. Milton and J. Treffers-Daller (eds.) *Testing and Modelling Lexical Knowledge.* Cambridge: Cambridge University Press.

ISBN: 978-0-521-87851-7

Pages: 1–32

Summary: Vocabulary is now considered integral to just about every aspect of language knowledge. This volume brings together contributions from internationally renowned researchers in this field to explain much of the background to study in this area. It introduces to a wider audience the concerns, the new approaches and developments in the field of vocabulary research and testing.

Descriptor(s): English language, Curriculum/syllabus, Assessment

Entered by: University of West of England (School of Humanities, Languages and Social Sciences)

Davidson, F. and G. Fulcher. 2007. 'The Common European Framework of Reference (CEFR) and the design of language tests: A matter of effect'. *Language Teaching* 40/3: 231–241.

Descriptor(s): Assessment

Entered by: University of Leicester (English Language Teaching and Applied Linguistics, School of Education)

Davidson, P., M. Al-Hamly, C. Coombe and S. Troudi. 2005. *Standards in English Language Teaching and Assessment.* UAE: TESOL Arabia.

Descriptor(s): ESOL/EAL, Assessment

Entered by: University of Exeter (School of Education and Lifelong Learning)

Davies, S., J. Gollin and T. Lynch. 2005. 'Identity in language learning: L2 learners' responses to English intonation teaching'. *Edinburgh Working Papers in Applied Linguistics* 14: 18–39.

Summary: A comparative study of Hong Kong and Japanese learners receiving instruction in English intonation patterns at the Institute for Applied Language Studies, Edinburgh.

Descriptor(s): Cultural issues, Pronunciation, Learner cognition, Classroom interaction

Entered by: University of Edinburgh (Institute for Applied Language Studies/Office of Lifelong Learning)

Deignan, A. 2005. 'A corpus-linguistic perspective on the relationship between metonymy and metaphor'. *Style* 39/1: 72–91.

Entered by: University of Leeds (School of Education)

D

D

Deignan, A. 2005. *Metaphor and Corpus Linguistics.* Amsterdam: John Benjamins.

ISBN: 9027238987

Entered by: University of Leeds (School of Education)

DeVelle, S. 2008. 'The revised IELTS pronunciation scale'. *Cambridge ESOL: Research Notes* 34: 36–39.

Summary: Sacha DeVelle describes a study to examiner raters' use and perceptions of the revised IELTS pronunciation scale.

www.cambridgeesol.org/rs_notes/rs_nts34. PDF

Entered by: University of Cambridge ESOL Examinations

Dewey, M. 2007. 'English as a lingua franca and globalization: An interconnected perspective'. *International Journal of Applied Linguistics* 17/3: 332–354.

Summary: This article reflects on the continued momentum of empirical research and debate regarding English as a lingua franca. The discussion considers the current situation in light of theoretical positions on globalization, arguing that a 'transformationalist' perspective is of most relevance to furthering our understanding of ELF.

Descriptor(s): Teacher education, English language

Country of research: United Kingdom

Entered by: King's College London (Department of Education and Professional Studies)

Dewey, M. 2008. 'Researching English as a lingua franca'. *IATEFL Research News* 22: 18–20.

Summary: This article provides a summary of recent research into English as a lingua franca and reflects on some of the key practical and theoretical concerns involved if language teachers are to adopt a World Englishes/ELF perspective in the classroom.

Descriptor(s): English language, Teacher education

Country of research: United Kingdom

Entered by: King's College London (Department of Education and Professional Studies)

Dewey, M. and A. Cogo. 2007. 'Adopting an ELF perspective in ELT'. *IATEFL Voices* 199: 11.

Descriptor(s): Cultural issues, Methodology, ESOL/EAL, ESP, English language, Curriculum/syllabus

Country of research: United Kingdom

Entered by: University of Southampton (Modern Languages, School of Humanities)

Diamantopoulou, S. 2007. 'A multimodal approach to the Ideas Factory Project's impact on children's literacy: A research report'.

Summary: This is an inquiry into the pedagogy of the Ideas Factory and EAL children's literacy practices that this approach facilitated. A multimodal social semiotic approach to teaching and learning in the gallery and the classroom is the framework for the understanding of children's literacy work.

www.tate.org.uk/britain/ideasfactory/2006/P DF/verbal-eyes-report.PDF

Descriptor(s): Teacher education, Cultural issues, Methodology, ESOL/EAL, Curriculum/syllabus, Classroom interaction

Country of research: United Kingdom

Learners' background: United Kingdom

Institutional level: primary

Entered by: Institute of Education, London (Department of Learning, Curriculum and Communication)

Díez Bedmar, M. and S. Papp. 2008. 'The use of the English article system by Chinese and Spanish learners' in G. Gilquin, S. Papp and M. Díez Bedmar (eds.) *Linking up Contrastive and Learner Corpus Research.* Amsterdam, New York: Rodopi.

D

ISBN: 978-90-420-2446-5

Pages: 147–176

Summary: In this paper we investigate the use of the English article system in two comparable learner corpora, Chinese-English and Spanish-English. Such investigation is significant as article use is at the interface of syntax, semantics and pragmatics.

Descriptor(s): Writing, Learner cognition, English language

Country of research: various

Learners' background: various

Institutional level: tertiary

Entered by: University of Cambridge ESOL Examinations

Donohue, J.P. 2006. 'How to support a one-handed economist: the role of modalisation in economic forecasting'. *English for Specific Purposes* 25: 200–216.

Descriptor(s): ESP, English language

Institutional level: adult

Entered by: The Open University (Faculty of Education and Languages)

Dörnyei, Z. 2005. *Teaching and Researching Motivation (Chinese edition)*. Beijing: Foreign Language Teaching and Research Press.

ISBN: 978-0582382381

Descriptor(s): Teacher education, Learner cognition, Learner autonomy/strategies, Curriculum/syllabus

Entered by: University of Nottingham (School of English Studies)

Dörnyei, Z. 2005. *The Psychology of the Language Learner: Individual Differences in Second Language Acquisition*. Mahwah, NJ: Lawrence Erlbaum.

ISBN: 0-8058-6018-5

Descriptor(s): Learner cognition, Learner autonomy/strategies

Entered by: University of Nottingham (School of English Studies)

Dörnyei, Z. 2005. 動機づけを高める英語指導ストラテジ *[Japanese translation of Motivational Strategies in the Language Classroom]*. Tokyo: Taishukan Publishing Co.

ISBN: 978-4-469-24508-0

Descriptor(s): Learner cognition, Learner autonomy/strategies

Entered by: University of Nottingham (School of English Studies)

Dörnyei, Z. 2006. 'Individual differences in second language acquisition'. *AILA Review* 19: 42–68.

Descriptor(s): Learner cognition, Learner autonomy/strategies

Entered by: University of Nottingham (School of English Studies)

Dörnyei, Z. 2006. 外国語教育学のための質問紙調査入門 ―作成・実施・データ処理 *[Japanese translation of Questionnaires in Second Language Research]*. Tokyo: Shohakusha Publishing Co.

ISBN: 978-4469244571

Descriptor(s): Assessment

Entered by: University of Nottingham (School of English Studies)

Dörnyei, Z. 2007. 'Creating a motivating classroom environment' in J. Cummins and C. Davison (eds.) *International Handbook of English Language Teaching*. New York: Springer.

ISBN: 9780387463001

Pages: 719–731

Descriptor(s): Management/innovation, Learner cognition, Learner autonomy/ strategies, Classroom interaction

D

Entered by: University of Nottingham
(School of English Studies)

Dörnyei, Z. 2008. *Estrategias de Motivación en el Aula de Lenguas [Spanish translation of Motivational Strategies in the Language Classroom].* Barcelona, Spain: Editorial UOC.

ISBN: 9788497887175

Descriptor(s): Learner cognition, Learner autonomy/strategies

Entered by: University of Nottingham
(School of English Studies)

Dörnyei, Z. 2008. *Estratègies de Motivació a L'aula de Llengües [Catalan translation of Motivational Strategies in the Language Classroom].* Barcelona, Spain: Editorial UOC.

ISBN: 9788497887021

Descriptor(s): Learner cognition, Learner autonomy/strategies

Entered by: University of Nottingham
(School of English Studies)

Dörnyei, Z. 2008. 'Generating and maintaining student motivation in the language classroom' in P. Bimmel, J. Canton, D. Fasoglio and G. Rijlaarsdam (eds.) *Handboek ontwerpen talen.* Amsterdam: Vossiuspers UvA.

ISBN: 9789056295097

Pages: 95–109

Descriptor(s): Learner cognition, Learner autonomy/strategies

Institutional level: secondary

Entered by: University of Nottingham
(School of English Studies)

Dörnyei, Z. 2008. 'New ways of motivating foreign language learners: Generating vision'. *Links* 38/Winter: 3–4.

Descriptor(s): Teacher education, Learner cognition, Learner autonomy/strategies

Entered by: University of Nottingham
(School of English Studies)

Dörnyei, Z. 2008.
외국어 연구를 위한 설문지 작성 방법론
[Korean translation of Questionnaires in Second Language Research]. Seoul, Korea: Hankook Munhwasa.

ISBN: 9788957264959

Descriptor(s): Assessment

Entered by: University of Nottingham
(School of English Studies)

Dörnyei, Z. and K. Csizér. 2005. 'The effects of intercultural contact and tourism on language attitudes and language learning motivation'. *Journal of Language and Social Psychology* 24/4: 327–357.

Descriptor(s): Cultural issues, Learner cognition

Country of research: Hungary

Institutional level: secondary

Entered by: University of Nottingham
(School of English Studies)

Dörnyei, Z. and T. Murphey. 2006. *Talde-Dinamika Hizkuntz Ikasgelan [Basque translation of Group Dynamics in the Language Classroom].* Donostia, Spain: HABE.

ISBN: 978-84-95827-93-7

Descriptor(s): Management/innovation, Learner cognition, Learner autonomy/strategies, Classroom interaction

Entered by: University of Nottingham
(School of English Studies)

Dörnyei, Z., K. Csizér and N. Németh. 2006. *Motivation, Language Attitudes and Globalisation: A Hungarian Perspective.* Clevedon, England: Multilingual Matters.

ISBN: 978-1-85359-885-2

Descriptor(s): Cultural issues, English language

Country of research: Hungary

Institutional level: secondary

E

Eckerth, J. 2008. 'Investigating consciousness-raising tasks: Pedagogically targeted and non-targeted learning gains'. *International Journal of Applied Linguistics* 18/2: 119–145.

Summary: This study investigates a series of dyadic consciousness-raising tasks which were introduced into an actual L2 classroom This research not only shows that consciousness-raising tasks can bring about significant learning gains in L2 explicit knowledge, but further reveals that many such learning opportunities lie outside the explicit linguistic focus of the tasks under scrutiny.

Descriptor(s): Learner cognition, Classroom interaction, Assessment

Country of research: Germany

Learners' background: various

Institutional level: tertiary

Entered by: King's College London (Department of Education and Professional Studies)

Eckerth, J. 2008. 'Task-based language learning and teaching: Old wine in new bottles?' in J. Eckerth and S. Siekmann (eds.) *Task-Based Language Teaching and Learning: Theoretical, Methodological and Pedagogical Perspectives*. Frankfurt am Main: Peter Lang.

ISBN: 9783631573303

Pages: 13–46

Summary: This paper provides a framework within which research into TBLT can be situated. It first focuses on tasks in SLA research. Several theoretical positions are reviewed. The use of tasks in L2 pedagogy is considered and tasks are suggested as a conceptual link between L2 teaching and learning.

Descriptor(s): Teacher education, Methodology, Materials, Management/innovation, Curriculum/syllabus

Entered by: King's College London (Department of Education and Professional Studies)

Economidou-Kogetsidis, M. and H. Woodfield. 2008. 'Interlanguage requests in academic encounters' in M. Edwardes (ed.) *Proceedings of the BAAL annual conference 2007*. London, UK: Scitsiugnil Press.

Principal format: CD-ROM

Entered by: University of Bristol (Graduate School of Education)

Edge, J. 2006. 'Background and overview' in J. Edge (ed.) *(Re-)Locating TESOL in an Age of Empire*. Basingstoke: Palgrave Macmillan.

ISBN: 9780230580060

Entered by: University of Manchester (School of Education)

Edge, J. 2007. 'Developing the community of practice in the Adult Migrant English Program'. *Prospect* 22/1: 3–18.

Descriptor(s): Management/innovation, Curriculum/syllabus

Institutional level: adult

Entered by: University of Manchester (School of Education)

Edge, J. 2008. 'Discourses in search of coherence' in S. Garton and K. Richards (eds.) *Professional Encounters in TESOL: Discourses of Teachers in Teaching*. Basingstoke: Palgrave.

ISBN: 978-0230553514

Pages: 232–247

Entered by: University of Nottingham (School of English Studies)

E

E

Descriptor(s): Teacher education, Teacher cognition, English language

Entered by: University of Manchester (School of Education)

El-Malik, A. and H. Nesi. 2008. 'Publishing research in a second language: The case of Sudanese contributors to international medical journals'. *Journal of English for Academic Purposes.* 7/2: 87–96.

Summary: This paper compares published writing produced by British and Sudanese medical researchers. Both sets of articles conformed to editorial requirements and followed the conventional IMRD structure to a large extent, but differences were noted in the realisation of these components, particularly in the discussion section.

Descriptor(s): Writing, Cultural issues, ESP, English language

Country of research: United Kingdom

Learners' background: Sudan

Institutional level: tertiary

Entered by: Coventry University

Enever, J. (ed.) 2008. 'Early language learning in Europe, first interim report'.

Summary: This report summarises key findings of the first year of the longitudinal, transnational study, highlighting attitudinal and linguistic progress; indicating the importance of in-school and out-of-school support (FL contexts: 6 English, 1 French/Spanish).

www.ellieresearch.eu/docs/ELLiE_1st_Interim_Report_Dec_08.PDF

Descriptor(s): Methodology, Management/innovation, English language, Curriculum/syllabus

Country of research: various

Learners' background: various

Institutional level: primary

Associated project: Early Language Learning in Europe (ELLiE)

Entered by: London Metropolitan University (Faculty of Humanities, Arts, Languages and Education)

Enever, J. 2005. 'Europeanisation or globalisation in early start EFL trends across Europe?' in C. Gnutzmann and F. Intermann (eds.) *The Globalisation of English and the English Language Classroom.* Tübingen, Germany: Gunter Narr Verlag.

ISBN: 3 8233 6136 8

Pages: 177–192

Summary: This study draws on interview data from Hungarian senior academics and ministry officials reviewing the process of language policy-making for an early start to foreign language learning (English) during the 1990s in Hungary. Implications of the decision against a mandatory early start are contextualised within a wider EU soft policy context.

Descriptor(s): Teacher education, Methodology, Management/innovation, Curriculum/syllabus

Country of research: Hungary

Institutional level: primary

Entered by: London Metropolitan University (Faculty of Humanities, Arts, Languages and Education)

Enever, J. 2006. 'The use of authentic picture books in the development of critical visual and written literacy in English as a foreign language' in J. Enever and G. Schmid-Schönbein (eds.) *Picture Books and Young Learners of English.* Munich, Germany: Langenscheidt.

ISBN: 10: 3-526-50836-4

Pages: 59–70

Summary: This paper focuses on the role of picture story books in the development of critical visual literacy and their potential contribution to the achievement of critical written literacy for young learners of English as a foreign language.

Descriptor(s): Reading, Methodology, Materials, Curriculum/syllabus

Institutional level: primary

Entered by: London Metropolitan University (Faculty of Humanities, Arts, Languages and Education)

Enever, J. 2007. 'Yet another early start. Language policy in Europe: Poland this time!'. *Current Issues in Language Planning* 8/2: 208–221.

Summary: This study interrogates contemporary drivers of Polish language-in-education planning, proposing their essentially political nature as a vehicle for the acquisition of linguistic cultural capital and questioning the extent to which this decision is founded on empirical evidence of the real advantages of an early start.

Descriptor(s): Teacher education, Management/innovation, Curriculum/syllabus

Country of research: Poland

Institutional level: primary

Entered by: London Metropolitan University (Faculty of Humanities, Arts, Languages and Education)

Erling, E.J. 2005. 'The many names of English'. *English Today* 21/1: 40–44.

Descriptor(s): ESOL/EAL, English language

Institutional level: adult

Entered by: The Open University (Faculty of Education and Languages)

Erling, E.J. 2005. 'Who is the global English speaker? A profile of students of English at the Freie Universität Berlin' in C. Gnutzmann and F. Intemann (eds.) *The Globalisation of English and the English Language Classroom*. Tubingen: Gunter Narr.

ISBN: 978 3823361367

Pages: 215–230

Descriptor(s): Speaking, Cultural issues, English language

Institutional level: adult

Entered by: The Open University (Faculty of Education and Languages)

Erling, E.J. 2007. 'Local identities and global connections: Affinities with English among student specialists at the Free University of Berlin'. *World Englishes* 26/2: 111–130.

Descriptor(s): Cultural issues, ESP, English language

Institutional level: adult

Entered by: The Open University (Faculty of Education and Languages)

Erling, E.J. 2008. 'Local investigations of global English: Teaching English as a global language at the Freie Universität Berlin' in S.H.J. Dogancay-Aktuna (ed.) *Global English Language Teacher Education*. Alexandria, VA: TESOL.

ISBN: 978 1931185516

Pages: 147–165

Descriptor(s): Cultural issues, English language, Curriculum/syllabus

Institutional level: adult

Entered by: The Open University (Faculty of Education and Languages)

Erling, E.J. and S.K. Hilgendorf. 2006. 'English at the German University: A means of disadvantage or empowerment?' in A. Weideman and B. Smieja (eds.) *Empowerment Through Language and Education*. Frankfurt: Peter Lang.

ISBN: 978 0820498829

Pages: 113–128

Descriptor(s): Cultural issues, English language

E

F

Institutional level: adult

Entered by: The Open University (Faculty of Education and Languages)

Erling, E. and T. Bartlett. 2006. 'Making English their own: The use of ELF among students of English at the FUB'. *Nordic Journal of English Studies, Special Issue on English as Lingua Franca* 5/2: 9–40.

Descriptor(s): Cultural issues, ESOL/EAL

Entered by: Cardiff University (School of English, Communication and Philosophy)

Erling, E.J. and T. Bartlett. 2006. 'Making English their own: The use of ELF among students of English at the Free University of Berlin'. *Nordic Journal of English Studies* 5/2: 9–40.

Descriptor(s): Cultural issues, English language, Classroom interaction

Institutional level: adult

Entered by: The Open University (Faculty of Education and Languages)

Erling, E. and T. Bartlett. 2008. 'Making space for us: German graduate student voices in English'. *Innovation in Language Learning and Teaching* 2/2: 174–188.

Descriptor(s): Cultural issues, English language

Entered by: Cardiff University (School of English, Communication and Philosophy)

Erling, E.J. and T. Bartlett. 2008. 'Making space for us: German graduate student voices in English'. *Innovation in Language Learning and Teaching* 2/2: 174–188.

Descriptor(s): English language

Institutional level: adult

Entered by: The Open University (Faculty of Education and Languages)

Evison, J., M. McCarthy and A. O'Keeffe. 2007. 'Looking out for love and all the rest of it: Vague category markers as shared social space' in J. Cutting (ed.) *Vague Language Explored.* Hampshire: Palgrave.

ISBN: 1-4039-8817-X

Pages: 138–157

Summary: This chapter used the British English CANCODE corpus and the Irish English LICE corpus to explore vague language in contexts where the participants have different degrees of shared knowledge and intimacy, notably casual conversation, spoken academic data, and calls to radio phone-ins. The implications for language teaching are considered.

Descriptor(s): Speaking, Cultural issues, ESP, English language, Classroom interaction

Entered by: University of Nottingham (School of Education)

F

Falvey, P. and S. Shaw. 2006. 'IELTS writing: Revising assessment criteria and scales (Phase 5)'. *Cambridge ESOL: Research Notes* 23: 7–12.

Summary: Peter Falvey and Stuart Shaw continue a series of articles on the IELTS Writing Revision project. They report the latest trial of new writing assessment criteria and describe how well they are being interpreted and applied, followed by a discussion of the process approach to developing tests which examines how tests fulfil their intended purpose.

www.cambridgeesol.org/rs_notes/rs_nts23.PDF

Entered by: University of Cambridge ESOL Examinations

Fay, R. and L. Davcheva. 2005. 'Developing professional intercultural competence: Reflections on DL programmes for language educators and translators/interpreters in Bulgaria' in B. Holmberg, M. Shelley and C. White (eds.) *Distance Education and Languages: Evolution and Change.* Clevedon: Multilingual Matters.

ISBN: 1853597759

Pages: 140–165

Descriptor(s): Teacher education, Cultural issues

Country of research: Bulgaria

Learners' background: Bulgaria

Institutional level: tertiary

Entered by: University of Manchester (School of Education)

Fay, R. and L. Davcheva. 2007. 'The development of language teachers' understandings of intercultural communicative competence: A Bulgarian distance learning case study' in M. Jimenez Raya and L. Sercu (eds.) *Challenges in Teacher Development: Learner Autonomy and Intercultural Competence.* Frankfurt am Main: Peter Lang.

ISBN: 3-631-55806-6

Pages: 191–212

Descriptor(s): Teacher education, Teacher cognition, Cultural issues

Country of research: Bulgaria

Learners' background: Bulgaria

Institutional level: tertiary

Entered by: University of Manchester (School of Education)

Ferguson, G. 2005. 'Is English really a Tyrannosaurus Rex? Scientific communication and the global spread of English' in P. Duran and A Riejos (eds.) *Reflections on Language Use in the Academic Context.* Madrid: Universidad Politecnica de Madrid Press.

ISBN: 84-96442-1-X

Pages: 73–94

Descriptor(s): English language

Entered by: University of Sheffield (School of English)

F

Ferguson, G. 2006. *Language Planning and Education.* Edinburgh: Edinburgh University Press.

ISBN: 0 7486 1262 9

Descriptor(s): Curriculum/syllabus, English language

Entered by: University of Sheffield (School of English)

Ferguson, G. 2007. 'The global spread of English, scientific communication and ESP: questions of equity, access and domain loss'. *Ibérica* 13/1: 7–38.

Descriptor(s): ESP, English language

Entered by: University of Sheffield (School of English)

Ferguson, G. 2008. 'Multilingual Sheffield' in C. Kenner and T. Hickey (eds.) Multilingual Europe: Diversity and Learning. Stoke-on-Trent: Trentham Books.

Pages: 21–28

ISBN: 978-185856-423-4

Descriptor(s): Cultural issues

Country of research: United Kingdom

Entered by: University of Sheffield (School of English)

Field, J. 2007. 'Looking outwards, not inwards'. *ELT Journal* 61/1: 30–38.

Summary: A call for second language teachers to prioritise the teaching of listening skills and compensatory strategies so as to enable learners to take full advantage of the rich linguistic resources which are now available outside the classroom

Descriptor(s): Listening, Learner autonomy/strategies, English language

Entered by: University of Reading (Department of Applied Linguistics)

F

Field, J. 2008. 'Bricks or mortar: Which parts of the input does a second language listener rely on?'. *TESOL Quarterly* 42/3: 411–432.

Summary: It is useful to know which parts of the signal L2 listeners are likely to recognize, and which are likely to be lost to them. This study investigated whether function or content words are processed more accurately. It found that the recognition of functors fell significantly behind that of lexical words, regardless of first language and level of proficiency.

Descriptor(s): Listening

Country of research: United Kingdom

Learners' background: various

Entered by: University of Reading (Department of Applied Linguistics)

Field, J. 2008. 'Emergent and divergent: A view of second language listening research'. *System* 36/1: 2–9.

Summary: Overview of current issues and recent developments in L2 listening research.

Descriptor(s): Listening

Country of research: United Kingdom

Institutional level: tertiary

Entered by: University of Reading (Department of Applied Linguistics)

Field, J. 2008. 'Face to face with the ghost in the machine: Psycholinguistics and TESOL'. *TESOL Quarterly* 42/3: 361–374.

Summary: Review of the many ways in which theory in psycholinguistics can extend our understanding of the processes underlying the acquisition, the storage and the use of a second language – especially in relation to the skills of speaking, listening, writing and reading.

Descriptor(s): Writing, Speaking, Reading, Listening

Entered by: University of Reading (Department of Applied Linguistics)

Field, J. 2008. *Listening in the Language Classroom.* Cambridge: Cambridge University Press.

ISBN: 978-0-521-68570-2

Summary: A comprehensive proposal for a new approach to the teaching of L2 listening, to supplement and replace the much-challenged comprehension approach. Accompanied by a detailed description of the nature of the listening process, both in L1 and in L2, to ensure a better understanding among teachers of their goals in teaching the skill.

Descriptor(s): Methodology, Listening

Country of research: various

Learners' background: various

Entered by: University of Reading (Department of Applied Linguistics)

Field, J. 2008. 'Revising segmentation hypotheses in first and second language listening'. *System* 36/1: 35–51.

Summary: Any online processing that takes place while an utterance is unfolding is extremely tentative, with early-formed hypotheses having to be revised as the utterance proceeds. This study examines how first and second language listeners adjust these segmentation assumptions as new perceptual evidence comes in. The results indicated a significant difference in the way in which first and second language listeners deal with incorrect hypotheses.

Descriptor(s): Listening

Country of research: United Kingdom

Learners' background: various

Institutional level: adult

Entered by: University of Reading (Department of Applied Linguistics)

Figura, K. and H. Jarvis. 2007. 'Computer-based materials: A study of learner autonomy and strategies'. *System* 35/4: 448–468.

Summary: This is a study of learner autonomy and specified cognitive, social, and metacognitive strategies across a range of computer-based materials. The work suggests a need for more social interaction in the target language and recognition that learner choices in a digitalised age may not match established practitioner beliefs.

Descriptor(s): Learning technologies, Learner autonomy/strategies, ESP

Country of research: United Kingdom

Learners' background: various

Institutional level: adult

Entered by: University of Salford (School of Languages)

Fitzpatrick, T. 2007. 'Word association patterns: Unpacking the assumptions'. *International Journal of Applied Linguistics* 17/ 3: 319–331.

Entered by: Swansea University (Department of Applied Linguistics)

Fitzpatrick, T. 2007. 'Productive vocabulary tests and the search for concurrent validity' in H. Daller, J. Milton and J. Treffers-Daller (eds.) *Modelling and Assessing Vocabulary Knowledge*. Cambridge: Cambridge University Press.

ISBN: 978-0-521-70327-7

Pages: 116–132

Entered by: Swansea University (Department of Applied Linguistics)

Fitzpatrick, T. and A. Wray. 2006. 'Breaking up is not so hard to do: Individual differences in L2 memorisation'. *Canadian Modern Languages Review* 63/1: 35–57.

Entered by: Swansea University (Department of Applied Linguistics)

Fitzpatrick, T. and A. Wray. 2008. 'Why can't you just leave it alone? Deviations from memorised language'

in F. Meunier and S. Granger (eds.) *Phraseology in Foreign Language Learning and Teaching*. Amsterdam: Benjamins.

ISBN: 978-90-272-3244-1

Pages: 123–148

Entered by: Swansea University (Department of Applied Linguistics)

Fitzpatrick, T., I. Al-Qarni and P. Meara. 2008. 'Intensive vocabulary learning: A case study'. *Language Learning Journal* 36/2: 239–248.

Entered by: Swansea University (Department of Applied Linguistics)

Flowerdew, J. 2006. 'Use of signalling nouns in a learner corpus'. *International Journal of Corpus Linguistics* 11/3: 345–362.

Entered by: University of Leeds (School of Education)

Flowerdew, J. 2008. 'The non-Anglophone scholar at the periphery of scientific communication'. *AILA Review* 20: 14–27.

Entered by: University of Leeds (School of Education)

Flowerdew, J. 2008. 'What can Goffman's "Stigma" tell us about scholarly writers who use English as an additional language?'. *Journal of English for Academic Purposes* 7/2: 77–86.

Entered by: University of Leeds (School of Education)

Flowerdew, J. and A. Wan. 2006. 'Genre analysis of tax computation letters: How and why tax accountants write the way they do'. *English for Specific Purposes* 25/2: 133–153.

Entered by: University of Leeds (School of Education)

Flowerdew, J. and L. Miller. 2005. *Second Language Listening: Theory and Practice*. Cambridge: Cambridge University Press.

F

F

ISBN: 978-0521786478

Descriptor(s): Listening

Entered by: University of Leeds
(School of Education)

Flowerdew, J. and L. Miller. 2008. 'Structure and agency in second language learning: Evidence from three life histories'. *Critical Inquiry in Language Studies* 5/4: 201–224.

Entered by: University of Leeds
(School of Education)

Flowerdew, J. and S. Leong. 2007. 'Metaphors in the discursive construction of patriotism: The case of Hong Kong's constitutional reform debate'. *Discourse and Society* 18/3: 273–294.

Entered by: University of Leeds
(School of Education)

Flowerdew, J. and Y-Y. Li. 2008. 'Language re-use among Chinese apprentice scientists writing for publication'. *Applied Linguistics* 28/3: 440–465.

Entered by: University of Leeds
(School of Education)

Flowerdew, J. and Y-Y. Li. 2008. 'Textual plagiarism'. *Annual Review of Applied Linguistics* 27: 161–183.

Entered by: University of Leeds
(School of Education)

Fortune, A. 2005. 'Learners' use of metalanguage in collaborative form-focused L2 output tasks'. *Language Awareness* 14/1: 21–38.

Summary: text reconstruction task is compared with that of intermediate learners in an earlier study. Grammatical and lexical Language Related Episodes containing metalanguage are categorised, and their frequency compared. Advanced learners are shown to be more frequent metalanguage users than their intermediate counterparts, particularly in lexical episodes.

Descriptor(s): Learner cognition, Classroom interaction

Country of research: United Kingdom

Learners' background: various

Institutional level: tertiary

Entered by: King's College London
(Department of Education and Professional Studies)

Fortune, A. 2008. 'Collaborative focus on form: What, why, when and how?' in M. Pawlak (ed.) *Investigating English Language Learning and Teaching.* Poznan-Kalisz: Adam-Mickiewicz University.

ISBN: 978-83-883354-5-7

Pages: 95–108

Principal format: Printed

Summary: This paper discusses the use of tasks during which learners focus on form, either incidentally or more particularly as a design feature of the task, focussing principally on research on the latter task type, especially work on collaborative output tasks.

Country of research: United Kingdom

Learners' background: various

Institutional level: tertiary

Entered by: King's College London
(Department of Education and Professional Studies)

Foster, P. and A. Ohta. 2005. 'Negotiation for meaning and peer assistance in classroom language tasks'. *Applied Linguistics* 26/3: 402–430.

Summary: This study used qualitative and quantitative analyses of classroom interaction in English and Japanese L2. It showed that negotiation for meaning is rare, and mostly lexical in nature, while learners provide themselves and each other with other kinds of potentially valuable opportunities for language development.

Descriptor(s): Methodology, Materials, Classroom interaction

Country of research: various

Learners' background: various

Institutional level: adult

Entered by: St. Mary's University College, Twickenham, London (School of Communication, Culture and Creative Arts)

Franson, C. 2005. 'A professional identity for the EAL teacher'. *NALDIC Quarterly* 2/4: 14–17.

Descriptor(s): ESOL/EAL

Entered by: Canterbury Christ Church University (Department of English and Language Studies)

Franson, C. 2007. 'Challenges and opportunities in EAL provision in the UK' in J. Cummins and C. Davison (eds.) *The International Handbook of English Language Teaching*. Norwell, Mass: Springer.

ISBN: 978-0-387-46300-1

Descriptor(s): ESOL/EAL

Entered by: Canterbury Christ Church University (Department of English and Language Studies)

Franson, C. and E. Vasquez. 2006. 'Teaching history to EAL learners in the mainstream classroom: Adaptation and contingency' in P. McKay (ed.) *Planning and Teaching Creatively Within a Required Curriculum for School Age Learners*. Alexandra, Virginia: TESOL.

ISBN: 1-9311-8530-1

Pages: 81–89

Descriptor(s): ESOL/EAL

Entered by: Canterbury Christ Church University (Department of English and Language Studies)

Fried-Booth, D. 2007. 'Reviewing part 1 of the FCE listening test'. *Cambridge ESOL: Research Notes* 30: 23–24.

Summary: A summary by Diana Fried-Booth of research into FCE Listening focusing on changes to the format of Part 1 of the paper. www.cambridgeesol.org/rs_notes/rs_nts30.PDF

Entered by: University of Cambridge ESOL Examinations

Frigols, M.J., D. Marsh and J. Naysmith. 2007. 'Competence building for teachers of CLIL: Vocational education' in D. Marsh and D. Wolff (eds.) *Diverse Contexts – Diverging Goals: CLIL in Europe*. Frankfurt am Main: Peter Lang.

ISBN: 9783631569054

Pages: 33–46

Summary: The chapter was an outcome from the EU–Funded Clilcom project, focussing on the development of CLIL teacher competences.

Descriptor(s): Management/innovation, Curriculum/syllabus

Entered by: University of Portsmouth (School of Languages and Area Studies)

Fulcher, G. 2006. 'Test architecture'. *Foreign Language Education Research* 9/1: 1-22.

Descriptor(s): Assessment

Entered by: University of Leicester (English Language Teaching and Applied Linguistics, School of Education)

Fulcher, G, 2007. 'Assessing the quality of language' in E. Shohamy (ed.) *Language Testing and Assessment (Encyclopaedia of Language and Education, Vol. 7)*. Amsterdam: Springer.

ISBN: 9780387328751

Descriptor(s): Assessment

F

G

Entered by: University of Leicester (English Language Teaching and Applied Linguistics, School of Education)

Fulcher, G. and F. Davidson. 2007. 'Tests in life and learning: A deathly dialogue'. *Educational Philosophy and Theory* 40/3: 407–417.

Descriptor(s): Assessment

Entered by: University of Leicester (English Language Teaching and Applied Linguistics, School of Education)

Furneaux, C. and M. Rignall. 2007. 'The effect of standardisation-training on rater judgements for the IELTS Writing Module' in L. Taylor and P. Falvey (eds.) *IELTS Collected Papers: Research in Speaking and Writing Assessment.* Cambridge: University of Cambridge ESOL Examinations and Cambridge University Press.

ISBN: 10: 0521542480

Pages: 422–445

Summary: This study investigates the judgements made by twelve trainee examiners (TEs) for the IELTS Writing Module. On successive occasions, before and during training, the TEs rated a set of eight scripts and wrote brief retrospective reports about their rating of four of the scripts.

Descriptor(s): Writing, English language, Assessment

Country of research: United Kingdom

Entered by: University of Reading (Department of Applied Linguistics)

Furneaux, C., A. Paran and B. Fairfax. 2007. 'Teacher stance as reflected in feedback on student writing: An empirical study of secondary school teachers in five countries'. *International Review of Applied Linguistics and Language Teaching* 45/1: 69–94.

Summary: This study examines the feedback practices of 110 EFL teachers from five different countries (Cyprus, France, Korea, Spain and Thailand), working in secondary school contexts. All provided feedback on the same student essay. Most teachers reacted as language teachers, rather than as readers of communication.

Descriptor(s): Writing, Methodology, English language

Country of research: various

Institutional level: secondary

Entered by: University of Reading (Department of Applied Linguistics)

Furneaux, C.L., A. Paran and B. Fairfax. 2007. 'Teacher stance as reflected in feedback on student writing: An empirical study of secondary school teachers in five countries'. *International Review of Applied Linguistics and Language Teaching* 45/1: 69–94.

Summary: 110 teachers from 5 countries provided feedback on the same student essay. Teachers overwhelmingly focused on grammar and assumed what was termed a Provider role, providing the correct forms for the student. Some teachers assumed an Initiator role, indicating errors and issues and expecting the learner to work on them.

Descriptor(s): Writing

Country of research: various

Learners' background: various

Entered by: Institute of Education, London (Department of Learning, Curriculum and Communication)

G

Galaczi, E. 2005. 'Upper Main Suite speaking assessment: Towards an understanding of assessment criteria and oral examiner behaviour'. *Cambridge ESOL: Research Notes* 20: 16–19.

Summary: Evelina Galaczi presents

performance data for FCE, CAE and CPE Speaking Tests for 2003, reporting on work to validate these Upper Main Suite tests through analysis of scoring criteria and examiner behaviour.

www.cambridgeesol.org/rs_notes/rs_nts20.PDF

Entered by: University of Cambridge ESOL Examinations

Galaczi, E. 2008. 'Peer-peer interaction in a speaking test: The case of the First Certificate in English examination'. *Language Assessment Quarterly* 5/2: 89–119.

Descriptor(s): Speaking, ESOL/EAL, Assessment

Country of research: various

Learners' background: various

Institutional level: tertiary

Entered by: University of Cambridge ESOL Examinations

Galaczi, E. and A. ffrench. 2007. 'Developing revised assessment scales for Main Suite and BEC speaking tests'. *Cambridge ESOL: Research Notes* 30: 28–31.

Summary: Evelina Galaczi and Angela ffrench describe the revision of assessment scales for Speaking tests for Main Suite and Business English Certificate (BEC) exams.

www.cambridgeesol.org/rs_notes/rs_nts30.PDF

Entered by: University of Cambridge ESOL Examinations

Gardner, S. 2006. 'Centre-stage in the instructional register: Partnership talk in primary EAL'. *International Journal of Bilingual Education and Biculturalism* 9/4: 476–494.

Descriptor(s): Methodology, ESOL/EAL, Classroom interaction

Country of research: United Kingdom

Learners' background: various

Institutional level: primary

Entered by: University of Birmingham (School of Education)

Gardner, S.F. 2007. 'Transforming talk and phonics practice: Or, how do crabs clap?'. *TESOL Quarterly* 42/2: 261–284.

Descriptor(s): ESOL/EAL, Classroom interaction

Country of research: United Kingdom

Learners' background: various

Institutional level: primary

Entered by: University of Birmingham (School of Education)

Gardner, S.F. 2008. 'Mapping ideational meaning in a corpus of student writing' in C. Jones and E. Ventola (eds.) *New Developments in the Study of Ideational Meaning: From Language to Multimodality.* London: Equinox Publishing.

ISBN: 978-1-84553-347-2

Country of research: United Kingdom

Learners' background: United Kingdom

Institutional level: adult

Entered by: University of Birmingham (School of Education)

Garrett, P. 2006. 'Language education: Language awareness' in K. Brown (ed.) *Encyclopaedia of Language and Linguistics (Second Edition).* Oxford: Elsevier.

ISBN: 0-08-044299-4

Pages: vol 6, 480–483

Descriptor(s): Learner autonomy/strategies

Entered by: Cardiff University (School of English, Communication and Philosophy)

Garrett, P. 2007. 'Language attitudes' in C. Llamas, L. Mullany and P. Stockwell (eds.) *Routledge Companion to Sociolinguistics.* London: Routledge.

ISBN: 978-0-415-33850-9

G

G

Pages: 116–121

Descriptor(s): Cultural issues

Entered by: Cardiff University (School of English, Communication and Philosophy)

Garrett, P., A. Williams and B. Evans. 2005. 'Attitudinal data from New Zealand, Australia, the USA and UK about each other's Englishes: Recent changes or consequences of methodologies?'. *Multilingua* 24: 211–236.

Descriptor(s): Cultural issues

Entered by: Cardiff University (School of English, Communication and Philosophy)

Garton, S. 2008. 'Teacher beliefs and interaction in the language classroom' in S. Garton and K. Richards (eds.) *Professional Encounters in TESOL: Discourses of Teachers in Teaching.* Basingstoke: Palgrave Macmillan.

ISBN: 9780230553514

Pages: 67–86

Summary: An investigation into the effects that teacher beliefs may have on the interaction patterns that teachers set up in their classrooms.

Descriptor(s): Teacher cognition, Classroom interaction

Entered by: Aston University (School of Languages and Social Sciences)

Garton, S. and K. Richards. 2007. 'Is distance education for teacher second best?'. *The Teacher Trainer* 21/3: 5–8.

Descriptor(s): Teacher education

Institutional level: tertiary

Entered by: Aston University (School of Languages and Social Sciences)

Garton, S. and K. Richards. 2007. 'Is distance education for teacher education second best?'. *The Teacher Trainer* 21/3: 5–8.

Summary: This paper examines the distinctive contribution that distance education can make to teacher development.

Descriptor(s): Teacher education

Entered by: University of Warwick (Centre for Applied Linguistics)

Garton, S. and K. Richards. 2008. 'Introduction' in S. Garton and K. Richards (eds.) *Professional Encounters in TESOL: Discourses of Teachers in Teaching.* Basingstoke: Palgrave Macmillan.

ISBN: 9780230553514

Pages: xiii–xxvii

Summary: An introduction to this edited collection looking at the career trajectory of those in TESOL, teacher cognition and the discourses of teachers

Descriptor(s): Teacher education, Teacher cognition

Entered by: Aston University (School of Languages and Social Sciences)

Geranpayeh, A. 2007. 'Differential Item Functioning in terms of age in the Certificate in Advanced English examination'. *Language Assessment Quarterly* 4/2: 190–222.

Descriptor(s): Listening, Assessment

Learners' background: various

Institutional level: tertiary

Entered by: University of Cambridge ESOL Examinations

Geranpayeh, A. 2007. 'Using structural equation modelling to facilitate the revision of high stakes testing: The case of CAE'. *Cambridge ESOL: Research Notes* 30: 8–12.

Summary: Ardeshir Geranpayeh reports on studies undertaken to investigate how Structural Equation Modelling (SEM) can aid the revision of high stakes testing, using CAE as a case study. He describes how SEM can be used to show that changes to the format of tests would not significantly change the underlying constructs of the CAE exam.

www.cambridgeesol.org/rs_notes/rs_nts30.PDF

Entered by: University of Cambridge ESOL Examinations

Geranpayeh, A. 2008. 'Using DIF to explore item difficulty in CAE listening'. *Cambridge ESOL: Research Notes* 32: 16–23.

Summary: Article explores sources of difficulty for test items in a General English Listening test using Differential Item Functioning (DIF). This procedure is used to show how tests are fair to candidates and as free from construct irrelevant variables as possible. This article investigates whether age is a source of unfairness in the Certificate in Advanced English (CAE) Listening paper.

www.cambridgeesol.org/rs_notes/rs_nts32.PDF

Entered by: University of Cambridge ESOL Examinations

Geranpayeh, A. and L. Taylor. 2008. 'Examining listening: Developments and issues in assessing second language listening'. *Cambridge ESOL: Research Notes* 32: 2–5.

Summary: Article describes the development of listening tests in Cambridge ESOL's examinations from 1913 to the present day, covering the nature of listening ability along three dimensions of a socio-cognitive framework: individual characteristics, extra-contextual factors and internal cognitive processing. They consider some of the issues with regard to assessing listening, such as the interplay of cognitive and contextual features.

www.cambridgeesol.org/rs_notes/rs_nts32.PDF

Entered by: University of Cambridge ESOL Examinations

Gieve, S. and R. Clark. 2005. 'The Chinese approach to learning: Cultural trait or situated response? The case of a self-directed learning programme'. *System* 33/2: 261–276

Descriptor(s): Cultural issues, Learner autonomy/strategies

Country of research: United Kingdom

Learners' background: China

Institutional level: tertiary

Entered by: University of Leicester (English Language Teaching and Applied Linguistics, School of Education)

Gieve, S. and R. Clark. 2005. 'The Chinese approach to learning: Cultural trait or situated response?'. *System* 33/2: 261–276.

Entered by: University of Portsmouth (School of Languages and Area Studies)

Gieve, S. and I. Miller. 2006. 'Introduction' in S. Gieve and I. Miller (eds.) *Understanding the Language Classroom.* Basingstoke: Palgrave Macmillan.

ISBN: 1403996628

Pages: 1–10

Descriptor(s): Teacher education, Curriculum/syllabus, Classroom interaction

Entered by: University of Leicester (English Language Teaching and Applied Linguistics, School of Education)

Gieve, S. and I. Miller. 2006. 'What do we mean by the quality of classroom life?' in S. Gieve and I. Miller (eds.) *Understanding the Language Classroom.* Basingstoke: Palgrave Macmillan.

ISBN: 1403996628

Pages: 18–46

Descriptor(s): Teacher education, Methodology, Learner cognition, Classroom interaction

Entered by: University of Leicester (English Language Teaching and Applied Linguistics, School of Education)

G

G

Gieve, S. and J. Norton. 2007. 'Dealing with linguistic difference in encounters with Others on British television' in A. Ensslin and S. Johnson (eds.) *Language in the Media: Representations, Identities, Ideologies.* London: Continuum Press.

ISBN: 0826495486

Pages: 118–212

Descriptor(s): Cultural issues

Country of research: United Kingdom

Entered by: University of Leicester (English Language Teaching and Applied Linguistics, School of Education)

Golovatch, Y. and R. Vanderplank. 2007. 'Unwitting agents: The role of adult learners' attributions of success in shaping language-learning behaviour'. *Adult and Continuing Education* 13/2: 127–155.

Summary: An investigation into the attributions of success and failure of adult EFL learners in the Department of Continuing Education, Minsk State Linguistic University, Belarus. Students attributed their limited progress mainly to the teacher's competence, the frequency and length of classes, the number of activities for listening and speaking, and teacher consultations.

Entered by: University of Oxford (Language Centre)

González-Diaz, V. 2006. 'On the origin of English periphrastic comparison'. *English Studies* 8: 707–734.

Descriptor(s): English language

Entered by: University of Liverpool (School of English)

González-Diaz, V. 2007. 'On the nature and distribution of English double periphrastic comparison'. *The Review of English Studies* 57: 623–664.

Descriptor(s): English language

Entered by: University of Liverpool (School of English)

González-Diaz, V. 2008. 'Worser and lesser in Modern English' in D. González-Alvarez J. Pérez-Guerra and E. Rama-Martínez (eds.) *Of Varying Language and Opposing Creed: New Insights into Late Modern English.* Bern: Peter Lang.

ISBN: 9783039107889

Pages: 237–278

Summary: González-Diaz, V. 2008. 'Worser and lesser in Modern English' in J. Pérez-Guerra, D. González-Alvarez, J.L. Bueno-Alonso and E. Rama-Martínez (eds.) *Of varying language and opposing creed. New insights into Late Modern English, Linguistic Insights 28.* Bern: Peter Lang.

Descriptor(s): English language

Entered by: University of Liverpool (School of English)

González-Diaz, V. and A. Auer. 2005. 'Eighteenth-century prescriptivism in English: A re-evaluation of its effects on actual language usage'. *Multilingua* 24: 317–341.

Descriptor(s): English language

Entered by: University of Liverpool (School of English)

Gray, C., R.M. Pilkington, L. Hagger-Vaughan and S. Tomkins. 2005. 'The pros and cons of interactive whiteboards'. *Language Learning Journal* 32/Winter: 38–44.

Descriptor(s): Learning technologies

Entered by: University of Birmingham (School of Education)

Green, A.B. 2005. 'EAP study recommendations and score gains on the IELTS Academic Writing test'. *Assessing Writing* 10/1: 44–60.

Descriptor(s): Writing, Curriculum/syllabus, Assessment

Country of research: United Kingdom

Learners' background: various

Institutional level: tertiary

Entered by: University of Bedfordshire (Centre for Research in English Language Learning and Assessment)

Green, A.B. 2005. 'Staying in touch: Tracking the career paths of CELTA graduates'. *Research Notes, Cambridge ESOL* 19: 7–12.

Descriptor(s): Teacher education

Country of research: various

Learners' background: various

Institutional level: adult

Entered by: University of Bedfordshire (Centre for Research in English Language Learning and Assessment)

Green, A.B. 2006. 'Washback to the learner: Learner and teacher perspectives on IELTS preparation course expectations and outcomes'. *Assessing Writing* 11/2: 113–134.

Summary: Learners and teachers on IELTS and non-IELTS EAP courses responded to questionnaires on academic writing instruction. Although test preparation courses, as predicted by washback theory, did appear to cover a relatively narrow range of skills, evidence was found that narrow preparation strategies were not driven primarily by learner expectations.

Descriptor(s): Writing, Cultural issues, Learner cognition, Learner autonomy/strategies, ESP, Assessment

Country of research: United Kingdom

Learners' background: China

Institutional level: tertiary

Entered by: University of Bedfordshire (Centre for Research in English Language Learning and Assessment)

Green, A.B. 2006. 'Watching for washback: Observing the influence of the IELTS academic writing test in the classroom'. *Language Assessment Quarterly* 3/4: 333–367.

Descriptor(s): Writing, Teacher cognition,

Methodology, Learner cognition, Learner autonomy/strategies, Curriculum/syllabus, Classroom interaction, Assessment

Country of research: United Kingdom

Learners' background: various

Institutional level: tertiary

Entered by: University of Bedfordshire (Centre for Research in English Language Learning and Assessment)

Green, A.B. 2007. *IELTS Washback in Context: Preparation for Academic Writing in Higher Education, Studies in Language Testing 25.* Cambridge: Cambridge University Press.

ISBN: 978-0-521-692922

Descriptor(s): Assessment

Entered by: University of Bedfordshire (Centre for Research in English Language Learning and Assessment)

Green, A.B. 2007. 'Washback to learning outcomes: A comparative study of IELTS preparation and university pre-sessional language courses'. *Assessment in Education* 14/1: 75–97.

Descriptor(s): Methodology, Learner autonomy/strategies, Curriculum/syllabus, Assessment

Country of research: United Kingdom

Learners' background: various

Institutional level: tertiary

Entered by: University of Bedfordshire (Centre for Research in English Language Learning and Assessment)

Green, A.B. and D. Jay. 2005. 'Quality assurance and quality control: Reviewing and pretesting examination material at Cambridge ESOL'. *Research Notes, Cambridge ESOL* 21: 5–7.

Descriptor(s): Teacher education, Assessment

G

G

Country of research: United Kingdom

Learners' background: various

Entered by: University of Bedfordshire (Centre for Research in English Language Learning and Assessment)

Green, A.B. and R.A. Hawkey. 2005. 'Test washback and impact: What do they mean and why do they matter?'. *Modern English Teacher* 13/4: 66–71.

Descriptor(s): Assessment

Entered by: University of Bedfordshire (Centre for Research in English Language Learning and Assessment)

Green, R. and D. Wall. 2005. 'Language testing in the military: Problems, politics and progress'. *Language Testing* 22/3: 379–398.

Summary: An overview of the development of the Standardization Agreement (STANAG) 6001 guidelines used for assessment purposes within NATO and a discussion of some of the challenges facing testing teams working to create assessment systems within their military organisations in Central and Eastern Europe.

Descriptor(s): ESP, English language, Assessment

Institutional level: adult

Entered by: Lancaster University (Linguistics and English Language)

Grenfell, M. and E. Macaro. 2007. 'Language learner strategies: Claims and critiques' in A. D. Cohen and E. Macaro (eds.) *Language Learner Strategies: 30 Years of Research and Practice*. Oxford: Oxford University Press.

ISBN: 978-0194422543

Descriptor(s): Learner autonomy/strategies

Entered by: University of Oxford (Department of Education)

Grimshaw, T. 2007. 'Critical perspectives on language in international education' in M. Hayden, J. Levy and J. Thompson (eds.)

Sage Handbook of Research in International Education. London: Sage.

ISBN: 978-1-4129-1971-5

Pages: 365–378

Summary: This chapter draws on recent literature from applied linguistics to inform our understanding of the role of language in international education. Particular emphasis is placed on the role of English as an International Language. The author proposes that international educators should critically interrogate this discourse, thereby playing a transformative role in the development of their discipline.

Descriptor(s): Teacher education, Teacher cognition, Cultural issues, English language

Country of research: various

Learners' background: various

Entered by: University of Bath (Department of Education)

Grimshaw, T. 2007. 'Problematizing the construct of 'the Chinese Learner': Insights from ethnographic research'. *Educational Studies* 33/3: 299–311.

Summary: Large numbers of students from the Chinese speaking world are nowadays enrolled in Western universities, prompting the need for awareness of their educational beliefs and practices. Although an established literature seeks to characterize 'the Chinese learner', much of this research results in stereotypical representations of a 'reduced other': passive, uncritical and over-reliant on the instructor.

Descriptor(s): Cultural issues

Country of research: United Kingdom

Learners' background: China

Institutional level: tertiary

Associated project: Chinese Learners' Perceptions and Constructions of British Academic Culture

Entered by: University of Bath (Department of Education)

Grimshaw, T. 2008. 'Negotiating an identity in English: The discursive construction and reconstruction of Chinese students' in R. Johnson (ed.). Southampton: *The Higher Education Academy Subject Centre for Social Policy and Social Work.*

ISBN: 9780854328901

Pages: 56–65

Summary: This paper explores the international student experience from the perspective of identity construction. Through case studies based on ethnographic interviews, it documents the cultural, linguistics and academic challenges of Chinese-speaking students.

www.swap.ac.uk/docs/monograph_ulu.PDF

Descriptor(s): Cultural issues, English language

Country of research: United Kingdom

Learners' background: China

Institutional level: tertiary

Associated project: Chinese Learners' Perceptions and Constructions of British Academic Culture

Entered by: University of Bath (Department of Education)

Grimshaw, T. and C. Morgan. 2006. 'Using a multicultural classroom to explore stereotypes: Moving towards intercultural competence' in J. Aden (ed.) *De Babel a la Mondialisation: Apports des Sciences Sociales a la Didactique des Langues.* Paris: CNDP.

ISBN: 2-86621-372-6

Pages: 385–402

Summary: Representations of other cultures often consist in the first place of stereotypes. People also often generate autostereotypes of their own culture: homogenous constructs which are not congruent with the diverse reality of their community (Wodak *et al*, 1999). It can be helpful for foreign and second language learners to consider stereotypes both of their own culture and the target language culture, as a first step to becoming interculturally aware.

Descriptor(s): Cultural issues

Country of research: United Kingdom

Learners' background: various

Institutional level: tertiary

Entered by: University of Bath (Department of Education)

Grimshaw, T. and C. Sears. 2008. '"Where am I from?" "Where do I belong?" The negotiation and maintenance of identity by international school students'. *Journal of research in International Education* 7/3: 257–276.

Summary: While the benefits of a mobile expatriate lifestyle are widely reported, it must also be recognized that many students who have attended international schools experience a confused sense of identity due to the fragmented nature of their personal histories. This article seeks to refine our understanding of how these globally mobile young people negotiate and maintain a sense of identity.

Descriptor(s): Cultural issues, ESOL/EAL

Country of research: Belgium

Learners' background: various

Institutional level: secondary

Entered by: University of Bath (Department of Education)

Gu, Q. and A.J. Brooks. 2008. 'Beyond the accusation of plagiarism: A case study of mainland Chinese students in UK HE'. *System* 36: 337–352.

Summary: The paper explores the complexity of the notion of plagiarism from sociocultural and psychological perspectives. A longitudinal study, it investigates 10 Chinese students' changing perceptions of plagiarism

G

H

during their UK-based Masters courses and compares these perceptions with those of their pre-sessional EAP tutors.

Descriptor(s): Writing, Teacher cognition, Cultural issues, Learner cognition, ESP

Country of research: United Kingdom

Learners' background: China

Institutional level: tertiary

Entered by: University of Sussex (The Sussex Language Institute)

Gu, Q. and M. Schweisfurth. 2005. 'Who adapts? Beyond cultural models of "the" Chinese learner'. *Language, Culture and Curriculum* 19/1: 74–89.

Learners' background: Canada

Institutional level: adult

Entered by: University of Birmingham (School of Education)

Guilloteaux, M.J. and Z. Dörnyei. 2008. 'Motivating language learners: A classroom-oriented investigation of the effects of motivational strategies on student motivation'. *TESOL Quarterly* 42/1: 55–77.

Descriptor(s): Teacher education, Learner cognition, Learner autonomy/strategies

Country of research: Korea, Republic of (South Korea)

Institutional level: secondary

Entered by: University of Nottingham (School of English Studies)

Gutteridge, M. 2006. 'ESOL special circumstances 2004: A review of Upper Main Suite provision'. *Cambridge ESOL: Research Notes* 23: 17–19.

Summary: Review of the 2004 Special Circumstances provision for candidates with special needs and an update of three key areas of research and development: computer-based testing (CBT), Asset Languages and ILEC, all of which are using technology in one form or another.

www.cambridgeesol.org/rs_notes/rs_nts23. PDF

Entered by: University of Cambridge ESOL Examinations

H

Hackett, E. 2005. 'The development of a computer-based version of PET'. *Cambridge ESOL: Research Notes* 22: 9–13.

Summary: Ed Hackett illustrates the development of CB PET, focusing on how paper-based materials have been adapted for computer-based testing to suit the candidature, which enables equivalence with the paper-based format.

www.cambridgeesol.org/rs_notes/rs_nts22. PDF

Entered by: University of Cambridge ESOL Examinations

Hackett, E. 2008. 'Adapting listening tests for on-screen use'. *Cambridge ESOL: Research Notes* 32: 23–25.

Summary: Ed Hackett reports on how paper-based listening tests are adapted for computer-based delivery. Hackett presents some key issues in adapting paper-based tests such as displaying items and determining how candidates respond to questions, focusing on the delivery of both Business English and General English exams.

www.cambridgeesol.org/rs_notes/rs_nts32. PDF

Entered by: University of Cambridge ESOL Examinations

Hale, L. and G. Lazar. 2007. 'Authoring online materials for academic writing: Issues and opportunities' in O. Alexander (ed.) *New Approaches to Materials Development for Language Learning. Proceedings of the 2005 Joint BALEAP/SATEFL Conference.* Bern: Peter Lang.

ISBN: 978-3-03910-909-8

Pages: 301–313

Principal format: Printed

Summary: This paper describes a project at Middlesex University to support students in academic writing skills. A collaborative authoring model was established to develop materials for the university's virtual learning environment. The writing team found the interaction between authorship, audience and medium to be problematic, and strategies for resolving this are explored.

Descriptor(s): Writing, Materials, Learning technologies, ESP

Institutional level: tertiary

Entered by: Middlesex University (English Language and Learning Support)

Hall, G. 2005. *Literature in Language Education.* Basingstoke, UK: Palgrave Macmillan.

ISBN: 1-4039-4336-2

Summary: Overview of relevant research literature with accounts of key studies and inclusive list of references and resources for research in this area. Research & Practice in Applied Linguistics series eds. Candlin and David Hall.

Descriptor(s): Teacher education, Cultural issues, Reading, English language, Curriculum/syllabus, Classroom interaction, Assessment

Entered by: Swansea University (Department of Applied Linguistics)

Hall, G. 2005. 'Symposium on English and other languages' in B. Beaven (ed.) *IATEFL 2005: Cardiff Conference Selections.*

Kent: IATEFL.

ISBN: 1 901095 02 9

Pages: 39–41

Principal format: Printed

Summary: A symposium summary discussing issues ranging from the role of English globally to local analyses; from linguistic description to socio-political orientation; and from the relationship between English and other languages in general to specific examples and case studies.

Descriptor(s): English language

Country of research: various

Entered by: University of Northumbria (Department of Humanities, School of Arts and Social Sciences)

Hall, G. 2005. 'Thinking locally: Addressing the dilemmas raised by Critical Pedagogy in ELT'.

Summary: Critical approaches to ELT argue that there is insufficient consideration of why we are teaching and what society we are teaching for. However, critical approaches are themselves criticised for being critical, impractical and not offering solutions to perceived problems. This paper argues for the development of local understandings to empower learners and teachers.

www.developingteachers.com/articles_tchtra ining/criticalpedagogy_graham.htm

Descriptor(s): Teacher education, Curriculum/syllabus

Entered by: University of Northumbria (Department of Humanities, School of Arts and Social Sciences)

Hall, G. 2008. 'An ethnographic diary study'. *ELT Journal* 62/2: 113–122.

Summary: This article examines a small-scale ethnographic survey of a single classroom. Drawing on the collected data, the discussion focuses on some of the problems encountered whilst collecting and interpreting data through self-report diaries. The article also discusses how variation within the data might be the result of the specific diary approach developed. The article concludes positively, however, suggesting that explicit recognition of these difficulties can still lead to fruitful,

H

H

localised approaches to the data.

Descriptor(s): Teacher education

Country of research: United Kingdom

Learners' background: various

Institutional level: adult

Entered by: University of Northumbria (Department of Humanities, School of Arts and Social Sciences)

Hall, G. 2008. 'English, Englishes and English language teaching – some thoughts'. *IATEFL Teacher Development SIG Newsletter* 59: 8–10.

Summary: This paper discusses the challenges to English language teachers presented by the emergence of local and regional varieties around the world.

Descriptor(s): Teacher education, Cultural issues, Curriculum/syllabus

Entered by: University of Northumbria (Department of Humanities, School of Arts and Social Sciences)

Hall, G. 2008. 'Values in English language teaching'. *IATEFL Teacher Development SIG Newsletter* 58: 9–11.

Summary: Teachers have values, and teachers also have power and responsibility. This paper discusses the need for teachers to examine and clarify their own beliefs about what is appropriate for their own learners and classrooms, and reflect upon how these values are realised in practice.

Descriptor(s): Teacher education, Cultural issues

Country of research: various

Entered by: University of Northumbria (Department of Humanities, School of Arts and Social Sciences)

Hall, G. and E. Angelinas. 2006. 'Teaching English as a missionary language'. *CALL Review: Journal of the Learning*

Technologies SIG Spring: 30–32.

Summary: This paper summarises debates surrounding the role of Christianity and Christian-based organizations in both the spread of English around the world and in the ELT profession today.

Descriptor(s): Cultural issues

Entered by: University of Northumbria (Department of Humanities, School of Arts and Social Sciences)

Hamp-Lyons, L. 2006. 'Feedback in portfolio-based writing courses' in K. Hyland and F. Hyland (eds.) *Feedback in Second Language Writing: Contexts and Issues.* New York: Cambridge University Press.

ISBN: 978-0-521-672580/978-0-521-856638

Pages: 140–161

Descriptor(s): Writing

Entered by: University of Bedfordshire (Centre for Research in English Language Learning and Assessment)

Hamp-Lyons, L. 2007. 'The impact of testing practices on teaching: ideologies and alternatives' in J. Cummins and C. Davison (eds.) *The International Handbook of English Language Teaching (Vol. 1).* Norwell, MA: Springer.

ISBN: 978-0-387-46300-1

Pages: 487–504

Descriptor(s): Assessment

Entered by: University of Bedfordshire (Centre for Research in English Language Learning and Assessment)

Hamp-Lyons, L. 2008. 'Best practice in writing assessment' in L. Taylor and C.J. Weir (eds.) *Multilingualism and Assessment in a Multilingual Context. Proceedings of the ALTE Conference, Berlin, May 2005.* Cambridge: University of Cambridge ESOL/Cambridge University Press.

Pages: 321–335

Principal format: Printed

Descriptor(s): Writing, Assessment

Entered by: University of Bedfordshire (Centre for Research in English Language Learning and Assessment)

Hamp-Lyons, L. and A. Davies. 2006. 'Bias revisited'. *Spaan Fellow Working Papers* 4: 97–108.

Descriptor(s): Assessment

Entered by: University of Bedfordshire (Centre for Research in English Language Learning and Assessment)

Hamp-Lyons, L. and A. Davies. 2008. 'The Englishes of English tests'. *World Englishes* 27/1: 26–29.

Descriptor(s): English language, Assessment

Entered by: University of Bedfordshire (Centre for Research in English Language Learning and Assessment)

Harrison, C. 2007. 'Reviewing the FCE and CAE Speaking tests'. *Cambridge ESOL: Research Notes* 30: 24–28.

Summary: Clare Harrison reports on research and consultation undertaken to review the FCE and CAE Speaking tests.

www.cambridgeesol.org/rs_notes/rs_nts30. PDF

Entered by: University of Cambridge ESOL Examinations

Harrison, C. 2007. 'Teaching knowledge test update – Adoptions and courses'. *Cambridge ESOL: Research Notes* 29: 30–32.

Summary: Clare Harrison's article on the uptake of TKT to date reveals a wide range of contexts in which it has been used to confirm teachers' knowledge about teaching.

www.cambridgeesol.org/rs_notes/rs_nts29. PDF

Entered by: University of Cambridge ESOL Examinations

Harsch, C. 2007. *Der gemeinsame europäische Referenzrahmen für Sprachen. Leistung und Grenzen [The Common European Framework of Reference for Languages: Attainment and Limitations].* Saarbrücken, Germany: VDM Verlag Dr. Müller.

ISBN: 9783836422826

Descriptor(s): Curriculum/syllabus, Assessment

Entered by: University of Warwick (Centre for Applied Linguistics)

Harsch, C. and K. Schröder. 2005. 'Schule zwischen Selbst- und Fremdbestimmung: Internationale Sprachtests, PISA, DESI und die, neue Evaluationskultur' [International large-scale assessment studies and the "new evaluative culture"]' in J. Maisch (ed.) *Evaluation und Analyse in der Schulentwicklung. Ansätze, Methoden und Beispiele für die Schulpraxis. [Evaluation and Analysis in School Development: Approaches, Methods, Examples].* Donauwörth: Auer.

ISBN: 3403043185

Pages: 22–36

Summary: The chapter examines the new demands placed on schools in the context of assessment and self-determination. Schools face new challenges and tensions as they are confronted with external means of quality management since the advent of large-scale assessment studies like PISA.

Descriptor(s): Teacher education, Management/innovation, ESOL/EAL, English language, Curriculum/syllabus, Assessment

Country of research: Germany

Learners' background: Germany

Institutional level: secondary

Entered by: University of Warwick (Centre for Applied Linguistics)

Harsch, C. and K. Schröder. 2006. 'Der mühsame Weg zur, Neuen Evaluationskultur' an unseren Schulen [The painstaking way towards the "new evaluative culture" in our

H

H

schools]' in I. Hosenfeldt and W. Schrader (eds.) *Schulische Leistung. Grundlagen, Bedingungen, Perspektiven [Achievement at School: Basics, Conditions, Perspectives].* Münster: Waxmann.

ISBN: 9783830915652

Pages: 275–288

Summary: The chapter gives an overview of necessary steps towards a new evaluative culture within the German school system, to use a complementary approach of informal and formal teacher assessments in combination with the use of internal and external means of assessment.

Descriptor(s): Teacher education, English language, Curriculum/syllabus, Assessment

Country of research: Germany

Learners' background: Germany

Institutional level: secondary

Entered by: University of Warwick (Centre for Applied Linguistics)

Harsch, C. and K. Schröder. 2007. 'Textrekonstruktion: C-Test [Text reconstruction: C-test]' in B. Beck and E. Klieme (eds.) *Sprachliche Kompetenzen: Konzepte und Messungen. DESI-Studie. [Language Proficiency: Concepts and Measurement. DESI study].* Weinheim: Beltz (Pädagogik).

ISBN: 9783407253989

Pages: 212–225

Summary: Account of the conceptualisation of communicative competences of 9th graders in the German school system (secondary level) in German and English as first foreign language. This chapter describes the concept and measurement model of the C-test as a means to assess global proficiency in English.

Descriptor(s): English language, Curriculum/syllabus, Assessment

Country of research: Germany

Learners' background: Germany

Institutional level: secondary

Entered by: University of Warwick (Centre for Applied Linguistics)

Harsch, C. and K. Schröder. 2008. 'Schülerkompetenzen im Englischen: Textrekonstruktion: C-Test [Students' competences in English as a foreign language: Text reconstruction: C-test]' in DESI-Konsortium (ed.) *Ergebnisse der DESI-Studie [Results of the DESI study].* Weinheim: Beltz.

ISBN: 9783407254917

Pages: 149–156

Summary: Report on the results of a large-scale assessment study in Germany to investigate 9th graders' proficiency in German and English as first foreign language. In this chapter, we report on the results of the C-test module as a measurement for global proficiency in English.

Descriptor(s): English language, Curriculum/syllabus, Assessment

Country of research: Germany

Learners' background: Germany

Institutional level: secondary

Entered by: University of Warwick (Centre for Applied Linguistics)

Harsch, C., A. Neumann, R. Lehmann and K. Schröder. 2007. 'Schreibfähigkeit [Writing proficiency]' in B. Beck and E. Klieme (eds.) *Sprachliche Kompetenzen: Konzepte und Messungen. DESI-Studie. [Language Proficiency: Concepts and Measurement. DESI study].* Weinheim: Beltz (Pädagogik).

ISBN: 9783407253989

Pages: 42–62

Summary: Account of the conceptualisation of communicative competences of 9th graders in the German school system (secondary level) in German and English as first foreign language. This chapter describes the concept and measurement model of the writing sub-tests for German and English.

Descriptor(s): Writing, English language, Curriculum/syllabus, Assessment

Country of research: Germany

Learners' background: Germany

Institutional level: secondary

Entered by: University of Warwick (Centre for Applied Linguistics)

Harsch, C., K. Schröder and A. Neumann. 2008. 'Schülerkompetenzen im Englischen: Semikreatives Schreiben [Students' competences in English as a foreign language: Semicreative writing]' in DESI-Konsortium (ed.) *Ergebnisse der DESI-Studie [Results of the DESI study].* Weinheim: Beltz.

ISBN: 9783407254917

Pages: 139–148

Summary: Report on the results of a large-scale assessment study in Germany to investigate 9th graders' proficiency in German and English as first foreign language. In this chapter, we report on the results of the writing sub-test for English.

Descriptor(s): Writing, English language, Curriculum/syllabus, Assessment

Country of research: Germany

Learners' background: Germany

Institutional level: secondary

Entered by: University of Warwick (Centre for Applied Linguistics)

Harwood, N. 2005. '"I hoped to counteract the memory problem, but I made no impact whatsoever": Discussing methods in computing science using I'. *English for Specific Purposes* 24/3: 243–267.

Descriptor(s): Writing, ESP, English language

Institutional level: tertiary

Entered by: University of Essex (Department of Language and Linguistics)

H

Harwood, N. 2005. '"Nowhere has anyone attempted...In this article I aim to do just that". A corpus-based study of self-promotional I and WE in academic writing across four disciplines'. *Journal of Pragmatics* 37/8: 1207–1231.

Descriptor(s): Writing, ESP, English language

Institutional level: tertiary

Entered by: University of Essex (Department of Language and Linguistics)

Harwood, N. 2005. '"We do not seem to have a theory...The theory I present here attempts to fill this gap": Inclusive and exclusive pronouns in academic writing'. *Applied Linguistics* 26/3: 343–375.

Descriptor(s): Writing, ESP, English language

Institutional level: tertiary

Entered by: University of Essex (Department of Language and Linguistics)

Harwood, N. 2005. 'What do we want EAP teaching materials for?'. *Journal of English for Academic Purposes* 4/2: 149–161.

Summary: This paper explores the various anti-textbook arguments in the literature to determine their relevance to the field of EAP. I distinguish between what I call a 'strong' and a 'weak' anti-textbook line, then review the corpus-based studies which compare the language EAP textbooks teach with corpora of the language academic writers use.

Descriptor(s): Writing, Materials, ESP, English language, Curriculum/syllabus

Institutional level: tertiary

Entered by: University of Essex (Department of Language and Linguistics)

Harwood, N. 2006. '(In)appropriate personal pronoun use in political science: A qualitative study and a proposed heuristic for future

H

research'. *Written Communication* 23/4: 424–450.

Descriptor(s): Writing, ESP, English language

Country of research: United Kingdom

Institutional level: tertiary

Entered by: University of Essex (Department of Language and Linguistics)

Harwood, N. 2007. 'Political scientists on the functions of personal pronouns in their writing: An interview-based study of "I" and "we"'. *Text and Talk* 27/1: 27–54.

Descriptor(s): Writing, ESP, English language

Country of research: United Kingdom

Institutional level: tertiary

Entered by: University of Essex (Department of Language and Linguistics)

Harwood, N. 2008. 'Citers' use of citees' names: Findings from a qualitative interview-based study'. *Journal of the American Society for Information Science and Technology* 59/6: 1007–1011.

Descriptor(s): Writing, ESP, English language

Country of research: United Kingdom

Entered by: University of Essex (Department of Language and Linguistics)

Harwood, N. 2008. 'Publication outlets and their effect on academic writers' citations.'. *Scientometrics* 77/2: 253–265.

Descriptor(s): ESP, English language, Writing

Country of research: United Kingdom

Entered by: University of Essex (Department of Language and Linguistics)

Hawkey, R. 2005. 'The CPE Textbook Washback Study'. *Cambridge ESOL: Research Notes* 20: 19–20.

Summary: Roger Hawkey reports on a study which explored the washback effects of the revised Certificate of Proficiency in English (CPE) on textbooks.

www.cambridgeesol.org/rs_notes/rs_nts20. PDF

Entered by: University of Cambridge ESOL Examinations

Hawkey, R. 2006. *Studies in Language Testing Vol 24: Impact Theory and Practice: Studies of the IELTS Test and Progetto Lingue 2000.* Cambridge: UCLES/CUP.

ISBN: 0521680972

Summary: This book focuses on the impact of language tests and language programmes on a range of stakeholders, including test-takers, teachers, textbook writers, testers and institutions. Two impact studies are cited: International English Language Testing System (IELTS), and the Progetto Lingue 2000, a state-school foreign-language education improvement programme undertaken by the Ministry of Education in Italy.

Descriptor(s): Assessment

Country of research: United Kingdom

Learners' background: various

Institutional level: adult

Entered by: University of Cambridge ESOL Examinations

Hawkey, R. 2007. 'The 2004–2008 FCE and CAE review project: Historical context and perennial themes'. *Cambridge ESOL: Research Notes* 30: 2–8.

Summary: Roger Hawkey gives an overview of the FCE and CAE review project, providing its historical context, previous revisions and updates, and some of the major themes which informed the review.

www.cambridgeesol.org/rs_notes/rs_nts30. PDF

Entered by: University of Cambridge ESOL Examinations

Hawkey, R. 2008. 'An impact study of a high-stakes test (IELTS): Lessons for test validation and linguistic diversity' in L. Taylor and C. Weir (eds.) *Studies in Language Testing Vol 27: Multilingualism and Assessment: Achieving Transparency, Assuring Quality, Sustaining Diversity – Proceedings of the ALTE Berlin Conference, May 2005.* Cambridge: UCLES/CUP.

ISBN: 9780521711920

Entered by: University of Cambridge ESOL Examinations

Hawkey, R. and S. Shaw. 2005. 'The Common Scale for Writing project: Implications for the comparison of IELTS band scores and Main Suite exam levels'. *Cambridge ESOL: Research Notes* 19: 19–24.

Summary: Roger Hawkey and Stuart Shaw draw implications, from developing a common descriptive scale for assessing writing to comparing Main Suite, IELTS and BEC writing scripts and scores.

www.cambridgeesol.org/rs_notes/rs_nts19. PDF

Entered by: University of Cambridge ESOL Examinations

Hawkey, R., S. Thompson and R. Turner. 2006. 'Developing a classroom video database for test washback research'. *Cambridge ESOL: Research Notes* 26: 5–9.

Summary: Roger Hawkey, Sue Thompson and Richard Turner describe the development of a video database of classroom data from three impact studies which will aid research into test washback for a range of different exams and contexts. This database is a form of multimodal corpus containing video clips, metadata and subtitling.

www.cambridgeesol.org/rs_notes/rs_nts26. PDF

Entered by: University of Cambridge ESOL Examinations

Hawkey, R.A. 2005. 'The CPE Textbook Washback Study'. *Research Notes, Cambridge ESOL* 20: 19–20.

Descriptor(s): Assessment

Entered by: University of Bedfordshire (Centre for Research in English Language Learning and Assessment)

Hawkey, R.A. 2006. *Impact Theory and Practice: Studies of the IELTS Test and Progetto Lingue 2000, Studies in Language Testing 24.* Cambridge: Cambridge University Press.

ISBN: 978-0-521-680974

Descriptor(s): Assessment

Entered by: University of Bedfordshire (Centre for Research in English Language Learning and Assessment)

Hawkey, R.A. 2006. 'Teacher and learner perceptions of language learning activity'. *English Language Teaching Journal* 60/3: 242–252.

Descriptor(s): Teacher cognition, Learner cognition

Entered by: University of Bedfordshire (Centre for Research in English Language Learning and Assessment)

Hawkey, R.A. 2007. 'The 2004–2008 FCE and CAE review project: Historical context and perennial themes'. *Research Notes, Cambridge ESOL* 30: 3–8.

Descriptor(s): Assessment

Entered by: University of Bedfordshire (Centre for Research in English Language Learning and Assessment)

Hawkey, R.A. 2008. 'An impact study of a high-stakes test (IELTS): Lessons for test validation and linguistic diversity' in L. Taylor and C.J. Weir (eds.) *Multilingualism and Assessment: Achieving Transparency, Assuring, Quality, Sustaining Diversity, Studies in Language Testing 27.* Cambridge: Cambridge University Press.

H

H

ISBN: 978-052-1-711920

Descriptor(s): Assessment

Entered by: University of Bedfordshire (Centre for Research in English Language Learning and Assessment)

Hawkey, R.A. and S.D. Shaw. 2005. 'The common scale for writing project: Implications for the comparison of IELTS band scores and Main Suite exam levels'. *Research Notes, Cambridge ESOL* 19: 19–24.

Descriptor(s): Writing, Assessment

Entered by: University of Bedfordshire (Centre for Research in English Language Learning and Assessment)

Hawkey, R.A., S. Thompson and R. Turner. 2006. 'Developing a classroom video database for test washback research purposes'. *Research Notes, Cambridge ESOL* 26: 5–8.

Descriptor(s): Assessment

Entered by: University of Bedfordshire (Centre for Research in English Language Learning and Assessment)

Hawkey, R.A., S. Thompson and R. Turner. 2007. 'The development of a video database for language educational research projects'. *Learning, Media and Technology* 32/1: 83–97.

Entered by: University of Bedfordshire (Centre for Research in English Language Learning and Assessment)

Hemchua, S. and N. Schmitt. 2006. 'An analysis of lexical errors in the English compositions of Thai learners'. *Prospect* 21/3: 3–25.

Descriptor(s): Learner cognition

Learners' background: Thailand

Entered by: University of Nottingham (School of English Studies)

Hobbs, V. 2007. 'Examining the effectiveness of the four-week ELT training course: Change or no change?' in B. Beaven

(ed.) *IATEFL 2006: Harrogate Conference Selections.* Canterbury: IATEFL.

Principal format: Printed

Descriptor(s): Teacher education, Teacher cognition

Country of research: United Kingdom; Institutional level: adult

Entered by: University of Sheffield (School of English)

Hobbs, V. 2007. 'Faking it or hating it: Can reflective practice be forced?'. *Reflective Practice* 8/3: 405–417.

Summary: Relying on research at a TESOL certificate course, this article examines the problematic nature of required reflective practice, namely, that requiring individuals to be open in the context of assessment tends to provoke strategic response and often hostility. These reactions point to an underlying problem with any required reflection that has serious implications for teacher education.

Descriptor(s): Teacher education, Teacher cognition

Country of research: United Kingdom

Institutional level: adult

Entered by: University of Sheffield (School of English)

Hobbs, V. and M. Kubanyiova. 2008. 'The challenges of researching language teachers: What research modules don't tell us'. *Language Teaching Research* 12/4: 495–513.

Descriptor(s): Teacher education, Teacher cognition, English language

Country of research: United Kingdom

Learners' background: Slovakia

Institutional level: adult

Entered by: University of Birmingham (School of Education)

Hobbs, V. and M. Kubanyiova. 2008. 'The challenges of researching language teachers: What research manuals don't tell us'. *Language Teaching Research* 12/4: 495–513.

Summary: This paper extends the existing discussion of the problematics of conducting classroom-based research in the field of applied linguistics by discussing specific challenges of engaging busy language teachers in one's research, sustaining their commitment throughout the project and handling the physical and emotional strain of the researcher.

Descriptor(s): Teacher education, Teacher cognition

Country of research: United Kingdom

Institutional level: adult

Entered by: University of Sheffield (School of English)

Hoey, M. 2005. 'Clause relations' in K. Brown (ed.) *Encyclopedia of Language and Linguistics (2nd Edition)*. Amsterdam: Elsevier.

ISBN: 9780080442990 (for 14 volume set)

Descriptor(s): Writing, Reading, English language

Country of research: United Kingdom

Entered by: University of Liverpool (School of English)

Hoey, M. 2005. *Lexical Priming: A New Theory of Words and Language*. Abingdon: Routledge.

ISBN: 0415328632

Summary: Drawing on psycholinguistic work on priming, the book describes how phenomena identified by corpus linguists are explicable in terms of the way language is acquired. The result is that the lexicon is seen as central to language.

Descriptor(s): Writing, Speaking, Reading, Listening, English language

Country of research: United Kingdom

Institutional level: adult

Entered by: University of Liverpool (School of English)

H

Hoey, M. 2005. 'Synonymy, polysemy and a drinking problem' in R. Bahous and N. Bacha (eds.) *Selected Papers from the Second Regional English Conference on Language and Change held at the Lebanese American University*. Beirut: Librairie du Liban.

Principal format: Printed

Descriptor(s): Writing, Speaking, Reading, Listening, English language

Country of research: United Kingdom

Entered by: University of Liverpool (School of English)

Hoey, M. 2005. 'Textuality, intertextuality and the mental lexicon' in Y-J. Chen and Y-N. Leung (eds.) *Selected Papers from the 14th International Symposium on English Teaching. English Teachers' Association*. Taipei: English Teachers' Association.

Principal format: Printed

Descriptor(s): Writing, Reading, English language

Country of research: United Kingdom

Entered by: University of Liverpool (School of English)

Hoey, M. 2006. 'Clumsy English'. *The European English Messenger* Autumn: 48–57.

Descriptor(s): Writing, Methodology, ESP, English language

Country of research: United Kingdom

Institutional level: tertiary

Entered by: University of Liverpool (School of English)

Hoey, M. 2006. 'Language as choice: What is chosen?' in G. Thompson and S. Hunston (eds.) *System and Corpus: Exploring Connections*. London: Equinox Publishing.

H

ISBN: 9781845532512

Descriptor(s): Writing, Speaking, English language

Country of research: United Kingdom

Entered by: University of Liverpool (School of English)

Hoey, M. 2006. 'Problem-solution patterns' in K. Brown (ed.) *Encyclopedia of Language and Linguistics (2nd Edition).* Amsterdam: Elsevier.

ISBN: 9780080442990 (for 14 volume set)

Descriptor(s): Writing, Reading, English language

Country of research: United Kingdom

Entered by: University of Liverpool (School of English)

Hoey, M. 2006. 'Talking, teaching, testing' in Y-J. Chen and Y-N. Leung (eds.) *Selected Papers from the Fifteenth International Symposium on English Teaching.* Taipei: English Teachers' Association.

Principal format: Printed

Descriptor(s): Speaking, English language, Classroom interaction, Assessment

Country of research: United Kingdom

Institutional level: tertiary

Entered by: University of Liverpool (School of English)

Hoey, M. 2007. 'Foreword' in M. Rundell and G. Fox (eds.) *Macmillan English Dictionary for Advanced Learners (2nd edition).* London: Macmillan.

ISBN: 9780230025455

Descriptor(s): Writing, Speaking, ESOL/EAL, ESP, English language

Institutional level: adult

Entered by: University of Liverpool (School of English)

Hoey, M. 2007. 'Lexical priming' in M. Rundell and G. Fox (eds.) *Macmillan English Dictionary for Advanced Learners (2nd edition).* London: Macmillan.

ISBN: 9780230025455

Descriptor(s): Writing, Speaking, ESOL/EAL, ESP, English language

Entered by: University of Liverpool (School of English)

Hoey, M. and M.B. O'Donnell. 2007. 'Death to the topic sentence: How we really paragraph' in Y-N. Leung (ed.) *Selected Papers from the Sixteenth International Symposium on English Teaching.* Taipei: English Teachers' Association/ ROC Taipei.

Principal format: Printed

Descriptor(s): Writing, ESP, English language

Country of research: United Kingdom

Institutional level: tertiary

Associated project: The Textual Priming of Hard News Stories

Entered by: University of Liverpool (School of English)

Hoey, M. and M.B. O'Donnell. 2008. 'Lexicography, grammar and textual position'. *International Journal of Lexicography* 21: 293–309.

Descriptor(s): Writing, Reading, English language

Country of research: United Kingdom

Institutional level: adult

Associated project: The Textual Priming of Hard News Stories

Entered by: University of Liverpool (School of English)

Hoey, M. and M.B. O'Donnell. 2008. 'The beginning of something important?: Corpus evidence on the text beginnings of hard news stories' in Lewandowska-Tomaszczyk and B. (eds.) *Corpus Linguistics,*

Computer Tools and Applications: State of the Art. Frankfurt am Main: Peter Lang.

ISBN: 9783631583111

Descriptor(s): Writing, English language

Country of research: United Kingdom

Institutional level: adult

Associated project: The Textual Priming of Hard News Stories

Entered by: University of Liverpool (School of English)

Hoey, M., M. Mahlberg, M. Stubbs and W. Teubert. 2007. *Text, Discourse and Corpora: Theory and Practice.* London: Continuum.

ISBN: 9780826491725

Descriptor(s): Writing, Speaking, Reading, Listening, ESP, English language

Institutional level: adult

Entered by: University of Liverpool (School of English)

Holliday, A.R. 2005. 'How is it possible to write?'. *Journal of Language, Identity & Education* 4/4: 304–309.

Summary: The validity of using personal narratives in research.

Descriptor(s): Cultural issues

Entered by: Canterbury Christ Church University (Department of English and Language Studies)

Holliday, A.R. 2005. *The Struggle to Teach English as an International Language.* Oxford: Oxford University Press.

ISBN: 978-0-19-442184-3

Summary: A discussion of how a native-speakerist cultural chauvinism operates within the professional structure of Western ELT.

Descriptor(s): Cultural issues, Methodology, Learner autonomy/strategies, English language, Curriculum/syllabus

Entered by: Canterbury Christ Church University (Department of English and Language Studies)

Holliday, A.R. 2005. 'What happens between people: Who we are and what we do' in S. Gieve and I. Miller (eds.) *Understanding the Language Classroom.* Basingstoke: Palgrave Macmillan.

ISBN: 1403996628

Pages: 47–63

Descriptor(s): Curriculum/syllabus

Entered by: Canterbury Christ Church University (Department of English and Language Studies)

Holliday, A.R. 2006. 'Native-speakerism'. *ELT Journal* 60/4: 385–387.

Summary: A description of cultural chauvinism in the ELT profession against 'non-native speaker' students and colleagues.

Descriptor(s): Cultural issues, English language, Curriculum/syllabus

Entered by: Canterbury Christ Church University (Department of English and Language Studies)

Holliday, A.R. 2007. 'Response to 'ELT and "the spirit of the times"''. *ELT Journal* 61/4: 360–366.

Summary: Discussion of research evidence for cultural chauvinism in ELT.

Descriptor(s): Cultural issues

Entered by: Canterbury Christ Church University (Department of English and Language Studies)

Holliday, A.R. 2007. 'The dangers of matrix thinking in international project design' in H. Coleman (ed.) *Language and Development: Africa and Beyond. Proceedings of the 7th International Language and Development Conference.* Addis Ababa: The British Council.

H

H

Pages: 130–137

Principal format: Printed

Summary: Discussion of how stakeholder-centredness is in effect an example of cultural chauvinism in which the 'non-native speaker' colleague is considered culturally deficient.

Descriptor(s): Cultural issues, Curriculum/syllabus

Entered by: Canterbury Christ Church University (Department of English and Language Studies)

Holliday, A.R. 2008. 'Standards of English and politics of inclusion'. *Language Teaching* 41/1: 115–126.

Summary: A discussion of how changes in the ownership of English affect the politics of speakerhood, the relevance of the native–non-native speaker distinction and the politics of English as a lingua franca.

Descriptor(s): Cultural issues, English language, Curriculum/syllabus

Entered by: Canterbury Christ Church University (Department of English and Language Studies)

Holliday, A.R., M. Hyde and J. Kullman. 2007. *Intercultural Communication.* London: Routledge.

ISBN: 0-415-27060

Summary: An advanced workbook for postgraduate students which explores a non-essentialist approach to intercultural communication.

Descriptor(s): Cultural issues

Entered by: Canterbury Christ Church University (Department of English and Language Studies)

Howarth, P. 2006. 'The phraseology of public international English'. *International Journal of English Studies (Special issue on New Advances in Phraseological Research)* 6/1: 109–129.

Summary: This study investigates the nature of the language used in public international settings (international press conferences in former Yugoslavia) between native and non-native speakers. It draws on a corpus of approximately 3 million words of transcribed press conferences, containing large numbers of exchanges between native and non-native spokespeople and journalists.

Descriptor(s): Materials, ESP, English language

Entered by: University of Leeds (The Language Centre)

Hua, Z., P. Seedhouse, L. Wei and V. Cook. 2007. 'Introduction' in Z. Hua, P. Seedhouse, L. Wei and V. Cook (eds.) *Language Learning and Teaching as Social Interaction.* Basingstoke: Palgrave Macmillan.

ISBN: 0230517005

Summary: Introduction to a volume which brings together contributions by leading researchers of the social interactional and socio-cultural approaches to language learning and teaching. It provides both an introduction to this important growth point and also an overview of cutting edge research, covering a wide range of language learning and teaching contexts.

Descriptor(s): Cultural issues, Methodology, ESOL/EAL, Curriculum/syllabus, Classroom interaction, Teacher education, Speaking

Country of research: various

Learners' background: various

Entered by: Newcastle University (School of Education, Communication and Language Sciences)

Hua, Z., P. Seedhouse, L. Wei and V. Cook. 2007. *Language Learning and Teaching as Social Interaction.* Basingstoke: Palgrave Macmillan.

ISBN: 0230517005

Summary: This volume brings together contributions by leading researchers of the social interactional and socio-cultural approaches to language learning and teaching. It provides both an introduction to this important growth point and also an overview of cutting edge research, covering a wide range of language learning and teaching contexts.

Descriptor(s): Teacher education, Speaking, Cultural issues, Methodology, ESOL/EAL, Curriculum/syllabus, Classroom interaction

Country of research: various

Learners' background: various

Entered by: Newcastle University (School of Education, Communication and Language Sciences)

Hubbard, C. 2005. 'ESOL staff seminar programme: Applied linguistics: A personal view and second language listening'. *Cambridge ESOL: Research Notes* 19: 14–15.

Summary: A review of former head of the University's Research Centre for English and Applied Linguistics Gillian Brown's recent staff seminar on applied linguistics and second language listening.

www.cambridgeesol.org/rs_notes/rs_nts19.PDF

Entered by: University of Cambridge ESOL Examinations

Hubbard, C., S. Gilbert and J. Pidcock. 2006. 'Assessment processes in speaking tests: A pilot verbal protocol study'. *Cambridge ESOL: Research Notes* 24: 14–19.

Summary: Chris Hubbard, Susan Gilbert and John Pidcock report on a Verbal Protocol Analysis (VPA) study into how CAE Speaking test raters make assessments in real time. They consider the appropriacy of a VPA methodology and how raters use a framework of assessment criteria (a rating scale).

www.cambridgeesol.org/rs_notes/rs_nts24.PDF

Entered by: University of Cambridge ESOL Examinations

H

Hughes, A. 2006. 'Patterns, problems and passions in YL action research' in R. Mitchell-Schuitevoerder and S. Mourao (eds.) *Teachers and Young Learners: Research in Our Classrooms. YLSIG Anniversary Publication.* Canterbury, Kent: IATEFL.

Summary: This article highlights the reasons for carrying out action research in the young language learner classroom and then reports on an investigation into the patterns, problems and passions found in a number of YL action research reports. This will aid those about to take part in YL action research.

Descriptor(s): Teacher education, Teacher cognition, Methodology, Management/innovation

Country of research: various

Learners' background: various

Institutional level: primary

Entered by: University of York (Department of Educational Studies)

Hughes, G. 2006. 'The effect of editing on language used in FCE reading texts: A case study'. *Cambridge ESOL: Research Notes* 26: 19–21.

Summary: Glyn Hughes compares texts used in the Reading component of FCE and the British National Corpus (BNC) to ascertain what impact edited reading texts have on candidates, basing his article on a case study of the word people.

www.cambridgeesol.org/rs_notes/rs_nts26.PDF

Entered by: University of Cambridge ESOL Examinations

H

Hughes, G. 2008. 'Text organisation features in an FCE reading gapped sentence task'. *Cambridge ESOL: Research Notes* 31: 26–31.

Summary: Glyn Hughes compares the text organisational features of reading passages from a First Certificate in English (FCE) paper with the original source text, seeking evidence for how candidates interact with reading passages and implications for training materials writers.

www.cambridgeesol.org/rs_notes/rs_nts31.PD

Entered by: University of Cambridge ESOL Examinations

Hunston, S. 2007. 'Grammar patterns and literacy' in A. McCabe, M. O'Donnell and R. Whittaker (eds.) *Advances in Language and Education.* London: Continuum.

ISBN: 9780826489609

Pages: 254–267

Summary: The paper investigates the contribution of recurring patterns of lexis and grammar to redundancy. This is linked to the role of redundancy in reading practices.

Descriptor(s): Reading, English language

Entered by: University of Birmingham (Centre for English Language Studies and Department of English)

Hyland, F. 2008. 'Scaffolding during the writing process: The role of informal peer interaction in writing workshops' in D. Becher and A. Hirvela (eds.) *The Oral-Literate Connection: Perspectives on L2 Speaking, Writing, and Other Media Interactions.* Michigan: University of Michigan Press.

ISBN: 9780472032327

Summary: This paper examines spoken interaction in writing workshops for EFL students. It discusses the different procedures adopted by two teachers in their management of their writing workshops and then focuses on the spoken interactions between the students in the two classes and examines the ways these provided scaffolding for their writing development.

Descriptor(s): Writing, ESOL/EAL

Country of research: New Zealand

Learners' background: various

Institutional level: tertiary

Entered by: Institute of Education, London (Department of Learning, Curriculum and Communication)

Hyland, F. and M. Lo. 2006. 'Examining interaction in the teaching practicum: Issues of language, power and control'. *Mentoring and Tutoring* 14/2: 163–186.

Summary: This study examines the post-observation interactions between six ESL student teachers and their tutors during their teaching practicum in Hong Kong. Case studies are used to examine the impact of the tutors' feedback and to highlight the importance of the power relations involved in the dialogue.

Descriptor(s): Teacher education, English language

Country of research: Hong Kong

Learners' background: Hong Kong

Institutional level: tertiary

Entered by: Institute of Education, London (Department of Learning, Curriculum and Communication)

Hyland, K. 2005. 'A convincing argument: Corpus analysis and academic persuasion' in U. Connor and T. Upton (eds.) *Discourse in the Professions: Perspectives from Corpus Linguistics.* Amsterdam: Benjamins.

ISBN: 90 272 2287 8

Pages: 87–114

Descriptor(s): Writing, ESP

Entered by: Institute of Education, London

(Department of Learning, Curriculum and Communication)

Hyland, K. 2005. *Metadiscourse.* London: Continuum.

ISBN: 9 780826 476111

Descriptor(s): Writing

Entered by: Institute of Education, London (Department of Learning, Curriculum and Communication)

Hyland, K. 2005. 'Stance and engagement: A model of interaction in academic discourse'. *Discourse Studies* 7/2: 173–191.

Descriptor(s): Writing, ESP

Institutional level: tertiary

Entered by: Institute of Education, London (Department of Learning, Curriculum and Communication)

Hyland, K. 2005. 'Texts, transcripts and identity: Confessions of a discourse analyst' in T. Silva and P. Matsuda (eds.) *Second Language Writing: Perspectives on the Process of Knowledge Construction.* Mahwah, NJ: Lawrence Erlbaum.

ISBN: 9 780805 850451

Pages: 177–189

Descriptor(s): Writing, Methodology

Entered by: Institute of Education, London (Department of Learning, Curriculum and Communication)

Hyland, K. 2006. 'Medical discourse: Hedges' in K. Brown (ed.) *Encyclopedia of Language and Linguistics 2nd edition.* Oxford: Elsevier.

ISBN: 0-08-044299-4

Pages: 694–697

Descriptor(s): Writing, ESP, English language

Entered by: Institute of Education, London (Department of Learning, Curriculum and Communication)

Hyland, K. 2006. 'Disciplinary differences: Language variation in academic discourses' in K. Hyland and M. Bondi (eds.) *Academic Discourse across Disciplines.* Frankfurt: Peter Lang.

ISBN: 978-3039111831

Pages: 17–45

Descriptor(s): Writing, ESP

Entered by: Institute of Education, London (Department of Learning, Curriculum and Communication)

Hyland, K. 2006. *English for Academic Purposes: An Advanced Resource Book.* London: Routledge.

ISBN: 9 780415 358705

Descriptor(s): Writing, Teacher education, Speaking, Cultural issues, Reading, Methodology, Materials, Listening, ESP, Curriculum/syllabus, Classroom interaction

Entered by: Institute of Education, London (Department of Learning, Curriculum and Communication)

Hyland, K. 2006. 'English for specific purposes: Some influences and impacts' in A. Cummins and C. Davison (eds.) *International Handbook of English Language Education Vol 1.* Norwell, Mass: Springer.

ISBN: 978-0-387-46300-1

Pages: 379–390

Entered by: Institute of Education, London (Department of Learning, Curriculum and Communication)

Hyland, K. 2006. 'Representing readers in writing: Student and expert practices'. *Linguistics and Education* 16: 363–377.

Descriptor(s): Writing

Institutional level: tertiary

Entered by: Institute of Education, London (Department of Learning, Curriculum and Communication)

H

H

Hyland, K. 2007. 'Applying a gloss: Exemplifying and reformulating in academic discourse'. *Applied Linguistics* 28: 266–285.

Descriptor(s): Writing

Institutional level: tertiary

Entered by: Institute of Education, London (Department of Learning, Curriculum and Communication)

Hyland, K. 2007. 'Different strokes for different folks: Disciplinary variation in academic writing' in K. Flottem (ed.) *Language and Discipline Perspectives on Academic Discourse.* Newcastle: Cambridge Scholars Press.

ISBN: 9781847180933

Pages: 89–108

Descriptor(s): Writing, Reading, ESP

Entered by: Institute of Education, London (Department of Learning, Curriculum and Communication)

Hyland, K. 2007. 'Genre pedagogy: Language, literacy and L2 writing instruction'. *Journal of Second Language Writing* 16/3: 148–164.

Descriptor(s): Writing, ESP

Entered by: Institute of Education, London (Department of Learning, Curriculum and Communication)

Hyland, K. 2007. 'Stance and engagement: A model of interaction in academic discourse' in T.A. Van Dijk (ed.) *Benchmarks in Discourse Studies, Vol. 3.* Thousand Oaks, CA: Sage.

ISBN: 9781412936170 (for 5 volume set)

Pages: 102–121

Descriptor(s): Writing, ESP

Institutional level: tertiary

Entered by: Institute of Education, London (Department of Learning, Curriculum and Communication)

Hyland, K. 2007. 'Understanding writing: Exploring texts, writers and readers'. *Journal of the British Assn of Teachers of Japanese* 8: 63–74.

Descriptor(s): Writing, English language

Entered by: Institute of Education, London (Department of Learning, Curriculum and Communication)

Hyland, K. 2008. '"Small bits of textual material": Voice and engagement in Swales' writing'. *English for Specific Purposes* 27/2: 143–160.

Descriptor(s): Writing, ESP

Institutional level: tertiary

Entered by: Institute of Education, London (Department of Learning, Curriculum and Communication)

Hyland, K. 2008. 'Academic clusters: Text patterning in published and postgraduate writing'. *International Journal of Applied Linguistics* 18/1: 41–62.

Descriptor(s): Writing, Methodology, ESP

Entered by: Institute of Education, London (Department of Learning, Curriculum and Communication)

Hyland, K. 2008. 'As can be seen: Lexical bundles and disciplinary variation'. *English for Specific Purposes.* 27/1: 4–21.

Descriptor(s): Writing, ESP

Institutional level: tertiary

Entered by: Institute of Education, London (Department of Learning, Curriculum and Communication)

Hyland, K. 2008. 'Disciplinary voices: Interactions in research writing'. *English Text Construction* 1/1: 5–22.

Descriptor(s): Writing, ESP

Entered by: Institute of Education, London (Department of Learning, Curriculum and Communication)

Hyland, K. 2008. 'Genre and academic writing in the disciplines'. *Language Teaching* 41/4: 543–562.

Descriptor(s): Writing, Methodology, ESP

Entered by: Institute of Education, London (Department of Learning, Curriculum and Communication)

Hyland, K. 2008. 'Make your academic writing assertive and certain' in J. Reid (ed.) *Writing Myths.* Ann Arbor, MI: University of Michigan Press.

ISBN: 9 780472 032570

Pages: 70–89

Descriptor(s): Writing, English language

Entered by: Institute of Education, London (Department of Learning, Curriculum and Communication)

Hyland, K. 2008. 'Persuasion, interaction and the construction of knowledge: Representing self and others in research writing'. *International Journal of English Studies* 8/2: 8–18.

Descriptor(s): Writing, ESP

Entered by: Institute of Education, London (Department of Learning, Curriculum and Communication)

Hyland, K. and E. Anan. 2006. 'Teachers' perceptions of error: The effects of first language and experience'. *System* 34/4: 509–519.

Descriptor(s): Writing, Teacher education

Entered by: Institute of Education, London (Department of Learning, Curriculum and Communication)

Hyland, K. and F. Hyland. 2006. 'Interpersonal aspects of response: Constructing and interpreting teacher written feedback' in K. Hyland and F. Hyland (eds.) *Feedback in Second Language Writing: Contexts and Issues.* Cambridge: Cambridge University Press.

ISBN: 9780521672580

Pages: 206–224

Summary: This chapter looks at the role of the interpersonal in constructing feedback. It discusses why the interpersonal is important in written feedback; how it is realised in comments through mitigation and the expression of praise, criticism or suggestion and looks at how students actively interpret, comprehend and respond to these comments.

Descriptor(s): Writing, English language

Entered by: Institute of Education, London (Department of Learning, Curriculum and Communication)

Hyland, K. and F. Hyland. 2006. 'State of the art article: Feedback on second language students' writing'. *Language Teaching* 39/2: 83–101.

Summary: This paper examines recent research related to feedback on second language students' writing, focusing first on the emerging and developing role of feedback in writing instruction. The paper then looks at current issues in research on teacher written and oral feedback and conferencing, collaborative peer feedback and computer-mediated feedback.

Descriptor(s): Writing, ESOL/EAL, English language

Entered by: Institute of Education, London (Department of Learning, Curriculum and Communication)

Hyland, K. and F. Salager-Meyer. 2008. 'Science writing'. *Annual Review of Information Science and Technology.* 42: 297–338.

Descriptor(s): ESP, Writing

Entered by: Institute of Education, London (Department of Learning, Curriculum and Communication)

H

I,J

Hyland, K. and P. Tse. 2005. 'Evaluative that constructions: Signalling stance in research abstracts'. *Functions of Language* 12/1: 39–64.

Descriptor(s): Writing, ESP

Institutional level: tertiary

Entered by: Institute of Education, London (Department of Learning, Curriculum and Communication)

Hyland, K. and P. Tse. 2005. 'Hooking the reader: A corpus study of evaluative that in abstracts'. *English for Specific Purposes* 24/2: 123–139.

Descriptor(s): Writing, ESP

Institutional level: tertiary

Entered by: Institute of Education, London (Department of Learning, Curriculum and Communication)

Hyland, K. and P. Tse. 2007. 'Is there an "academic vocabulary"?'. *TESOL Quarterly* 41/2: 235–254.

Descriptor(s): Reading, ESP, English language

Entered by: Institute of Education, London (Department of Learning, Curriculum and Communication)

I

Ingham, K. 2008. 'The Cambridge ESOL approach to item writer training: The case of ICFE Listening'. *Cambridge ESOL: Research Notes* 32: 5–9.

Summary: Kate Ingham describes Cambridge ESOL's training program for new item writers. All item writers undergo both general and paper-specific training; training activities for new and established item writers for the Listening component of the new International Certificate in Financial English (ICFE) are described.

www.cambridgeesol.org/rs_notes/rs_nts32.PDF

Entered by: University of Cambridge ESOL Examinations

Ingham, K. and D. Thighe. 2006. 'Issues with developing a test in LSP: The International Certificate in Financial English'. *Cambridge ESOL: Research Notes* 25: 5–9.

Summary: Kate Ingham and David Thighe describe some of the issues involved in developing LSP tests, focusing on the International Certificate in Financial English (ICFE), including the relationship of test specificity to test generalisability and the importance of ensuring authenticity of test content.

www.cambridgeesol.org/rs_notes/rs_nts25.PDF

Entered by: University of Cambridge ESOL Examinations

J

Jackson, S. and K. Johnson. 2007. 'Exploring the repair procedures used in non-linguistic skill teaching and assessing their relevance for language teaching: The "START" Project'. *Indonesian Journal of English Language Teaching* 3/1: 33–50.

Summary: Describing the 'Exploring the procedures' research project.

Descriptor(s): Teacher education, Teacher cognition, Materials, Learner cognition, Curriculum/syllabus, Classroom interaction

Country of research: United Kingdom

Learners' background: United Kingdom

Institutional level: tertiary

Associated project: Exploring the Procedures Used in Non-linguistic Skill Teaching and Assessing their Relevance for Language Teaching

Entered by: Lancaster University (Linguistics and English Language)

Jarvis, H. 2005. 'Computer-based materials in EAP: History, trends and issues' in B. Beaven (ed.) *IATEFL 2005 Cardiff Conference Selections.*

Kent, UK: IATEFL.

ISBN: 1-901095-02-9

Pages: 141–143

Principal format: Printed

Summary: This paper documents the changing role of computers in English for academic purposes and argues that a computers for academic purposes (CAP) should now form a component of most EAP courses if they are to adequately equip non-native speakers for academic study at British universities.

Descriptor(s): Learning technologies, ESP, Curriculum/syllabus

Learners' background: various

Institutional level: adult

Entered by: University of Salford (School of Languages)

Jarvis, H. 2005. 'Integrating information and communication technology (ICT) by exploiting the skills of practitioners and their students' in G. Lovtsevich (ed.) *Sharing Challenges, Sharing Solutions: Teaching Languages in Diverse Contexts. Conference Proceedings PAC5 at FEELTA 2004.*

Vladivostock, Russia: Far Eastern National University.

ISBN: 5-7444-1702-8

Pages: 200–204

Principal format: Printed

Summary: This paper demonstrates how computers can be usefully integrated into classroom practice by making full use of the technology skills of our students.

Descriptor(s): Learning technologies, ESP, Curriculum/syllabus

Learners' background: various

Institutional level: adult

Entered by: University of Salford (School of Languages)

Jarvis, H. 2005. 'Technology and change in English language teaching (ELT)'. *Asian EFL Journal* 7/4: 213–227.

Summary: This state-of-the-art discussion paper considers the impact of technology on long-established notions of English as a foreign or second language. It goes on to argue and illustrate a role for computers in shifting away from traditional notions of curriculum and syllabus towards task-based approaches.

www.asian-efl-journal.com/ December_05_hj.php

Descriptor(s): Learning technologies, English language

Entered by: University of Salford (School of Languages)

Jarvis, H. 2006. 'Issues of computer-mediated communication for English language teaching'. *British Journal of Education Technology* 37/4: 643–645.

Summary: This paper discusses the implications of computer-mediated-communication (CMC) for English language teaching (ELT).

Descriptor(s): English language

Country of research: United Kingdom

Entered by: University of Salford (School of Languages)

Jarvis, H. 2008. 'Computers and independent study: Practices and perceptions of students' in P. Torres and R. Marriot (eds.) *Handbook of Research on E-Learning Methodologies for Language Acquisition.*

Hershey: Information Science Reference.

J

J

ISBN: 9781599049946

Pages: 367–386

Summary: This study considers established Computer Assisted Language Learning frameworks in relation to learner actions and perceptions of computer-based materials in less controlled self-study contexts where there is free choice regarding the range of materials to use, the place in which to use them and the time to spend on them.

Descriptor(s): Learning technologies, Learner autonomy/strategies

Country of research: United Kingdom

Learners' background: various

Institutional level: adult

Entered by: University of Salford (School of Languages)

Jarvis, H. 2008. 'Resource centres and self-study: Issues in computer assisted language learning' in E. O'Doherty (ed.) *The Fourth Education in a Changing Environment Conference Book 2007.*

Santa Rosa, California: Informing Science Press.

ISBN: 978-1-932886-13-9

Pages: 137–154

Summary: This paper reports on a languages-based study, which employs a combination of quantitative and qualitative research methodologies in order to examine a number of issues related to the title above.

Descriptor(s): Learning technologies, Learner autonomy/strategies

Country of research: United Kingdom

Learners' background: various

Institutional level: tertiary

Entered by: University of Salford (School of Languages)

Jarvis, H. and L. Pastuszka. 2008. 'Electronic literacy, reading skills and

non-native speakers: Issues for EAP'.

CALL-EJ Online 10/1: n/a.

Summary: This paper reports on a study which investigates electronic literacy reading skills amongst non-native speakers studying a range of academic subjects and levels in English at two British universities. The findings are considered in relation to implications for English for Academic Purposes (EAP) programmes.

www.tell.is.ritsumei.ac.jp/callejonline/journal/10-1/jarvis.html

Descriptor(s): Learning technologies, ESP

Country of research: United Kingdom

Learners' background: various

Institutional level: adult

Entered by: University of Salford (School of Languages)

Jendli, A., C. Coombe and S. Troudi. 2008. *Best Practice in English Language Teaching.*

Dubai: TESOL Arabia.

Descriptor(s): Teacher education

Entered by: University of Exeter (School of Education and Lifelong Learning)

Jendli, A., S. Troudi and C. Coombe. 2007. *The Power of Language: Perspectives from Arabia.* UAE: TESOL Arabia.

Descriptor(s): Cultural issues, English language

Entered by: University of Exeter (School of Education and Lifelong Learning)

Jenkins, J. 2006. 'Current perspectives on teaching World Englishes and English as a Lingua Franca'. *TESOL Quarterly* 40/1: 157–181.

Summary: This article explores recent research into WE and ELF and the extent to which it is being taken into account by English language professionals, applied linguists and SLA researchers. It also addresses the implications of WE and ELF for English language standards and for the native-nonnative English teacher debate.

Descriptor(s): Cultural issues, English language

Institutional level: adult

Entered by: University of Southampton (Modern Languages, School of Humanities)

Jenkins, J. 2006. 'Points of view and blind spots: ELF and SLA'. *International Journal of Applied Linguistics* 16/2: 137–162.

Summary: This article argues that mainstream SLA research can no longer afford to ignore the massive growth in the use of ELF, highlights the irrelevance for ELF of concepts such as interference and fossilization, and explores the extent to which alternative perspectives offer greater promise for ELF.

Descriptor(s): Cultural issues, English language

Institutional level: tertiary

Entered by: University of Southampton (Modern Languages, School of Humanities)

Jenkins, J. 2006. 'The spread of EIL: A testing time for testers'. *ELT Journal* 60/1: 42–50.

Summary: This article argues that recent changes in users and uses of English have reached the point when a major rethink of the goals of ELT is needed, but that this will first require a substantial overhaul of English language testing, given that curriculum change will not be accepted if it isn't reflected in assessment targets.

Institutional level: tertiary

Entered by: University of Southampton (Modern Languages, School of Humanities)

Jenkins, J. 2007. *English as a Lingua Franca: Attitude and Identity.* Oxford: Oxford University Press.

ISBN: 9780194422376

Summary: An investigation of attitudes towards the phenomenon of English as a Lingua Franca. The research involved a questionnaire using folk-linguistic methods completed by (mainly non-native) teachers of English in a range of countries, and interviews with non-native English teachers to explore their sense of identity in English, relating especially to their accents.

Descriptor(s): Teacher education, Cultural issues, English language

Country of research: various

Institutional level: adult

Entered by: University of Southampton (Modern Languages, School of Humanities)

Jenks, C. 2007. 'Floor management in task-based interaction: The interactional role of participatory structures'. *System* 35/4: 609–622.

Descriptor(s): Speaking, English language

Entered by: Newcastle University (School of Education, Communication and Language Sciences)

Jin, L. and M. Cortazzi. 2006. 'Changing practices in Chinese culture of learning'. *Language, Culture and Curriculum* 19/1: 5–20.

Entered by: University of Warwick (Centre for Applied Linguistics)

Jin, L. and M. Cortazzi. 2007. 'Narrative learning, EAL and metacognitive development'. *Childhood Development and Care* 177/6: 645–660.

Entered by: University of Warwick (Centre for Applied Linguistics)

Jin, L. and M. Cortazzi. 2008. 'Images of teachers, learning and questioning in Chinese cultures of learning' in E. Berendt (ed.) *Metaphors for Learning: Cross-cultural Perspectives.* Amsterdam: Benjamins.

ISBN: 978 90 272 2376 0

Pages: 177–202

J

Entered by: University of Warwick (Centre for Applied Linguistics)

Johns, A., A. Bawashi, R. Coe, K. Hyland, B. Paltridge, M. Reiff and C. Tardy. 2006. 'Crossing the boundaries of genres studies: Commentaries by experts'. *Journal of Second Language Writing* 15/3: 234–249.

Descriptor(s): Writing, English language

Entered by: Institute of Education, London (Department of Learning, Curriculum and Communication)

Johnson, K. (ed.) 2005. *Expertise in Second Language Learning and Teaching.* Basingstoke: Palgrave Macmillan.

ISBN: 978-0-230-55436-8

Summary: Describing expertise research undertaken in areas related to language learning and teaching

Descriptor(s): Teacher education, Teacher cognition, Learner cognition

Entered by: Lancaster University (Linguistics and English Language)

Johnson, K. 2005. 'The "general" study of expertise' in K. Johnson (ed.) *Expertise in Second Language Learning and Teaching.* Basingstoke: Palgrave Macmillan.

ISBN: 978-0-230-55436-8

Pages: 11–34

Summary: Considering expertise studies in non-language-teaching areas and discussing ways in which similar research might be done in the language teaching area.

Descriptor(s): Teacher cognition, Methodology

Entered by: Lancaster University (Linguistics and English Language)

Johnson, K. 2006. 'Forty years of language teaching: The 1970s'. *Language Teaching* 40: 8–9.

Summary: Describing language teaching developments in the nineteen seventies.

Descriptor(s): Teacher education, Teacher cognition, Methodology, Materials, Curriculum/syllabus

Entered by: Lancaster University (Linguistics and English Language)

Johnson, K. 2007. 'Expertise research in language teaching: Some examples and some issues'. *Indonesian Journal of English Language Teaching* 3/1: 51–71.

Summary: Considering the development of expertise research in the language teaching field and describing some examples of small-scale research undertaken at Lancaster.

Descriptor(s): Teacher education, Teacher cognition, English language

Country of research: United Kingdom

Entered by: Lancaster University (Linguistics and English Language)

Johnson, K. 2008. *An Introduction to Foreign Language Learning and Teaching; second edition.* London: Pearson Education.

ISBN: 978-1-4058-3617-3

Summary: Describing research and developments in the fields of language learning and teaching.

Descriptor(s): Writing, Teacher education, Teacher cognition, Speaking, Cultural issues, Reading, Pronunciation, Methodology, Materials, Listening, Learning technologies, Learner cognition, Learner autonomy/ strategies, ESOL/EAL, ESP, English language, Curriculum/syllabus, Classroom interaction, Assessment

Entered by: Lancaster University (Linguistics and English Language)

Johnson, K. and S. Jackson. 2006. 'Comparing language teaching and other-skill teaching: Has the language teacher anything to learn?'. *System* 34: 532–546.

Summary: Describing the main findings of the 'Exploring the procedures' project.

J

Descriptor(s): Teacher education, Methodology, Materials, English language, Curriculum/syllabus, Classroom interaction

Country of research: United Kingdom

Learners' background: United Kingdom

Institutional level: tertiary

Associated project: Exploring the Procedures Used in Non-linguistic Skill Teaching and Assessing their Relevance for Language Teaching

Entered by: Lancaster University (Linguistics and English Language)

Johnson, K., M. Kim, Y-F. Liu, A. Nava, D. Perkins, A-M. Smith, O. Soler-Canela and W. Lu. 2008. 'A step forward: Investigating expertise in materials evaluation'. *ELTJ* 62: 157–163.

Summary: Describing a research project which observed the way teachers evaluate a textbook for possible classroom use with their students. Uses think-alouds.

Descriptor(s): Teacher education, Teacher cognition, Methodology, Materials, Learner cognition, English language, Curriculum/syllabus

Country of research: United Kingdom

Institutional level: tertiary

Entered by: Lancaster University (Linguistics and English Language)

Jones, N. 2005. 'Raising the languages ladder: Constructing a new framework for accrediting foreign language skills'. *Cambridge ESOL: Research Notes* 19: 15–19.

Summary: Neil Jones describes how tests for 26 different languages are being related to the Languages Ladder framework, focusing on how objectively marked components (reading and listening) can be linked to it.

www.cambridgeesol.org/rs_notes/rs_nts19.PDF

Entered by: University of Cambridge ESOL Examinations

Jones, N. 2006. 'Assessment systems: Conceptual, human, technological'. *Cambridge ESOL: Research Notes* 23: 2–3.

Summary: Neil Jones gives a unique view of assessment systems, describing the complex system of language assessment in terms of its conceptual, human and technological facets that have evolved over the last decade at Cambridge ESOL.

www.cambridgeesol.org/rs_notes/rs_nts23.PDF

Entered by: University of Cambridge ESOL Examinations

Jones, N. 2008. 'SurveyLang: A European survey of language competences' in *IAEA: Re-interpreting Assessment: Society, Measurement and Meaning.* Cambridge: Cambridge Assessment.

Principal format: Online

www.iaea2008.cambridgeassessment.org.uk/ca/digitalAssets/180411_Jones.PDF

Descriptor(s): Assessment

Entered by: University of Cambridge ESOL Examinations

Jones, N. and L. Maycock. 2007. 'The comparability of computer-based and paper-based tests: Goals, approaches, and a review of research'. *Cambridge ESOL: Research Notes* 27: 11–14.

Summary: Neil Jones and Louise Maycock address the issue of comparability between the computer-based mode and paper-based mode of tests such as BEC and BULATS.

www.cambridgeesol.org/rs_notes/rs_nts27.PDF

Entered by: University of Cambridge ESOL Examinations

Jones, N., K. Ashton and A.S-Y. Chen. 2005. 'Rising to the challenge of asset languages'. *Cambridge ESOL: Research Notes* 19: 2–4.

Summary: Neil Jones, Karen Ashton and Ann Shih-yi Chen introduce asset languages, an assessment system being developed by UCLES to implement the Languages Ladder, a voluntary recognition system in the UK which seeks to give people credit for their language skills across 26 languages.

www.cambridgeesol.org/rs_notes/rs_nts19.PDF

Entered by: University of Cambridge ESOL Examinations

Kelly, G. 2005. 'Can intonation be taught'. *English Teaching Professional* Issue 39: 11–12.

Summary: An argument that intonation can and should be taught, using a discourse model.

Descriptor(s): Pronunciation, Methodology, ESOL/EAL, English language

Entered by: University of Northumbria (Department of Humanities, School of Arts and Social Sciences)

Kelly, G. 2006. 'Can the DELTA help you to teach EAP?'.

Summary: An article generally in support of the Cambridge ESOL DELTA course, and its appropriacy for EAP teachers.

www.developingteachers.com/articles_tchtraining/eapdelta1_gerald.htm

Descriptor(s): Methodology, ESOL/EAL, ESP, English language, Curriculum/syllabus, Assessment, Teacher education

Entered by: University of Northumbria (Department of Humanities, School of Arts and Social Sciences)

Kelly, G. 2006. 'Teaching pronunciation'.

Summary: A short guide to pronunciation teaching, written for the Pearson Longman methodology website.

www.pearsonlongman.com/methodology/PDF/Pronunciation.PDF

Descriptor(s): Speaking, Pronunciation, Methodology, Materials, Learner autonomy/strategies, ESOL/EAL, ESP, English language

Entered by: University of Northumbria (Department of Humanities, School of Arts and Social Sciences)

Kemp, C. 2007. 'Strategic processing in grammar learning: Do multilinguals use more strategies?'. *International Journal of Multilingualism* 4: 241–261.

Descriptor(s): Learner autonomy/strategies

Entered by: Cardiff University (School of English, Communication and Philosophy)

Kemp, C. 2008. 'A pilot to investigate multilinguals' use of grammar learning strategies' in M. Gibson, B. Hufeisen and C. Personne (eds.) *Multilingualism: Learning and Instruction. Selected Papers from the L3 Conference in Freiburg, Switzerland 2005.* Berlin: Schneider Verlag.

ISBN: 978-3-8340-0407-9

Pages: 51–60

Descriptor(s): Teacher cognition, Learner cognition

Entered by: Cardiff University (School of English, Communication and Philosophy)

Kennedy, C. 2005. 'Just perfect! The pragmatics of evaluation in holiday postcards' in A. Jaworski and A. Pritchard (eds.) *Discourse, Communication and Tourism.* Clevedon: Channel View Publications.

ISBN: 1-84541-020-3

Pages: 223–246

Summary: Examines the use of evaluation lexis in holiday postcards – applications to classroom analysis of genre, and student and teacher language awareness.

Descriptor(s): Methodology, Materials, English language, Curriculum/syllabus

Entered by: University of Birmingham (Centre for English Language Studies and Department of English)

Kennedy, C. 2007. 'A corpus-based investigation of linguistic responses to an IELTS academic writing task' in L. Taylor and P. Falvey (eds.) *Research in Speaking and Writing Assessment.* Cambridge: CUP.

ISBN: 9780521542487

Pages: 316–377

Summary: Investigation into a corpus of writing assessments in the IELTS examination to compare distinguishing linguistic features of the different levels.

Descriptor(s): Writing, English language, Assessment

Learners' background: various

Institutional level: tertiary

Entered by: University of Birmingham (Centre for English Language Studies and Department of English)

Kennedy, J., R. Smith and E. Ushioda. 2008. 'Taking stock of *ELTED* (A conversation)'. *ELTED (English Language Teacher Education and Development)* 11: 52–57.

www.elted.net/issues/volume-11/8%20Kennedy%20et%20al.PDF

Descriptor(s): Writing, Teacher education

Entered by: University of Warwick (Centre for Applied Linguistics)

Kerr, R. 2008. 'International development and the New Public Management: Projects and logframes as discursive technologies of governance' in S. Dar and B. Cooke (eds.)

The New Development Management. London: Zed.

ISBN: 978 1842779224

Pages: 91–110

Descriptor(s): Management/innovation, English language

Institutional level: adult

Entered by: The Open University (Faculty of Education and Languages)

Khalifa, H. 2005. 'Are test taker characteristics accounted for in Main Suite Reading papers?'. *Cambridge ESOL: Research Notes* 21: 7–10.

Summary: Hanan Khalifa considers whether test taker characteristics are accounted for in the Reading papers of the Cambridge Main Suite. She suggests how candidates' responses to Reading tasks may be affected by their physical/physiological, psychological and experiential characteristics, all of which form part of Cyril Weir's Validity framework.

www.cambridgeesol.org/rs_notes/rs_nts21.PDF

Descriptor(s): Reading, Assessment

Entered by: University of Cambridge ESOL Examinations

Khalifa, H. 2008. 'Co-operating in setting and monitoring standards for language assessment' in *Beijing 6th National Public Tests Forum.* China: Ministry of Education.

ISBN: n/a

Pages: n/a

Principal format: Printed

Descriptor(s): Assessment

Entered by: University of Cambridge ESOL Examinations

Khalifa, H. 2008. 'Testing teaching knowledge: Developing a quality instrument to support professional development' in L. Taylor and C. Weir (eds.) *Studies in Language Testing Vol 27: Multilingualism*

K

K

and Assessment: Achieving Transparency, Assuring Quality, Sustaining Diversity – Proceedings of the ALTE Berlin Conference, May 2005. Cambridge: UCLES/CUP.

ISBN: 9780521711920

Entered by: University of Cambridge ESOL Examinations

Khalifa, H. and A. Ffrench. 2008. 'Aligning Cambridge ESOL examinations to the CEFR: Issues & practice' in IAEA: *Re-interpreting Assessment: Society, Measurement and Meaning.* Cambridge: Cambridge Assessment.

Principal format: Online

www.iaea2008.cambridgeassessment.org.uk/ca/digitalAssets/180399_Khalifa.PDF

Descriptor(s): Speaking, ESOL/EAL, Curriculum/syllabus, Assessment

Entered by: University of Cambridge ESOL Examinations

Kiely, R. 2005. 'Cultural mirrors – Television drama in the EFL classroom'.

www.developingteachers.com/articles_tchtraining/tv21_richard.htm

Descriptor(s): Speaking, Cultural issues, Methodology, Curriculum/syllabus

Entered by: University of Bristol (Graduate School of Education)

Kiely, R. 2005. 'Television in TESOL – The research agenda'.

Summary: A discussion of the use of television as a new technology in ELT and the issues and approaches in examining these in research.

www.developingteachers.com/articles_tchtraining/tv31_richard.htm

Descriptor(s): Teacher education, Cultural issues, Methodology, Learning technologies

Entered by: University of Bristol (Graduate School of Education)

Kiely, R. 2005. 'The role of television and televisual literacy in language teaching and learning'.

www.developingteachers.com/articles_tchtraining/tv1_richard.htm

Descriptor(s): Curriculum/syllabus, Learning technologies, Methodology, Cultural issues, Teacher education

Entered by: University of Bristol (Graduate School of Education)

Kiely, R. 2006. '"In fact I can't really lose": Laure's struggle to become an academic writer' in S. Trahar (ed.) *Narrative Research on Learning: Comparative and International Perspectives.* Oxford, UK: Symposium Books.

ISBN: 187 3927 60 6

Pages: 183–198

Summary: A single case study of an undergraduate student developing second language writing skills in the context of an EAP programme in a UK university, drawing on ethnographic data examined in the light of narrative theory.

Descriptor(s): Writing, Cultural issues, Materials, ESP, Curriculum/syllabus, Classroom interaction

Entered by: University of Bristol (Graduate School of Education)

Kiely, R. 2006. 'Evaluation, innovation and ownership in language programs'. *Modern Language Journal,* 90/3: 597–602.

Summary: A discussion of the factors which influence teacher and curriculum development through teacher-led programme evaluation

Descriptor(s): Teacher education, Management/innovation, Curriculum/syllabus

Country of research: United Kingdom

Learners' background: various

Institutional level: tertiary

Entered by: University of Bristol (Graduate School of Education)

Kiely, R. 2007. 'Teachers into researchers: Learning to research in TESOL' in S. Borg (ed.) *Language Teacher Research in Europe.* Virginia, USA: TESOL Publications.

ISBN: 978 1931 1853 7 0

Pages: 67–80

Summary: A report and discussion of the issues involved in teachers' shift from a professional teacher identity to a researcher identity in the context of a masters programme in the UK. The chapter draws on the Teachers into Researchers project, University of Bristol, 2002–2004.

Entered by: University of Bristol (Graduate School of Education)

Kiely, R. and J. Askham 2008. 'Socialisation and identity in learning in applied linguistics. *Report to the Languages, Linguistics and Area Studies (LLAS) Learning and Teaching Support Network (LTSN)'.* HEA/University of Southampton.

Summary: Project report, focussing on the pedagogical implications of the findings.

www.llas.ac.uk/resourcedownloads/2631/kiely.pdf

Descriptor(s): Teacher education, Cultural issues, Management/innovation, ESP

Country of research: United Kingdom

Learners' background: various

Institutional level: tertiary

Associated project: SAIL: Socialisation and Identity in Learning in Applied Linguistics

Entered by: University of Bristol (Graduate School of Education)

Kiely, R. 2008. 'The purpose, promise and potential of teacher research' in M. Pawlak (ed.) *Investigating English Language Teaching and Learning.* Poznan: IATEFL/University of Poznan.

ISBN: 978 83 88 33 54 5 7

Pages: 11–30

Summary: An examination of the contexts and characteristics of teacher research in ELT, drawing on finding of the Teachers into Researchers project, University of Bristol 2002–2004.

Descriptor(s): Teacher education, Cultural issues, Management/innovation, Curriculum/syllabus

Country of research: various

Learners' background: various

Entered by: University of Bristol (Graduate School of Education)

Kiely, R. and J. Askham. 2008. '"Visiting locals' houses" and "English without noticing": The nature and potential of informal language development' in M. Edwardes (ed.) *Proceedings of the BAAL Annual Conference 2007.* London, UK: Scitsiugnil Press.

ISBN: 978-0-9559533-1-6

Principal format: CD-ROM

Summary: Paper presenting findings of the SAIL project, later published as Observing, noticing and understanding: Two case studies in language awareness in the development of academic literacy (Kiely) in the journal Language Awareness 2009.

Descriptor(s): Writing, Cultural issues, Management/innovation, ESP, Curriculum/syllabus

Country of research: United Kingdom

Learners' background: various

Institutional level: tertiary

Associated project: SAIL: Socialisation and Identity in Learning in Applied Linguistics

Entered by: University of Bristol (Graduate School of Education)

Kiely, R. and P. Rea-Dickins. 2005. *Program Evaluation in Language Education.* Basingstoke: Palgrave Macmillan.

ISBN: 1-4039 4571 3

Summary: A textbook on language programme evaluation within a series on

K

K

teaching and researching applied linguistics, with sections on theoretical issues, case studies and strategies for implementation.

Descriptor(s): Teacher education, Methodology, Materials, Learning technologies, Curriculum/syllabus, Assessment

Country of research: various

Learners' background: various

Entered by: University of Bristol (Graduate School of Education)

Kiely, R., M. Davis, G. Carter and C. Nye. 2008. 'The craft of the experienced language teacher'. *Voices* 205: 12–13.

Summary: A brief report on initial findings on the InSITE project.

Descriptor(s): Teacher education, Methodology, Management/innovation, Curriculum/syllabus

Country of research: United Kingdom

Learners' background: various

Institutional level: adult

Associated project: InSITE: Integrating Systematic Investigation into Teaching of English

Entered by: University of Bristol (Graduate School of Education)

Kiely, R., P. Rea-Dickins and G. Yu. 2007. 'Student Identity, Learning and Progression (SILP): The affective and academic impact of IELTS on "successful" candidates' in *IELTS Research Reports Volume 7*. Canberra, Australia: IELTS Australia Pty and British Council.

ISBN: 978 0 977 5875 2 0

Pages: 59–136

Descriptor(s): Writing, Speaking, Reading, Listening, ESP, Assessment

Country of research: United Kingdom

Learners' background: various

Entered by: University of Bristol (Graduate School of Education)

Kiely, R., P.M. Rea-Dickins, H. Woodfield and G.M. Clibbon. 2006. 'Introduction' in R. Kiely, P.M. Rea-Dickins, H. Woodfield and G.M. Clibbon (eds.) *Language, Culture and Identity in Applied Linguistics: Proceedings of the 2005 Annual Meeting of the British Association for Applied Linguistics.* London: Equinox.

Principal format: Printed

Summary: A collection of papers on language culture and identity, with an introduction on ways in which the conference (BAAL AM 2005) interpreted the theme. Issues include identity and language learning, academic writing, and contact issues in adjacent language and professional communities.

Descriptor(s): Writing, Cultural issues, Pronunciation, Materials, Curriculum/syllabus

Country of research: various

Learners' background: various

Entered by: University of Bristol (Graduate School of Education)

Kormos, J. and K. Csizér. 2007. 'An interview study of inter-ethnic contact and its role in language learning in a foreign language environment'. *System* 35: 241–258.

Summary: The research reported in this paper investigates what types of inter-cultural contact Hungarian schoolchildren have, what kind of language-related attitudes they can give account of and how they see the role of contact situations in affecting their attitudinal and motivational dispositions towards the L2, the L2 speaking communities and the process of L2 learning.

Descriptor(s): Cultural issues

Country of research: Hungary

Learners' background: Hungary

Institutional level: primary

Entered by: Lancaster University (Linguistics and English Language)

K

Kormos, J. and K. Csizér. 2008. 'Age-related differences in the motivation of learning English as a foreign language: Attitudes, selves and motivated learning behavior'. *Language Learning* 58: 327–355.

Summary: Our study describes the motivation for learning English as a foreign language in three distinct learner populations: secondary school pupils, university students, and adult language learners. The main factors affecting students' second language (L2) motivation were language learning attitudes and the Ideal L2 self.

Descriptor(s): Learner autonomy/strategies

Country of research: Hungary

Learners' background: Hungary

Entered by: Lancaster University (Linguistics and English Language)

Kormos, J. and E.H. Kontra. 2007. 'Nyelvtanárok a diszlexiáról [Language teachers on dyslexia]'. *Új Pedagógiai Szemle* 9.

Summary: This study investigated language teachers' knowledge concerning dyslexia and its effect on language learning as well as attitudes to dyslexic children in the foreign language classroom.

www.oki.hu/oldal.php?tipus=cikk&kod=2007-09-ta-Tobbek-Nyelvtanarok

Descriptor(s): Teacher education

Country of research: Hungary

Learners' background: Hungary

Entered by: Lancaster University (Linguistics and English Language)

Kormos, J. and E.H. Kontra. 2008. 'Hungarian teachers' perceptions of dyslexic language learners' in J. Kormos and E. Kontra (eds.) *Language Learners with Special Needs: An International Perspective.* Bristol: Multilingual Matters.

ISBN: 1-84769-089-0

Pages: 189–214

Summary: This paper reports on an interview study conducted in Hungary with teachers involved in a special compensatory program for dyslexic language learners. The interviews examined the teachers' perception of the nature of the problems dyslexia causes in foreign language learning.

Descriptor(s): Teacher education, Methodology

Country of research: Hungary

Learners' background: Hungary

Entered by: Lancaster University (Linguistics and English Language)

Kormos, J. and A. Sáfár. 2008. 'Phonological short term-memory, working memory and foreign language performance in intensive language learning.'. Bilingualism: *Language and Cognition* 11: 261–271.

Summary: In our research we addressed the question what the relationship is between phonological short-term and working memory capacity and performance in an end-of-year reading, writing, listening, speaking and use of English test.

Descriptor(s): Learner cognition, Assessment

Country of research: Hungary

Learners' background: Hungary

Institutional level: secondary

Entered by: Lancaster University (Linguistics and English Language)

Kormos, J., K. Csizér, A. Menyhárt and D. Török. 2008. '"Great Expectations": The motivational profile of Hungarian English language students'. *Arts and Humanities in Higher Education* 7: 65–82.

Summary: In this article we investigate what characterizes the language learning motivation of Hungarian English language students. The interview data revealed that the respondents did not invest sufficient energy in maintaining and improving their

L

language competence. This is explained with reference to a low level of learner autonomy primarily caused by teacher-centered instruction.

Descriptor(s): Learner autonomy/strategies

Country of research: Hungary

Learners' background: Hungary

Institutional level: tertiary

Entered by: Lancaster University (Linguistics and English Language)

Kubanyiova, M. 2005. 'Promoting cohesive groups in the language classroom' in E. Szoradova (ed.) *Retrospective and Perspectives in Education: Proceedings from an International Research Conference.* Nitra, Slovakia: Constantine the Philosopher University in Nitra.

ISBN: 80-80-50-918-2

Pages: 315–321

Principal format: Printed

Country of research: Slovakia

Learners' background: Slovakia

Entered by: University of Birmingham (School of Education)

Kubanyiova, M. 2006. 'Developing a motivational teaching practice in EFL teachers in Slovakia: Challenges of promoting teacher change in EFL contexts'. *TESL-EJ* 10/2: 1–17.

http://tesl-ej.org/ej38/a5.PDF

Descriptor(s): Teacher education, Teacher cognition, Management/innovation

Country of research: Slovakia

Learners' background: Slovakia

Institutional level: adult

Entered by: University of Birmingham (School of Education)

Kurtes, S. and N. Saville. 2008. 'The English Profile Programme – An overview'. *Cambridge ESOL: Research Notes* 33: 2–4.

Summary: Article describes the birth of English Profile, a programme rooted in – and building on – the Common European Framework of Reference (CEFR) and other Council of Europe initiatives. They outline the approach to producing Reference Level Descriptions (RLD) begun by Cambridge ESOL and describe current research projects and the various events through which we disseminate research findings.

www.cambridgeesol.org/rs_notes/rs_nts33.PDF

Entered by: University of Cambridge ESOL Examinations

Kurtoglu-Hooton, N. 2008. 'The design of feedback and its effect on student teachers' in S. Garton and K. Richards (eds.) *Professional Encounters in TESOL.* Basingstoke: Palgrave Macmillan.

ISBN: 978-0-230-55351-4

Pages: 24–41

Descriptor(s): Teacher education

Entered by: Aston University (School of Languages and Social Sciences)

L

Lamb, M. 2007. 'The impact of school on EFL learning motivation: An Indonesian case-study'. *TESOL Quarterly* 41/4: 757–780.

Entered by: University of Leeds (School of Education)

Lazar, G. 2008. 'Some approaches to literature, language teaching and the Internet'. *Fremdsprachen Lehren und Lernen (FLuL)* 37: 154–163.

Summary: This article focuses on how the Internet can be used to exploit the use of literary texts with language learners. Drawing on critical theory, it is suggested that hypermedia and fan fiction sites are two possible classroom resources. Pedagogic principles for developing generic activities exploiting these resources are discussed.

Descriptor(s): Writing, Reading, Materials, Learning technologies, ESOL/EAL

Country of research: United Kingdom

Institutional level: secondary

Entered by: Middlesex University (English Language and Learning Support)

Leung, C. 2005. 'Convivial communication: Recontextualizing communicative competence'. *International Journal of Applied Linguistics* 15/2: 119–144.

Entered by: King's College London (Department of Education and Professional Studies)

Leung, C. 2005. 'Language and content in bilingual education'. *Linguistics and Education* 16/2: 238–252.

Entered by: King's College London (Department of Education and Professional Studies)

Leung, C. 2006. 'Is there a critical point for language learners?'. *TESOL Research Newsletter* 13: 1–2.

Entered by: King's College London (Department of Education and Professional Studies)

Leung, C. 2007. 'Dynamic assessment – assessment as teaching?'. *Language Assessment Quarterly* 4/3: 257–278.

Entered by: King's College London (Department of Education and Professional Studies)

Leung, C. 2008. 'Second language academic literacies: Converging understandings' in E. Shohamy and N.H. Hornberger (eds.) *Encyclopedia of Language and Education volume 2.* New York: Springer.

ISBN: 978038732875

Pages: 143–161

Entered by: King's College London (Department of Education and Professional Studies)

Leung, C. and J. Lewkowicz. 2006. 'Expanding horizons and unresolved conundrums: Language testing and assessment'. *TESOL Quarterly* 40/1: 211–234.

Entered by: King's College London (Department of Education and Professional Studies)

Leung, C. and J. Lewkowicz. 2008. 'Assessing second/additional language of diverse populations' in E. Shohamy and N.H. Hornberger (eds.) *Encyclopedia of Language and Education volume 7.* New York: Springer.

ISBN: 978038732875

Pages: 301–317

Descriptor(s): Assessment

Entered by: King's College London (Department of Education and Professional Studies)

Leung, C. and P. Rea-Dickins. 2007. 'Teacher assessment as policy instrument – contradictions and capacities'. *Language Assessment Quarterly* 4/4: 16–36.

Entered by: University of Bristol (Graduate School of Education)

Li, Y-Y. and J. Flowerdew. 2007. 'Shaping Chinese novice scientists' manuscripts for publication'. *Journal of Second Language Writing* 16/2: 100–117.

Entered by: University of Leeds (School of Education)

Linse, C. 2008. 'Language issue or learning disability?'. *TESOL Essential Teacher* 5/4: 28–31.

Summary: This article is designed to help teachers consider issues related to learners who are struggling in the EFL or ESL classroom.

Descriptor(s): Learner autonomy/strategies, ESOL/EAL

Entered by: Queen's University, Belfast (School of Education)

L

L

Linse, C. 2008. 'Meet the parents'. *English Teaching Professional* 60: 23–25.

Summary: This article addresses strategies that teachers can utilise to foster positive relationships with parents of children learning English as a foreign and/or additional language.

Descriptor(s): Teacher education, Learner autonomy/strategies

Entered by: Queen's University, Belfast (School of Education)

Littlemore, J. 2008. 'The relationship between associative thinking, analogical reasoning, image formation and metaphoric competence' in M. Zanotto, L. Cameron and M. Cavalcanti (eds.) *Confronting Metaphor in Use: An Applied Linguistic Approach.* Amsterdam/Philadelphia: John Benjamins.

ISBN: 9789027254177

Pages: 199–222

Summary: This chapter explores the cognitive processes involved in understanding metaphor in a second language.

Descriptor(s): English language

Entered by: University of Birmingham (Centre for English Language Studies and Department of English)

Littlemore, J. and G. Low. 2006. *Figurative Thinking and Foreign Language Learning.* Basingstoke: Palgrave MacMillan.

ISBN: 1403-996024

Summary: This book explores the ways in which language learners deal with and learn from figurative language.

Descriptor(s): Cultural issues, Learner cognition, English language

Entered by: University of Birmingham (Centre for English Language Studies and Department of English)

Littlemore, J. and G. Low. 2006. 'Metaphoric competence and communicative language ability'. *Applied Linguistics* 27/2: 268–294.

Summary: This article looks at how an ability to understand and produce metaphor can contribute to various aspects of communicative competence.

Descriptor(s): Learner cognition, English language

Entered by: University of Birmingham (Centre for English Language Studies and Department of English)

Lo, J. and F. Hyland. 2007. 'Enhancing students' engagement and motivation in writing: The case of primary students in Hong Kong'. *Journal of Second Language Writing* 16 /4: 219–237.

Summary: This study describes the implementation of a new ESL primary writing programme. The study examines both the students' and teacher-researchers' perspectives on the new programme and looks at its impact on writing engagement, motivation and interest in writing as well as on the overall development of the students' writing skills.

Descriptor(s): Writing, Cultural issues, Methodology, English language

Country of research: Hong Kong

Learners' background: Hong Kong

Institutional level: primary

Entered by: Institute of Education, London (Department of Learning, Curriculum and Communication)

Lynch, T. 2005. 'Self-transcribing and noticing in EAP speaking classes'. *Edinburgh Working Papers in Applied Linguistics* 14: 54–67.

Summary: A study comparing two approaches to feedback on spoken English performance (teacher-led and learner-led) and their impact on learning.

Descriptor(s): Speaking, Methodology, Learner cognition, English language

Entered by: University of Edinburgh (Institute for Applied Language Studies/Office of Lifelong Learning)

Lynch, T. 2006. 'Academic listening: Marrying top and bottom' in E. Uso-Juan and A. Martinez-Flor (eds.) *Current Trends in the Development and Teaching of the Four Language Skills.* Berlin: Mouton de Gruyter.

ISBN: 3110189682

Pages: 91–110

Summary: A discussion of the need for attention to both top and bottom level processing in the teaching of L2 listening skills, with practical illustrations from the author's EAP materials.

Descriptor(s): Teacher education, Listening, Learner autonomy/strategies

Entered by: University of Edinburgh (Institute for Applied Language Studies/Office of Lifelong Learning)

Lynch, T. 2007. 'Checks, lies and videotape: Developing international academics' lecturing skills in English' in T. Lynch and J. Northcott (eds.) *Symposia for Language Teacher Educators.* Edinburgh: Institute for Applied Language Studies.

Principal format: CD-ROM

Descriptor(s): Teacher education, Speaking

Entered by: University of Edinburgh (Institute for Applied Language Studies/Office of Lifelong Learning)

Lynch, T. 2007. 'Learning from the transcripts of an oral communication task'. *ELT Journal* 61/4: 311–320.

Summary: A classroom study comparing alternative feedback techniques on spoken task performance.

Descriptor(s): Writing, Speaking, Listening, Learner cognition, English language, Classroom interaction

Entered by: University of Edinburgh (Institute for Applied Language Studies/Office of Lifelong Learning)

M

Macaro, E. 2005. 'Codeswitching in the L2 classroom: A communication and learning strategy' in E. Llurda (ed.) *Non-Native Language Teachers: Perceptions, Challenges, and Contributions to the Profession.* Boston, MA: Springer.

ISBN: 978-0387328225

Pages: 63–84

Descriptor(s): Teacher education, Learner autonomy/strategies

Entered by: University of Oxford (Department of Education)

Macaro, E. 2006. 'Strategies for language learning and for language use: Revising the theoretical framework'. *Modern Language Journal* 90/3: 320–337.

Descriptor(s): Learner autonomy/strategies

Country of research: United Kingdom

Entered by: University of Oxford (Department of Education)

Macaro, E. 2008. 'The shifting dimensions of language learner autonomy' in T.E. Lamb and H. Reinders (eds.) *Learner and Teacher Autonomy: Concepts, Realities and Responses.* Amsterdam: John Benjamins.

ISBN: 978 90 272 9169 1

Pages: 47–62

Descriptor(s): Learner autonomy/strategies

Country of research: United Kingdom

Entered by: University of Oxford (Department of Education)

Macaro, E. and E. Masterman. 2006. 'Does intensive explicit grammar instruction make all the difference?'. *Language Teaching Research* 10/3: 297–327.

Descriptor(s): Classroom interaction, Learner cognition, Methodology

Country of research: United Kingdom

M

Entered by: University of Oxford
(Department of Education)

Macaro, E., S. Graham and R. Vanderplank.
2007. 'Listening strategies' in A. D. Cohen
and E. Macaro (eds.) *Language Learner
Strategies: 30 Years of Research and
Practice.* Oxford: Oxford University Press.

ISBN: 978-0194422543

Descriptor(s): Learner autonomy/strategies

Entered by: University of Oxford
(Department of Education)

Macaro, E., S. Graham and R. Vanderplank.
2007. 'A review of listening strategies: Focus
on sources of knowledge and success' in A.
Cohen and E. Macaro (eds.) Language
Learner Strategies: *30 years of Research and
Practice.* Oxford: Oxford University Press.

ISBN: 978-0-19-442254-3

Descriptor(s): Learner autonomy/strategies,
Listening

Entered by: University of Oxford (Language
Centre)

Macaro, E., R. Vanderplank and S. Graham.
2005. *A Systematic Review of the Role of
Prior Knowledge in Unidirectional Listening
Comprehension.* London: EPPI-Centre, Social
Science Research Unit, Institute of Education,
University of London.

ISBN: None. Available online:
http://eppi.ioe.ac.uk/cms/LinkClick.aspx?fileti
cket=cRyM1w3AGg8%3d&tabid=299&mid=1
149&language=en-US

Descriptor(s): Methodology, Listening,
Learner autonomy/strategies, Assessment

Entered by: University of Oxford (Language
Centre)

MacArthur, F. and J. Littlemore. 2008.
'Exploring the figurative continuum:
A discovery approach using corpora
in the foreign language classroom' in
F. Boers and S. Lindstromberg (eds.)

*Cognitive Linguistic Approaches to
Teaching Vocabulary and Phraseology.*
Amsterdam: Moutin de Gruyter.

ISBN: 9783110196306

Pages: 159–188

Summary: The chapter explores the ways
in which learners of English and Spanish
interact with corpora to learn figurative
language.

Descriptor(s): English language

Country of research: Spain

Learners' background: Spain

Institutional level: tertiary

Entered by: University of Birmingham
(Centre for English Language Studies
and Department of English)

Macdonald, M. and J. Spiro. 2008. '"Read
Write": Assessing cultural awareness and
creativity in literary response'. *Literature,
Media & Cutural Studies* 32/1: 21–27.

Descriptor(s): Cultural issues, Reading

Entered by: University of Exeter
(School of Education and Lifelong Learning)

Macdonald, M.N., R. Badger and M. Dasli.
2006. 'Authenticity, culture and language
learning'. *Language and Intercultural
Communication* 6/3-4: 250–261.

Descriptor(s): Cultural issues

Entered by: University of Exeter
(School of Education and Lifelong Learning)

MacDonald, M.N., R. Badger and M. Dasli.
2006. 'Authenticity, culture and language'.
Language and Intercultural Communication
6/3-4: 251–261.

Entered by: University of Leeds
(School of Education)

Mahlberg, M. 2006. 'Lexical cohesion:
Corpus linguistic theory and its application
in ELT'. *International Journal of Corpus
Linguistics* 11/3: 363–383.

Descriptor(s): Methodology, Learning technologies, English language

Country of research: United Kingdom

Learners' background: various

Institutional level: tertiary

Entered by: University of Liverpool (School of English)

Malderez, A. and M. Wedell. 2007. *Teaching Teachers: Processes and Practices.* London: Continuum.

ISBN: 9780826484918

Descriptor(s): Teacher education

Entered by: University of Leeds (School of Education)

Mann, S. 2005. 'Researching reflective teaching'. *Perspectives (Journal of TESOL Italy)* 21/2: 7–28.

Summary: This article is based on a plenary given at TESOL-Italy in 2004. It incorporates some research arising from a workshop given with Donald Freeman. It provides evidence of a non-judgemental teacher development process.

Descriptor(s): Teacher education, Teacher cognition

Entered by: University of Warwick (Centre for Applied Linguistics)

Mann, S. 2005. 'State-of-the-art: The language teacher's development'. *Language Teaching* 38/3: 103–118.

Summary: A review of important research related to teacher development, reflective practice, action research, collaborative and peer development and CPD.

Entered by: University of Warwick (Centre for Applied Linguistics)

Mann, S. 2008. 'Metaphors keep cropping up: Features of exploratory talk' in S. Garton and K. Richards (eds.) *Professional Encounters.* London: Palgrave.

Pages: 151–172

Summary: Reports on research that shows teachers using metaphor as exploratory vehicles in articulating their developing ideas. The study points to the importance of metaphors as a heuristic.

Entered by: University of Warwick (Centre for Applied Linguistics)

Mann, S. 2008. 'Teachers' use of metaphor in making sense of the first year of teaching' in T. Farrell (ed.) *Novice Language Teachers.* London: Equinox.

Pages: 11–28

Summary: Reports on evidence of the development of teachers' use of metaphor in coming to terms with the first year of teaching. The evidence points to metaphor use as changeable and dependent on context. There is little evidence to support the idea of 'core' metaphors for teachers.

Descriptor(s): Teacher cognition, Teacher education

Entered by: University of Warwick (Centre for Applied Linguistics)

Márquez, R.M., I. Rainey and G. Fulcher. 2005. 'A comparative study of conventional indirectness in British English and Peninsular Spanish'. *Applied Linguistics* 26/1: 1–31.

Descriptor(s): Cultural issues

Learners' background: Spain

Entered by: University of Leicester (English Language Teaching and Applied Linguistics, School of Education)

Marshall, H. 2006. 'The Cambridge ESOL item banking system'. *Cambridge ESOL: Research Notes* 23: 3–5.

Summary: Helen Marshall describes key aspects of our item banking system, the database of test items which are used to construct all of our examinations and tests. Helen describes how this system

M

M

maintains quality assurance through a number of different stages that all test material goes through, drawing on current technology to do so.

www.cambridgeesol.org/rs_notes/rs_nts23. PDF

Entered by: University of Cambridge ESOL Examinations

Martin, D.M. 2005. 'English as an additional language; and speech, language and communication difficulties' in A.L. Lewis and B. Norwich (eds.) *Special Teaching for Special Children? Pedagogies for Inclusion.* Milton Keynes: Open University Press.

ISBN: 0335214053

Pages: 96–109

Entered by: University of Birmingham (School of Education)

Martin-Jones, M. 2006. 'Sociolinguistics and second language teaching' in U. Ammon, N. Dittmar, K. Matthier and P. Trudgill (eds.) *Sociolinguistics: International Handbook of the Science of Language and Society.* Berlin and New York: Mouton de Gruyter.

ISBN: 3110184184

Pages: 2367–2376

Entered by: University of Birmingham (School of Education)

Martin-Jones, M. 2007. 'Bilingualism, education and the regulation of access to language resources' in M. Heller (ed.) *Bilingualism: A Social Approach.* Basingstoke: Palgrave Macmillan.

ISBN: 9781403996787

Pages: 161–182

Entered by: University of Birmingham (School of Education)

Matei, G., M. Bernaus, F. Heyworth, U-J. Pohl and T. Wright. 2007. *First steps in Teacher Training: A Practical Guide.*

[The TrainEd Kit].

Summary: Booklet (61pp.) and CD-ROM of resources for novice teacher trainers. Deals with role shift from teacher to trainer, professional identity and the teacher training process. Produced as an ECML-funded project. Also available from ECML [ISBN: 9789287161390] in printed form.

www.ecml.at/mtp2/publications/C7_TrainED _E_internet.PDF

Descriptor(s): Teacher education

Entered by: University College Plymouth St Mark & St John (Department of International Education)

Matei, G.S., M. Bernaus, F. Heyworth, U. Pohl and T. Wright. 2007. *First Steps in Teacher Training: A Practical Guide [The TrainEd Kit].* Graz, Austria: European Centre for Modern Languages/Council of Europe.

ISBN: 9789287161390

Summary: Booklet (61pp.) and CD-ROM of resources for novice teacher trainers. Deals with role shift from teacher to trainer, professional identity and the teacher training process. Also available as PDF: www.ecml.at/mtp2/publications/C7_TrainED _E_internet.PDF

Descriptor(s): Teacher education

Institutional level: tertiary

Entered by: University College Plymouth St Mark & St John (Department of International Education)

Maycock, L. and A.B. Green. 2005. 'The effects on performance of computer familiarity and attitudes towards CBIELTS'. *Research Notes, Cambridge ESOL* 20: 3–9.

Descriptor(s): Assessment

Entered by: University of Bedfordshire (Centre for Research in English Language Learning and Assessment)

M

Maynard, J. and S. Troudi. 2008. 'Female Emirati students' perceptions of using a chat room to learn English' in P. Davidson, J. Shewell and W.J. Moore (eds.) *Educational Technology in the Arabian Gulf: Theory, Research and Pedagogy.* Dubai: TESOL Arabia.

Pages: 249–262

Descriptor(s): Cultural issues, ESOL/EAL

Country of research: United Arab Emirates

Institutional level: adult

Entered by: University of Exeter (School of Education and Lifelong Learning)

Mayor, B.M. 2006. 'Dialogic and hortatory features in the writing of Chinese candidates for the IELTS test'. *Journal of Language, Culture and Curriculum* 19/1: 104–121.

Descriptor(s): Writing, Cultural issues, English language, Assessment

Institutional level: adult

Entered by: The Open University (Faculty of Education and Languages)

Mayor, B.M., A. Hewings, S. North, J. Swann and C. Coffin. 2007. 'A linguistic analysis of Chinese and Greek L1 scripts for IELTS Academic Writing Task 2' in L. Taylor and P. Falvey (eds.) *IELTS Collected Papers: Research in Speaking and Writing Assessment (Studies in Language Testing Vol 19).* Cambridge: Cambridge University Press.

ISBN: 978 0521542487

Pages: 250–313

Descriptor(s): Writing, Reading, ESP, English language, Assessment

Institutional level: adult

Entered by: The Open University (Faculty of Education and Languages)

McGonigal, J. and E. Arizpe. 2007. 'Learning to read a new culture: How immigrant and asylum-seeking children experience Scottish identity through classroom books'.

Summary: This is a report for the Scottish Government on a project involving immigrant pupils' responses to Scottish texts, from picturebooks to short stories and comics. The aim was to explore what pupils made of Scottish culture and identity through text but also their understanding of Scots (and its relationship to English) as a foreign language.

www.scotland.gov.uk/Publications/2007/10/3 1125406/0

Descriptor(s): Cultural issues, Reading, Methodology, Materials, English language, Classroom interaction

Country of research: United Kingdom

Learners' background: various

Institutional level: primary

Entered by: University of Glasgow (Language and Literature, Faculty of Education)

McGrath, I., B. Sinclair and Z-H. Chen. 2007. 'Designing an innovative online course in language teaching methodology for middle school teachers of English in China: Encouraging learner and teacher autonomy' in H. Spencer-Oatey (ed.) *e-Learning Initiatives in China: Pedagogy, Policy and Culture.* Hong Kong: Hong Kong University Press.

ISBN: 9789622098678

Pages: 57–78

Summary: This chapter reports on the piloting of innovative e-learning materials and tools for secondary school teachers of English in China, developed collaboratively by multi-cultural, multi-disciplinary teams of educators and technical experts at Beijing Normal University and the University of Nottingham, as part of the E-China-UK projects funded by HEFCE.

M

Descriptor(s): Teacher education, Cultural issues, Learning technologies, Learner autonomy/strategies, Curriculum/syllabus

Country of research: China

Learners' background: China

Institutional level: tertiary

Entered by: University of Nottingham (School of Education)

Mehmedbegovic, D. 2007. '"Miss, who needs the languages of immigrants?": London's multilingual schools' in T. Brighouse and L. Fullick (eds.) *Education in a Global City: Essays from London.* London: Institute of Education.

ISBN: 9780854737925

Pages: 221–252

Summary: This chapter explores London's linguistic wealth and the way education policies and practices have impacted on this wealth and on its many multilingual pupils. The chapter makes recommendations for a more inclusive model of engaging with multilingualism in London schools than the one that currently prevails.

Descriptor(s): Teacher education, Cultural issues, ESOL/EAL, Classroom interaction

Country of research: United Kingdom

Entered by: Institute of Education, London (Department of Learning, Curriculum and Communication)

Mehmedbegovic, D. 2008. 'Bilingual theatre' in C. Kenner and T. Hickey (eds.) *Multilingual Europe: Diversity and Learning.* Stoke-on-Trent: Trentham Books.

ISBN: 9781858564234

Summary: Bilingual theatre was a creative response to children rejecting their first language. It was an attempt to counterbalance the factors which contribute to the low value of first languages in mainstream society and their consequent loss.

Descriptor(s): Writing, Cultural issues, ESOL/EAL

Learners' background: Bosnia and Herzegovina

Institutional level: secondary

Entered by: Institute of Education, London (Department of Learning, Curriculum and Communication)

Mehmedbegovic, D. 2008. 'Leading increasingly linguistically diverse schools'. *Educate, The Journal of Doctoral Research in Education* 8/2: 4–21.

Summary: Engaging with bilingual parents, students and teachers with little awareness of the benefits of bilingualism has initiated a search for factors resulting in the low value attached to certain types of bilingualism. Working on the hypothesis that prevalent practice is influenced more by attitudes to bilingualism rather than relevant research and pedagogical theory, this research focuses on attitudes. This small-scale qualitative study conducted with a group of London headteachers provides an insight into the attitudes to bilingualism and how they impact on policy and practice in schools with significant proportions of multilingual learners.

www.educatejournal.org/index.php?journal=educate&page=article&op=view&path%5B%5D=174&path%5B%5D=171

Descriptor(s): Teacher education, Cultural issues, ESOL/EAL

Country of research: United Kingdom

Institutional level: secondary

Entered by: Institute of Education, London (Department of Learning, Curriculum and Communication)

Memon, R. and R.G. Badger. 2007. 'Purposeful change? Changing the teaching of reading in a regional university in Pakistan'. *System* 35/4: 551.

M

Entered by: University of Leeds (School of Education)

Milton, J. 2007. 'Lexical profiles, learning styles and the construct validity of lexical size tests' in H. Daller, J. Milton and J. Treffers-Daller (eds.) *Modelling and Assessing Vocabulary Knowledge*. Cambridge: Cambridge University Press.

ISBN: 978-0-521-70327-7

Pages: 47–58

Summary: This chapter presents evidence to support the frequency effect in vocabulary acquisition in EFL learners. It also examines systematic differences in vocabulary acquisition which appear to derive from differences in learning aptitude.

Descriptor(s): Assessment

Country of research: Greece

Learners' background: Greece

Institutional level: secondary

Entered by: Swansea University (Department of Applied Linguistics)

Milton, J. 2008. 'Vocabulary uptake from informal learning tasks'. *Language Learning Journal* 36/2: 227–237.

Summary: Demonstrates that very large quantities of EFL vocabulary can be gained from informal language tasks such as reading comic books, listening to songs and watching sub-titled films, provided these activities are supported by directed vocabulary tests.

Descriptor(s): Learner autonomy/strategies

Country of research: United Kingdom

Learners' background: various

Institutional level: secondary

Entered by: Swansea University (Department of Applied Linguistics)

Milton, J. and N. Hopkins. 2007. 'Comparing phonological and orthographic vocabulary size'. *Canadian Modern Language Review* 63/1: 127–147.

Summary: Most vocabulary tests examine learners' ability to recognise words in writing. This paper examine scores from vocabulary breadth tests, which are comparably constructed to be either aural or orthographic in form. It appears learners have a pre-disposition to learn aural word forms initially, but after about 1,000-word knowledge is reached, knowledge of orthographic form predominates.

Descriptor(s): Learner cognition

Country of research: various

Learners' background: various

Entered by: Swansea University (Department of Applied Linguistics)

Mitchell, S. and A. Evison. 2006. 'Exploiting the potential of writing for educational change at Queen Mary, University of London' in L. Ganobcsik-Williams (ed.) *Teaching Academic Writing in UK Higher Education. Theories, Practices and Models*. Basingstoke: Palgrave Macmillan.

ISBN: 1-4039-4535-7

Pages: 68–84

Summary: This chapter addresses some of the issues associated with the development of ways of talking or thinking about writing, and associated relationships to learning at university. It highlights an innovative project at Queen Mary that has worked towards creating more informed and productive thinking, writing, disciplinarity and teaching and learning.

Descriptor(s): Writing

Country of research: United Kingdom

Learners' background: various

Institutional level: adult

Entered by: Queen Mary, University of London (Language and Learning Unit)

N

Mitchell, S. and M. Riddle. 2005. 'Developing a toolkit for tackling academic discourse' in A. Goodwyn and A. Stables (eds.) *Learning to Read Critically in Language and Literacy.* London: Sage Publications Ltd.

ISBN: 978-0761944744

Pages: 65–86

Summary: The authors tackle students' ability to construct an argument in writing. They raise three questions: how are arguments (on paper) constructed, what are students' existing understandings of argument, and what can we do to help students develop their powers of argumentation?

Descriptor(s): Writing

Country of research: United Kingdom

Learners' background: various

Institutional level: adult

Entered by: Queen Mary, University of London (Language and Learning Unit)

Morris-Adams, M. 2008. 'Going outside the classroom' in S. Garton and K. Richards (eds.) *Professional Encounters in TESOL.* Basingstoke: Palgrave Macmillan.

ISBN: 978-0-230-55351-4

Pages: 105–122

Summary: The chapter looks at topic management strategies employed by learners during informal interactions with native English-speaking peers.

Descriptor(s): Speaking, Learner autonomy/strategies, English language, Classroom interaction

Country of research: United Kingdom

Learners' background: various

Institutional level: tertiary

Entered by: Aston University (School of Languages and Social Sciences)

Morrison, B. and L. Hamp-Lyons. 2007. 'Writing up grounded theory research: Increasing credibility through the use of the "worked example"'. *The International Journal of Interdisciplinary Social Sciences* 2/3: 413–424.

Entered by: University of Bedfordshire (Centre for Research in English Language Learning and Assessment)

Morton, T. and J. Gray. 2008. 'The mediating role of talk-in-interaction in guided lesson planning in a pre-service TESOL training course: An ethnomethodological and activity-theoretic perspective'.

Summary: This paper locates guided lesson planning within the context of wider issues in teacher education, and the move away from a 'technical-rational' model towards a more sociocultural orientation. The case study data are initially analysed using applied conversation analysis methodology and then explored from the perspective of activity theory.

http://ora.ouls.ox.ac.uk/objects/uuid%3Ae3fa6c0b-c065-4c1a-a701-9f39ce684099

Descriptor(s): Teacher education, Teacher cognition

Entered by: University of East London (Cass School of Education)

N

Nakatsuhara, F. 2006. 'The impact of proficiency level on conversational styles in paired speaking tests'. *Research Notes, Cambridge ESOL* 25: 15–20.

Descriptor(s): Speaking, Assessment

Entered by: University of Bedfordshire (Centre for Research in English Language Learning and Assessment)

Nakatsuhara, F. 2008. 'Inter-interviewer variation in oral interview tests'. *English Language Teaching Journal* 62/3: 266–275.

Descriptor(s): Speaking, Assessment

Entered by: University of Bedfordshire (Centre for Research in English Language Learning and Assessment)

Nathan, P. 2007. 'Teaching against plagiarism in the EAP classroom' in B. Beaven (ed.) *IATEFL 2006: Harrogate Conference Selections. 40th International Annual Conference, Harrogate 8–12 April 2006.* Canterbury: IATEFL.

ISBN: 1901095096

Pages: 102–104

Principal format: Printed

Summary: This paper proposes that practice and learning activities in which students engage in writing activities based on the integration of different source material provide a useful and effective way of teaching students how to use sources effectively and thereby avoid plagiarism.

Descriptor(s): Writing, ESOL/EAL, ESP

Country of research: United Kingdom

Learners' background: various

Institutional level: tertiary

Entered by: Durham University (Language Centre)

Naysmith, J. 2008. 'New direction in the teaching of English as a foreign language: A personal journey to CLIL' in I. Kemble (ed.) *Essays on Language and Translation: From Textual Analysis To Pedagogical Applications.* Krasnodar & Portsmouth: Kuban State University/University of Portsmouth.

ISBN: 9785934911905

Pages: 107–116

Summary: The chapter describes the authors growing discontent with the lack of application of SLA research to language teaching and proposes CLIL as a better alternative to current EFL approaches.

Descriptor(s): Methodology, Curriculum/syllabus

Entered by: University of Portsmouth (School of Languages and Area Studies)

Nesi, H. 2008. 'BAWE: An introduction to a new resource' in A. Frankenberg-Garcia, R. Carvalho, C. Direito and D. Santos-Rosa (eds.) *Proceedings of the 8th Teaching and Language Corpora Conference.* Lisbon, Portugal: ISLA.

Pages: 239–246

Principal format: Printed

Summary: An overview of the BAWE corpus

Descriptor(s): Writing, ESP, English language

Country of research: United Kingdom

Institutional level: tertiary

Associated project: An Investigation of Genres of Assessed Writing in British Higher Education

Entered by: Coventry University

Nesi, H. 2008. 'Corpora in EAP' in Z. Zainal (ed.) *LSP: Interfacing Language with other Realms: Proceedings of the 6th Languages for Specific Purposes International Seminar.* Johor Bahru, Malaysia: Universiti Teknologi Malaysia.

Principal format: CD-ROM

Summary: An overview of the types of corpus data available to EAP syllabus and materials developers.

Descriptor(s): Materials, ESP, Curriculum/syllabus

Institutional level: tertiary

Entered by: Coventry University

Nesi, H. 2008. 'Dictionaries in electronic form' in A.P. Cowie (ed.) *The Oxford History of English Lexicography.* Oxford: Oxford University Press.

ISBN: 978-0-19-928562-4

Pages: 458–478

Summary: This chapter describes the history of the electronic dictionary, and particularly monolingual or bilingual dictionaries intended for use by English speakers, whether natives or foreign

N

N

learners. It considers electronic dictionaries accessible via hand-held mobile devices, laptop or desktop computers, and the Internet.

Descriptor(s): Learning technologies, English language

Entered by: Coventry University

Nesi, H. 2008. 'The form, meaning and purpose of university-level assessed reflective writing' in M. Edwardes (ed.) *Proceedings of the BAAL Annual Conference 2007.* London: Scitsiugnil Press.

ISBN: ISBN-10: 0955953308
ISBN-13: 978-0955953309

Principal format: CD-ROM

Summary: An examination of the role and language of reflection in assessed university-level writing tasks, with implications for the teaching of reflective writing.

Descriptor(s): Writing, ESP

Country of research: United Kingdom

Learners' background: various

Institutional level: tertiary

Associated project: An Investigation of Genres of Assessed Writing in British Higher Education

Entered by: Coventry University

Nesi, H. and H. Basturkmen. 2006. 'Lexical bundles and discourse signalling in academic lectures'. *International Journal of Corpus Linguistics* 11/3: 147–168.

Summary: This paper investigates the cohesive role of lexical bundles in a corpus of 160 university lectures (120 from the BASE corpus and 40 from MICASE). The majority of frequently occurring bundles were found to be used to signal discourse relations. This has implications for EAP listening skills development.

Descriptor(s): Listening, ESP, English language

Country of research: United Kingdom

Institutional level: tertiary

Associated project: Enhancement of the British Academic Spoken English Corpus

Entered by: Coventry University

Nesi, H. and S. Gardner. 2006. 'Variation in disciplinary culture: University tutors' views on assessed writing tasks' in R. Kiely, G. Clibbon, H. Woodfield and P. Rea-Dickins (eds.) *Language, Culture and Identity in Applied Linguistics.* London: Equinox Publishing.

ISBN: 1845532198
978-1845532192

Pages: 99–117

Summary: This paper reports on the findings from 55 semi-structured interviews with academic staff, leading to an inventory of genres of assessed student writing, and the identification, from the perspective of the academic, of a number of trends in the assignment of writing tasks.

Descriptor(s): Writing, Teacher education, ESP

Country of research: United Kingdom

Institutional level: tertiary

Associated project: An Investigation of Genres of Assessed Writing in British Higher Education

Entered by: Coventry University

Nitta, R. and S.F. Gardner. 2005. 'Consciousness-raising and practice in ELT coursebooks'. *ELT Journal* 59/1: 3–13.

Descriptor(s): Methodology, Materials, Learner cognition, Curriculum/syllabus

Country of research: United Kingdom

Learners' background: various

Institutional level: secondary

Entered by: University of Birmingham (School of Education)

Niu, J. and L. Hamp-Lyons. 2006. 'Progress assessment in Chinese distance education: The voices of learners'. *Open Learning* 21/2: 111–123.

Descriptor(s): Assessment

Entered by: University of Bedfordshire (Centre for Research in English Language Learning and Assessment)

Northcott, J. 2006. 'Law and language, or language and law?' in D. Bartol, A. Duszak, H. Izdebski and J. Pierrel (eds.) *Langue, Droit, Societe*. Nancy, France: Presses Universitaires de Nancy.

ISBN: ISSN 1773-7737

Descriptor(s): Teacher education, ESP

Entered by: University of Edinburgh (Institute for Applied Language Studies/Office of Lifelong Learning)

Northcott, J. 2007. 'LSAP teacher development and course development: An English for the LIM case study' in T. Lynch and J. Northcott (eds.) *Symposia for Language Teacher Educators*. Edinburgh: Institute for Applied Language Studies.

Principal format: CD-ROM

Descriptor(s): Teacher education, ESP

Entered by: University of Edinburgh (Institute for Applied Language Studies/Office of Lifelong Learning)

Northcott, J. 2008. 'Language education for legal professionals' in J. Gibbons and M.T. Turrell (eds.) *Dimensions of Forensic Linguistics*. Amsterdam: John Benjamins Publishing Company.

ISBN: 9789027205216

Descriptor(s): Teacher education, ESP

Entered by: University of Edinburgh (Institute for Applied Language Studies/Office of Lifelong Learning)

Northcott, J. and G.D. Brown. 2006. 'Legal translator training: Partnership between teachers of English for legal purposes and legal specialists'. *English for Specific Purposes* 25/3: 358–375.

Descriptor(s): Teacher education, Cultural issues, ESP

Entered by: University of Edinburgh (Institute for Applied Language Studies/Office of Lifelong Learning)

Norton, J.E. 2005. 'The paired format in the Cambridge Speaking Tests'. *ELT Journal* 59/4: 287–297.

Entered by: University of Leicester (English Language Teaching and Applied Linguistics, School of Education)

Novakovic, N. 2006. 'Profile of Skills for Life candidature'. *Cambridge ESOL: Research Notes* 25: 14–15.

Summary: Nadezda Novakovic reports on the candidate profile after the first year of the Cambridge ESOL certificates in Skills for Life (SfL). This modular exam suite follows the Adult ESOL Core Curriculum in England and is used to ascertain migrants' language proficiency.

www.cambridgeesol.org/rs_notes/rs_nts25. PDF

Entered by: University of Cambridge ESOL Examinations

Novakovic, N. 2006. 'TKT – A year on'. *Cambridge ESOL: Research Notes* 24: 22–24.

Summary: Nadezda Novakovic describes the first year of the Teaching Knowledge Test (TKT) in terms of the candidates' profile and their performance. She explains how Cambridge ESOL is measuring TKT candidates' language proficiency to determine if this affects their performance on the TKT.

www.cambridgeesol.org/rs_notes/rs_nts24. PDF

N

O

O'Keefe, A., M.J. McCarthy and R.A. Carter. 2007. *From Corpus to Classroom: Language Use and Language Teaching.* Cambridge: Cambridge University Press.

ISBN: 9780521616867

Descriptor(s): Teacher education, Materials, Learning technologies, English language

Entered by: University of Nottingham (School of English Studies)

Onat-Stelma, Z. and J. Stelma. 2007. 'Understanding dynamics supportive of learning in the young learner classroom' in B. Beaven (ed.) *IATEFL 2006: Harrogate Conference Selections.* Canterbury, Kent: IATEFL.

Principal format: Printed

Descriptor(s): Teacher education, Classroom interaction

Country of research: Turkey

Learners' background: Turkey

Institutional level: primary

Entered by: University of Manchester (School of Education)

O'Regan, J., J. Macdonald 2007. 'Cultural relativism and the discourse of intercultural communication: Aporias of praxis in the intercultural public sphere'. *Languages and Intercultural Communication* 7/4: 267–278.

Descriptor(s): Cultural issues

Entered by: University of Exeter (School of Education and Lifelong Learning)

Orsini, M. 2008. 'Troublesome language knowledge: Identifying threshold concepts in grammar learning' in R. Land, H.F. Meyer and J. Smith (eds.) *Threshold Concepts within the Disciplines.* Rotterdam: Sense.

ISBN: 978-90-8790-267-4

Pages: 213–226

Summary: This chapter focuses on the troublesome knowledge experienced by students in the first year undergraduate module Academic and Professional Skills for Language Learning when carrying out a socio-collaborative grammar project.

Descriptor(s): Management/innovation, Learning technologies, Learner cognition, Learner autonomy/strategies, Curriculum/syllabus, Assessment

Country of research: United Kingdom

Learners' background: various

Institutional level: tertiary

Associated project: Grammar: Researching Activities for Student Progress

Entered by: Coventry University

Orsini-Jones, M. and C. Sinclair. 2008. 'Helping students to GRASP (Grammar: Researching Activities for Student Progress) the rules of grammar' in C. Rust (ed.) *Improving Student Learning for What?* Oxford: OCSLD.

ISBN: 978-1-873576-76-2

Pages: 72–86

Principal format: Printed

Summary: Building on previous cycles of action research (Orsini-Jones and Jones 2007), the project illustrated (GRASP) has explored students' understanding of grammar further and has also used grammatical exercises and materials to attempt to support the enhanced understanding of grammar categories.

Descriptor(s): Management/innovation, Learning technologies, Learner cognition, Learner autonomy/strategies, Curriculum/syllabus, Assessment

Country of research: United Kingdom

Learners' background: various

Institutional level: tertiary

Associated project: Grammar: Researching Activities for Student Progress

Entered by: Coventry University

Orsini-Jones, M. and D. Jones. 2007. 'Supporting grammar learning via a virtual learning environment: A case study from Coventry University'. *Arts and Humanities in Higher Education: An International Journal of Theory, Research and Practice* 6/1: 90–106.

Summary: This article reports the results of an investigation into the issues encountered by undergraduate language students when engaging in the 'grammar project' – a collaborative assessment task for the module Academic and Professional Skills for Language Learning – and shows how encouraging students to take ownership of their learning process with a VLE can increase their motivation.

Descriptor(s): Methodology, Management/innovation, Learning technologies, Learner cognition, Learner autonomy/strategies, Assessment

Country of research: United Kingdom

Learners' background: various

Institutional level: tertiary

Associated project: Grammar: Researching Activities for Student Progress

Entered by: Coventry University

P

Papp, S. 2006. 'A relevance-theoretic account of the development and deficits of Theory of Mind in normally developing children and individuals with autism'. *Theory & Psychology* 16/2: 141–161.

Descriptor(s): Learner cognition, English language

Entered by: University of Cambridge ESOL Examinations

Papp, S. 2007. 'Inductive learning and self-correction with the use of learner and reference corpora' in E. Hidalgo, L. Quereda and J. Santana (eds.) *Corpora in the Foreign Language Classroom.* Amsterdam, New York: Rodopi.

ISBN: 978-9-04202-142-6

Pages: 207–220

Descriptor(s): Writing, Cultural issues, Methodology, Learning technologies, Learner cognition, Learner autonomy/strategies, English language

Country of research: United Kingdom

Learners' background: China

Institutional level: tertiary

Entered by: University of Cambridge ESOL Examinations

Papp, S. and M. Robinson. 2008. 'A framework for addressing issues related to migration and language assessment' in *IAEA: Re-interpreting Assessment: Society, Measurement and Meaning.* Cambridge: Cambridge Assessment.

Principal format: Online

www.iaea2008.cambridgeassessment.org.uk/ ca/digitalAssets/180464_Papp.PDF

Descriptor(s): Assessment

Entered by: University of Cambridge ESOL Examinations

Paran, A. 2006. 'The stories of literature and language teaching' in A. Paran (ed.) *Literature in Language Teaching and Learning.* Alexandria, Virginia, US: TESOL.

ISBN: 1931185247

Pages: 1–10

Summary: Surveys recent changes in the use of literature in language teaching, focusing on methodological aspects as well as on text choice and curricula. Concludes by pointing out current issues and future research agendas.

P

Descriptor(s): Curriculum/syllabus, Materials, Reading

Country of research: various

Learners' background: various

Entered by: Institute of Education, London (Department of Learning, Curriculum and Communication)

Paran, A. 2008. 'The role of literature in instructed foreign language learning and teaching: An evidence-based survey'. *Language Teaching* 41/4: 465–496.

Summary: This is a state-of-the-art paper which summarises research on the use of literature in language teaching from a variety of aspects (methodology, training, learner views, teacher views, etc.). It looks mainly at ELT, but also includes references to teaching German, French and Spanish as foreign languages.

Descriptor(s): Cultural issues, Reading, Methodology, Materials

Country of research: various

Learners' background: various

Entered by: Institute of Education, London (Department of Learning, Curriculum and Communication)

Pérez-Llantada, C. and Ferguson, G. 'Editors' introduction' in C. Pérez-Llantada and G. Ferguson.(eds). 2006. *English as a GloCalization Phenomenon: Observations from a Linguistic Microcosm.*Valencia: University of Valencia Press.

ISBN: 978-84-370-6445-1

Descriptor(s): ESP, English language

Entered by: University of Sheffield (School of English)

Perrin, S. and M. Davies. 2008. 'Internationalising the university: Acclimatising the student' in B. Beaven (ed.) *IATEFL 2007.*

Aberdeen Conference Selections. Canterbury: IATEFL.

ISBN: 1 901095 14 2

Pages: 106–107

Principal format: Printed

Summary: This summarises a presentation that detailed a year-long case study looking at how pre-university courses such as International Foundation Programmes help students to adapt to a different learning culture. It argues that such programmes prepare them both academically and personally for their life at university.

Descriptor(s): Cultural issues, Learner cognition, Classroom interaction

Country of research: United Kingdom

Learners' background: various

Institutional level: adult

Entered by: Queen Mary, University of London (Language and Learning Unit)

Petric, B. 2005. 'Contrastive rhetoric in the writing classroom: A case study'. *English for Specific Purposes* 24/2: 213–228.

Summary: This article explores the role of contrastive rhetoric in writing pedagogy, focusing on the teaching of the argumentative essay genre to a group of students from the Russian Federation studying at an English medium university in Central Europe.

Descriptor(s): Writing, Cultural issues

Country of research: Hungary

Learners' background: Russia

Institutional level: tertiary

Entered by: University of Essex (Department of Language and Linguistics)

Petric, B. 2006. 'Interdisciplinarity and writer identity: Students' views and experiences' in R. Kiely, G. Clibbon, P. Rea-Dickins and H. Woodfield (eds.) *Language, Culture, and*

Identity in Applied Linguistics. London: Equinox.

ISBN: 1845532198

Pages: 119–131

Summary: This study explores disciplinary affiliation as an aspect of writer identity in an interdisciplinary field by focusing on student writers' views and experiences of writing a master's dissertation in an interdisciplinary master's programme.

Descriptor(s): Writing, ESP

Learners' background: various

Institutional level: tertiary

Entered by: University of Essex (Department of Language and Linguistics)

Petric, B. 2007. 'Rhetorical functions of citations in high- and low-rated master's theses'. *Journal of English for Academic Purposes* 6/3: 238–253.

Summary: This study compares the rhetorical functions of citations in eight high- and eight low-graded master's dissertations in the field of gender studies, written in English as a second language.

Descriptor(s): Writing

Country of research: Hungary

Learners' background: various

Institutional level: tertiary

Entered by: University of Essex (Department of Language and Linguistics)

Petric, B. 2007. '"This English writing thing": Students' perceptions of their writing experiences at an English-medium university'. *Porta Linguarum* 7: 45–55.

Summary: This article explores five students' perceptions of their writing experiences at an English-medium university in a non-English speaking country as compared to writing in their home country universities in their native languages. Three types of differences are found to be relevant:

language and rhetorical differences, disciplinary differences, and differences in educational systems.

Descriptor(s): Writing, Cultural issues

Country of research: Hungary

Learners' background: various

Institutional level: tertiary

Entered by: University of Essex (Department of Language and Linguistics)

Petric, B. 2008. 'Autonomy, culture and training'. *Independence (IATEFL Learner Autonomy SIG)* 43: 19.

Descriptor(s): Cultural issues, Learner autonomy/strategies

Entered by: University of Essex (Department of Language and Linguistics)

Phipps, S. and S. Borg. 2007. 'Exploring the relationship between teachers' beliefs and their classroom practice'. *The Teacher Trainer* 21/3: 17–19.

Entered by: University of Leeds (School of Education)

Phongphio, T. and N. Schmitt. 2006. 'Learning English multi-word verbs in Thailand'. *Thai TESOL Bulletin* 19: 122–136.

Descriptor(s): Learner autonomy/strategies

Learners' background: Thailand

Entered by: University of Nottingham (School of English Studies)

Pickering, A. 2005. 'Facilitating reflective learning: An example of practice in TESOL teacher education'. *Subject Centre for Languages, Linguistics and Area Studies Guide to Good Practice Online:* no page numbers.

Summary: This article is based on a study of the use of Statements of Relevance to facilitate reflection in language teacher education.

www.llas.ac.uk/resources/gpg/2395

P

P

Descriptor(s): Teacher education, Teacher cognition

Country of research: United Kingdom

Entered by: University of Brighton (School of Humanities)

Pickering, A. 2005. 'Harnessing influences for change'. *IATEFL Teacher Trainers and Educators SIG Newsletter* 3: 17–25.

Summary: This article is based on research into influences for pedagogic change, and presents a view of professional change as being highly complex, with an unpredictable relationship between teaching experience, teacher education 'input', and other factors affecting change. It identifies implications for TESOL teacher education.

Descriptor(s): Teacher education, Teacher cognition

Country of research: United Kingdom

Entered by: University of Brighton (School of Humanities)

Pigada, M. and N. Schmitt. 2006. 'Vocabulary acquisition from extensive reading: A case study'. *Reading in a Foreign Language* 18/1: 1–28.

Descriptor(s): Learner autonomy/strategies

Entered by: University of Nottingham (School of English Studies)

Pinter, A. 2005. 'Task repetition with 10-year-old children' in C. Edwards and J. Willis (eds.) *Teachers Exploring Tasks in English Language Teaching.* Palgrave Macmillan.

ISBN: 9781403945563

Pages: 113–126

Summary: The effects of task repetition with low proficiency child learners of L2 English.

Descriptor(s): Speaking, Materials, English language, Classroom interaction

Country of research: Hungary

Learners' background: Hungary

Institutional level: primary

Entered by: University of Warwick (Centre for Applied Linguistics)

Pinter, A. 2006. *Teaching Young Language Learners.* Oxford: Oxford University Press.

ISBN: 0-19-4422070

Summary: A comprehensive overview of links between research and practice in the area of teaching languages to young learners.

Descriptor(s): Teacher education

Country of research: United Kingdom

Learners' background: United Kingdom

Institutional level: primary

Entered by: University of Warwick (Centre for Applied Linguistics)

Pinter, A. 2006. 'Verbal evidence of task-related strategies: Child versus adult interactions'. *System* 34: 615–630.

Summary: 10-year-old Hungarian children's and adults' observable strategies are contrasted when they interact in L2 English using a communication task.

Descriptor(s): Speaking, Learner autonomy/strategies, English language, Classroom interaction

Country of research: Hungary

Learners' background: Hungary

Institutional level: primary

Entered by: University of Warwick (Centre for Applied Linguistics)

Pinter, A. 2007. 'Benefits of peer-peer interaction: 10-year-old children practising with a communication task'. *Language Teaching Research* 11/2: 189–208.

Summary: Hungarian children interact in L2 English in pairs using a Spot the Differences task and the paper describes different learning benefits.

Descriptor(s): Speaking, Materials, English language, Classroom interaction

Country of research: Hungary

Learners' background: Hungary

Institutional level: primary

Entered by: University of Warwick
(Centre for Applied Linguistics)

Pinter, A. 2007. 'Towards teacher autonomy' in P. Benson (ed.) *Learner Autonomy Series No 8: Teacher and Learner Perspectives.* Dublin: Authentik.

ISBN: 978-1-905275-00-7

Pages: 104–120

Summary: Some Russian primary teachers who worked in collaborative project teams describe their own professional development.

Descriptor(s): Teacher education, Materials, English language

Country of research: United Kingdom

Learners' background: Russia

Institutional level: adult

Entered by: University of Warwick
(Centre for Applied Linguistics)

Pinter, A. 2007. 'What children say: Benefits of task repetition' in K. Van den Branden, K. Van Gorp and M. Verhelst (eds.) *Tasks in Action: Task-based Language Education for a Classroom-based Perspective.* Newcastle, UK: Cambridge Scholars Publishing.

ISBN: 9 781847 182432

Pages: 131–158

Summary: 10-year-old Hungarian children's views and opinions about task-based learning.

Descriptor(s): Speaking, Materials, Learner autonomy/strategies, English language, Classroom interaction

Country of research: Hungary

Learners' background: Hungary

Institutional level: primary

Entered by: University of Warwick
(Centre for Applied Linguistics)

Poulter, M. 2007. 'Cambridge ESOL teacher training and development – Future directions'. *Cambridge ESOL: Research Notes* 29: 2–4.

Summary: Article describes the origins and evolution of the various teaching qualifications, as well as current trends and future directions; Cambridge ESOL's aspiration that those who opt for a Cambridge ESOL product will be engaged in a high quality, positive learning experience and will, as a result, be better equipped to help learners of English succeed in their own language learning endeavours.

www.cambridgeesol.org/rs_notes/rs_nts29. PDF

Entered by: University of Cambridge ESOL Examinations

Poulter, M. 2007. 'Setting international standards for teaching'. *Cambridge ESOL: Research Notes* 29: 16–18.

Summary: Monica Poulter considers the challenges involved in setting international standards for English language teaching, and the extent to which Cambridge ESOL seeks rigour through its standardised procedures for CELTA centres and assessors when assessing teaching practice.

www.cambridgeesol.org/rs_notes/rs_nts29. PDF

Entered by: University of Cambridge ESOL Examinations

R

Rayson, P., S. Sharoff and A. Adolphs. 2006. 'Preface' in P. Rayson, S. Sharoff and S. Adolphs (eds.) *Multi-Word-Expressions in a Multilingual Context, April 3rd 2006, Trento, Italy.* East Stroudsburg, PA, USA: Association for Computational Linguistics.

Principal format: Online

www.aclweb.org/anthology/W/W06/W06-2400.PDF

R

R

Descriptor(s): Speaking, Cultural issues, Learner cognition

Entered by: University of Nottingham (School of English Studies)

Rea-Dickins, P. 2006. 'Currents and eddies in the discourse of assessment: A learning-focused interpretation'. *International Journal of Applied Linguistics* 16/2: 163–188.

Entered by: University of Bristol (Graduate School of Education)

Rea-Dickins, P. 2007. 'Classroom-based assessment: Possibilities and pitfalls' in J. Cummins and C. Davison (eds.) *The International Handbook of English Language Teaching*. Norwell, MA: Springer Publications.

ISBN: 9780387463001

Pages: 505–520

Entered by: University of Bristol (Graduate School of Education)

Rea-Dickins, P. 2007. 'Learning or measuring? Exploring teacher decision-making in planning for classroom-based assessment' in S. Fotos and N. Nassaji (eds.) *Form-focused Instruction and Teacher Education: Studies in Honour of Rod Ellis*. Oxford: Oxford University Press.

ISBN: 9780194422505

Pages: 193–210

Entered by: University of Bristol (Graduate School of Education)

Rea-Dickins, P. 2008. 'Classroom-based assessment' in N.H. Hornberger (ed.) *Encyclopedia of Language and Education (2nd edition)*. New York: Springer Science.

ISBN: 9780387354200

Pages: 257–272

Entered by: University of Bristol (Graduate School of Education)

Rea-Dickins, P. and C. Scott. 2007. 'Washback from language tests on teaching, learning and policy: Evidence from diverse settings'. *Assessment in Education, Special Issue* 14/1: 1–7.

Entered by: University of Bristol (Graduate School of Education)

Rea-Dickins, P. and C. Scott. 2007. 'Washback in language testing and assessment'. *Assessment in Education, Special Issue* 14/1: 1–7.

Entered by: University of Bristol (Graduate School of Education)

Rea-Dickins, P., I. Scott and G. Yu. 2008. 'Language testing and assessment in applied linguistics: Identifying reciprocity in applied linguistic research'. *Language Teaching* 41/4: 575–577.

Entered by: University of Bristol (Graduate School of Education)

Rea-Dickins, P., R. Kiely and G. Yu. 2007. 'Student identity, learning and progression: With specific reference to the affective and academic impact of IELTS on "successful" candidates'. *IELTS Impact Studies* 7: 59–136.

Entered by: University of Bristol (Graduate School of Education)

Rich, S. and L. Davis. 2007. 'Insights into the strategic ways in which two bilingual children in the early years seek to negotiate the competing demands on their identity in their home and school worlds'. *International Journal of Early Years Education* 15/1: 35–47.

Descriptor(s): Cultural issues, ESOL/EAL

Country of research: United Kingdom

Learners' background: various

Institutional level: primary

Entered by: University of Exeter (School of Education and Lifelong Learning)

Rich, S. and S. Troudi. 2006. 'Hard Times: Arab TESOL students' experiences of racialization and othering in the United Kingdom'. *TESOL Quarterly* 40/3: 615–627.

Descriptor(s): Teacher education, Cultural issues

Entered by: University of Exeter (School of Education and Lifelong Learning)

Richards, K. 2005. 'Introduction' in K. Richards and P. Seedhouse (eds.) *Applying Conversation Analysis.* Basingstoke: Palgrave Macmillan.

ISBN: 1-4039-4233-1

Pages: 1–15

Summary: This introduction explores the ways in which conversation analysis can contribute to informed practice across a range of professions, including language teaching, where its focus on competencies rather than deficits is particularly relevant.

Descriptor(s): Speaking, ESP

Country of research: various

Entered by: University of Warwick (Centre for Applied Linguistics)

Richards, K. 2006. '"Being the teacher": Identity and classroom conversation'. Applied Linguistics 27/1: 51–77.

Summary: The paper proposes an approach to the analysis of classroom talk which takes account of the dynamic nature of identity construction and its relationship to the development of ongoing talk. It demonstrates how shifts in the orientation to different aspects of identity produce distinctively different interactional patterns in teacher-fronted talk.

Descriptor(s): Classroom interaction

Country of research: various

Learners' background: various

Institutional level: adult

Entered by: University of Warwick (Centre for Applied Linguistics)

R

Richards, K. 2007. 'Knowing when to "no": Aspects of alignment in professional relationships' in H. Bowles and P. Seedhouse (eds.) *Conversation Analysis and Languages for Specific Purposes.* Bern: Peter Lang.

ISBN: 978-3-03911-469-6

Pages: 69–98

Summary: This chapter explores how the use of 'no' is negotiated in different professional contexts and highlights the implications of this for teaching ESP in such contexts.

Descriptor(s): ESP

Country of research: United Kingdom

Institutional level: adult

Entered by: University of Warwick (Centre for Applied Linguistics)

Richards, K. 2008. 'Making the break: Establishing a new school' in S. Garton and K. Richards (eds.) *Professional Encounters in TESOL: Discourses of Teachers in Teaching.* Basingstoke: Palgrave Macmillan.

ISBN: 978-0-230-55351

Pages: 173–196

Summary: This chapter describes how a group of teachers established their own school and how a distinctive discourse of caring and professional engagement developed as part of this.

Descriptor(s): Management/innovation

Country of research: United Kingdom

Entered by: University of Warwick (Centre for Applied Linguistics)

Rixon, S. 2007. 'Cambridge ESOL YLE tests and children's first steps in reading and writing in English'. *Cambridge ESOL Research Notes* 28: 7–14.

Summary: An analysis of the word lists for the syllabuses of the 'Starters', 'Movers' and 'Flyers' tests, for orthographic depth, and a comparison with the National Literacy Strategy sight word lists.

S

www.cambridgeesol.org/rs_notes/rs_nts28.PDF

Descriptor(s): English language, Assessment

Learners' background: various

Institutional level: primary

Entered by: University of Warwick (Centre for Applied Linguistics)

Roach, P., J. Hartman and J. Setter. 2006. *Daniel Jones' English Pronouncing Dictionary (17th edition).* Cambridge: Cambridge University Press.

ISBN: 978-0521680875

Descriptor(s): Pronunciation, English language

Entered by: University of Reading (Department of Applied Linguistics)

Roberts, C., M. Baynham, M. Cooke and J. Simpson. 2008. 'Adult ESOL in the UK: Policy and research'. *Prospect* 22/3: 18–31.

Entered by: University of Leeds (School of Education)

Roberts, C., M. Cooke, P. Bushell, M. Hepworth, J. McGoldrick, J. O'Neill, K. Dudley, A. Goodband and J. Simpson. 2007. *Developing Adult Teaching and Learning: Practitioner Guides: ESOL.* Leicester and London: NIACE and NRDC.

ISBN: 978-1-86201-336-0

Descriptor(s): ESOL/EAL

Entered by: University of Leeds (School of Education)

Rogerson-Revell, P. 2005. 'A hybrid approach to developing CALL materials: authoring with Macromedia's Dreamweaver/Coursebuilder'. *ReCALL* 17/1: 122–138.

Entered by: University of Leicester (English Language Teaching and Applied Linguistics, School of Education)

Rose, D. 2008. 'Vocabulary use in the FCE listening test'. *Cambridge ESOL: Research Notes* 32: 9–16.

Summary: Dittany Rose reports on a study which investigates whether vocabulary in the First Certificate in English (FCE) Listening paper is more like spoken or written language. Rose compares lexical density and word frequency patterns in this General English paper versus corpora of exam materials, source texts and native speaker material.

www.cambridgeesol.org/rs_notes/rs_nts32.PDF

Entered by: University of Cambridge ESOL Examinations

Rupp, A., M. Vock, C. Harsch and O. Köller. 2008. *Developing Standards-based Assessment Tasks for English as a First Foreign Language: Context, Processes and Outcomes in Germany.* Münster, Germany: Waxmann.

ISBN: 9783830919

Descriptor(s): Assessment

Entered by: University of Warwick (Centre for Applied Linguistics)

S

Salamoura, A. 2008. 'Aligning English Profile research data to the CEFR'. *Cambridge ESOL: Research Notes* 33: 5–7.

Summary: Angeliki Salamoura discusses how research data being collected for English Profile can be aligned to the CEFR.

www.cambridgeesol.org/rs_notes/rs_nts33.PDF

Entered by: University of Cambridge ESOL Examinations

Salter-Dvorak, H. 2005. 'Plagiarism explained through copyright and intertextuality in music and film' in A. Pulverness (ed.) *IATEFL 2004 Liverpool Conference Selections.* Kent: IATEFL.

ISBN: 1-901095-26-6

Pages: 146–7

Principal format: Printed

Summary: This paper describes pedagogic materials from music and film to enable university students in Britain to explore plagiarism, copyright and intertextuality. It also presents a rationale for the materials.

Descriptor(s): Materials

Institutional level: adult

Entered by: University of Westminster (Centre for English Learning and Teaching)

Salter-Dvorak, H. 2007. '"Academic Tourism" or "a truly multi-cultural community"? Why international students need pragmatic training for British H.E.' in O. Alexander (ed.) *New Approaches to Materials Development for Language Learning.* Proceedings of the joint 2005 BALEAP/SATEFL conference. Oxford: Peter Lang.

ISBN: 978-3-03910-909-8

Pages: 37–48

Principal format: Printed

Summary: This paper argues that international students are prevented from integrating into British higher education through lack of interactional competence. It presents a rationale for pragmatic training for such students and intercultural competence training for home students and university staff.

Descriptor(s): ESOL/EAL, Curriculum/syllabus

Entered by: University of Westminster (Centre for English Learning and Teaching)

Sataporn, S. and M. Lamb. 2005. 'Accommodation zone: Two learners' struggle to complete a distance learning English course' in P. Benson and D. Nunan (eds.) *Learners' Stories: Difference and Diversity in Language Learning.* Cambridge: Cambridge University Press.

ISBN: 9780521614146

Pages: 119–133

Entered by: University of Leeds (School of Education)

Samuda, V. and M. Bygate. 2008. *Tasks in Second Language Learning.* Basingstoke: Palgrave Macmillan.

ISBN: 978-1-4039-1187-2

Descriptor(s): Methodology, Materials, ESOL/EAL, ESP, Curriculum/syllabus

Entered by: Lancaster University (Linguistics and English Language)

Saville, N. 2005. 'Setting and monitoring professional standards: A QMS approach'. *Cambridge ESOL: Research Notes* 22: 2–5.

Summary: Nick Saville describes how the Association of Language Testers in Europe (ALTE) sets professional standards for its members through a Quality Management approach. This involves the adoption of a code of practice and associated systems and practices. For Cambridge ESOL this means a continual process of striving to maintain the quality of all of our products.

www.cambridgeesol.org/rs_notes/rs_nts22. PDF

Entered by: University of Cambridge ESOL Examinations

Saville, N. 2006. 'Language testing for migration and citizenship'. *Cambridge ESOL: Research Notes* 25: 2–4.

Summary: Nick Saville discusses the role of language testing in migration and citizenship, as language testers are contributing to the ongoing debate about policy and practice in this area. ALTE, including Cambridge ESOL, is keen to ensure that language tests are used by governments or other institutions in a fair and appropriate manner.

www.cambridgeesol.org/rs_notes/rs_nts25. PDF

S

S

Entered by: University of Cambridge ESOL Examinations

Saville, N. 2008. 'Auditing the quality profile' in *IAEA: Re-interpreting Assessment: Society, Measurement and Meaning.* Cambridge: Cambridge Assessment.

Principal format: Online

www.iaea2008.cambridgeassessment.org.uk/ ca/digitalAssets/180500_Saville.PDF

Entered by: University of Cambridge ESOL Examinations

Saville, N. and N. Jones. 2007. 'Scales and frameworks' in B. Spolsky and F. Hult (eds.) *The Handbook of Educational Linguistics.* Oxford: Blackwell Publishing.

ISBN: 978-1-4051-5410-9

Descriptor(s): Learner cognition, English language, Assessment

Country of research: various

Learners' background: various

Entered by: University of Cambridge ESOL Examinations

Saville, N. and P. Van Avermaet. 2008. 'Language testing for migration and citizenship: Contexts and issues' in L. Taylor and C. Weir (eds.) *Studies in Language Testing Vol 27: Multilingualism and Assessment: Achieving Transparency, Assuring Quality, Sustaining Diversity – Proceedings of the ALTE Berlin Conference, May 2005.* Cambridge: UCLES/CUP.

ISBN: 9780521711920

Entered by: University of Cambridge ESOL Examinations

Schauer, G.A. 2006. 'The development of ESL learners' pragmatic competence: A longitudinal investigation of awareness and production' in K. Bardovi-Harlig, C. Felix-Brasdefer and A. Omar (eds.) *Pragmatics and Language Learning.* Manoa, HI: Second

Language teaching and Curriculum Center University of Hawaii.

ISBN: 9780824831370

Pages: 135–163

Summary: The present paper presents the results of a longitudinal study into the development of ESL learners' pragmatic awareness and their productive pragmatic competence.

Descriptor(s): Speaking, Cultural issues, English language

Country of research: United Kingdom

Learners' background: Germany

Institutional level: tertiary

Entered by: Lancaster University (Linguistics and English Language)

Schauer, G.A. 2006. 'Pragmatic awareness in ESL and EFL contexts: Contrast and development'. *Language Learning* 56/2: 269–318.

Summary: The study replicates and extends Bardovi-Harlig and Dornyei's (1998) investigation of pragmatic awareness by addressing two research questions: (a) Do learners in EFL and ESL contexts display differences in their recognition and rating of pragmatic and grammatical errors? (b) Do learners increase their pragmatic awareness whilst in the target country?

Descriptor(s): Speaking, Cultural issues, English language

Country of research: United Kingdom

Learners' background: Germany

Institutional level: tertiary

Entered by: Lancaster University (Linguistics and English Language)

Schauer, G.A. 2007. 'Finding the right words in the study abroad context: The development of German learners' use of external modifiers in English'. *Intercultural Pragmatics* 4/2: 193–220.

Summary: This paper examines the pragmatic development of nine German university students in a study abroad context over the period of one academic year. The investigation focuses on learners' ability to soften the illocutionary force of request utterances by employing a range of external modifiers.

Descriptor(s): Speaking, Cultural issues, English language

Country of research: various

Learners' background: Germany

Institutional level: tertiary

Entered by: Lancaster University (Linguistics and English Language)

Schauer, G.A. 2008. 'Getting better in getting what you want: Language learners' pragmatic development in requests during study abroad sojourns' in M. Puetz and J. Neff-van Aertselaer (eds.) *Developing Contrastive Pragmatics: Interlanguage and Cross-cultural Perspectives.* Berlin: Mouton de Gruyter.

ISBN: 978-3-11-019670-2

Pages: 399–426

Summary: This chapter investigates the impact of the study abroad context on language learners' pragmatic development by focusing on request strategies. Requests were selected as the focus of the investigation, since being able to appropriately ask for their interlocutor's help or cooperation is an essential skill for language learners.

Descriptor(s): Speaking, Cultural issues, English language

Country of research: various

Learners' background: Germany

Institutional level: tertiary

Entered by: Lancaster University (Linguistics and English Language)

Schauer, G.A. and S. Adolphs. 2006. 'Expressions of gratitude in corpus and DCT data: Vocabulary, formulaic sequences, and pedagogy'. *System* 34/1: 119–134.

Summary: Our study explores the similarities and differences between a discourse completion task (DCT)and corpus data and discusses potential implications for using the two in a pedagogic context.

Descriptor(s): Materials, Learning technologies, English language, Curriculum/syllabus

Entered by: Lancaster University (Linguistics and English Language)

Schauer, G. and S. Adolphs. 2006. 'Expressions of gratitude in corpus and DCT data: Vocabulary, formulaic sequences and pedagogy'. *System* 34/1: 119–134.

Descriptor(s): Teacher education

Entered by: University of Nottingham (School of English Studies)

Schmitt, D. 2005. 'Writing in the international classroom' in J. Carroll and J. Ryan (eds.) *Teaching International Students: Improving Learning for All.* London: Routledge.

ISBN: 9780415350655

Pages: 63–74

Descriptor(s): Writing, ESP

Country of research: United Kingdom

Learners' background: various

Institutional level: tertiary

Entered by: Nottingham Trent University (School of Arts and Humanities)

Schmitt, D. and N. Schmitt. 2005. *Focus on Vocabulary.* New York: Longman.

ISBN: 978-0131833081

Descriptor(s): Learner autonomy/strategies, English language, Curriculum/syllabus

S

S

Entered by: University of Nottingham
(School of English Studies)

Schmitt, N. 2005. 'Formulaic language:
Fixed and varied'. *ELIA: Estudios de
Lingüística Inglesa Aplicada* 6: 13–39.

Descriptor(s): English language

Entered by: University of Nottingham
(School of English Studies)

Schmitt, N. 2007. 'Current trends
in vocabulary learning and teaching'
in J. Cummins and C. Davison (eds.)
*The International Handbook of English
Language Teaching.* New York: Springer.

ISBN: 978038746300-1

Pages: 827–841

Descriptor(s): Teacher education

Entered by: University of Nottingham
(School of English Studies)

Schmitt, N. 2008. 'State-of-the-art:
Instructed second language vocabulary
acquisition'. *Language Teaching Research*
12/3: 329–363.

Descriptor(s): Teacher education,
Learning technologies

Entered by: University of Nottingham
(School of English Studies)

Schmitt, N. and R. Marsden. 2006.
Why is English Like That? Michigan:
University of Michigan Press.

ISBN: 978-0-472-03134-4

Descriptor(s): Teacher education,
Materials, English language

Entered by: University of Nottingham
(School of English Studies)

Schröder, K., C. Harsch and G. Nold.
2006. 'DESI – Die sprachpraktischen
Kompetenzen unserer Schülerinnen
und Schüler im Bereich Englisch.
Zentrale Befunde [DESI: The communicative

competencies of German students]'.
Neusprachliche Mitteilungen 03/2006: 11–32.

Summary: The article gives an overview
of the results of the large-scale assessment
study reporting on English proficiency of
9th graders in the German school system.

Descriptor(s): Teacher education, ESOL/EAL,
English language, Curriculum/syllabus,
Assessment

Country of research: Germany

Learners' background: Germany

Institutional level: secondary

Entered by: University of Warwick
(Centre for Applied Linguistics)

Seargeant, P. 2005. 'More English than
England itself: The simulation of authenticity
in foreign language practice in Japan'.
International Journal of Applied Linguistics
15/3: 326–345.

Descriptor(s): Cultural issues,
English language

Institutional level: adult

Entered by: The Open University
(Faculty of Education and Languages)

Seargeant, P. 2008. 'Ideologies of English
in Japan: The perspective of policy and
pedagogy'. *Language Policy* 7/2: 121–142.

Descriptor(s): Cultural issues,
English language, Curriculum/syllabus,
Classroom interaction

Institutional level: adult

Entered by: The Open University
(Faculty of Education and Languages)

Seedhouse, P. 2005. 'Conversation
analysis and language learning'.
Language Teaching 38/4: 165–187.

Summary: Conversation Analysis (CA)
is a methodology for the analysis of
naturally-occurring spoken interaction.
It is a multi-disciplinary methodology

which is now applied in a very wide range of professional and academic areas.

http://eprints.ncl.ac.uk/deposit_details.php?deposit_id=651

Descriptor(s): Speaking, Methodology, Classroom interaction

Country of research: various

Learners' background: various

Entered by: Newcastle University (School of Education, Communication and Language Sciences)

Seedhouse, P. 2005. 'Task as research construct'. *Language Learning* 55/3: 533–570.

Summary: The article examines 'task' as research construct as predominantly conceived in terms of task-as-workplan in the Task-based Learning/SLA literature. It is suggested that 'task' has weak construct validity and ontology in an overwhelmingly quantitative paradigm because the construct has a 'split personality'.

http://eprints.ncl.ac.uk/deposit_details.php?deposit_id=5775

Descriptor(s): Methodology, Curriculum/syllabus, Classroom interaction

Country of research: various

Learners' background: various

Entered by: Newcastle University (School of Education, Communication and Language Sciences)

Seedhouse, P. 2007. 'Interaction and constructs' in Z. Hua, P. Seedhouse, L. Wei and V. Cook (eds.) *Language Learning and Teaching as Social Interaction*. Basingstoke: Palgrave Macmillan.

ISBN: 0230517005

Pages: 9–21

Summary: There is currently considerable interest in the relationship between Conversation Analysis (CA) and sociocultural or Social Constructionist (SC) approaches

to language learning. This chapter analyses extracts of L2 classroom interaction to discover the extent to which SC constructs may or may not be manifest in the details of the interaction.

Descriptor(s): Speaking, Methodology, Classroom interaction

Country of research: various

Learners' background: various

Entered by: Newcastle University (School of Education, Communication and Language Sciences)

Seedhouse, P. 2007. 'On ethnomethodological CA and "Linguistic CA": A reply to all'. *Modern Language Journal* 91/4: 526–532.

http://eprints.ncl.ac.uk/deposit_details.php?deposit_id=5774

Descriptor(s): Methodology, Classroom interaction

Country of research: various

Learners' background: various

Entered by: Newcastle University (School of Education, Communication and Language Sciences)

Seedhouse, P. 2008. 'Learning to talk the talk: Conversation analysis as a tool for induction of trainee teachers' in S. Garton and K. Richards (eds.) *Professional Encounters in TESOL*. Basingstoke: Palgrave Macmillan.

ISBN: 9780230553514

Pages: 42–57

Summary: A particular puzzle for trainee teachers is how it is that experienced teachers manage to create a pedagogical focus; that is, to get students to do what they want, in an apparently effortless manner.

Descriptor(s): Teacher education, Teacher cognition, Methodology, Classroom interaction

S

S

Country of research: various

Learners' background: various

Entered by: Newcastle University (School of Education, Communication and Language Sciences)

Seedhouse, P. 2008. 'The interactional architecture of the language classroom'. *Babylonia* 3: 22–24.

Descriptor(s): Speaking, Methodology, Classroom interaction

Country of research: various

Learners' background: various

Entered by: Newcastle University (School of Education, Communication and Language Sciences)

Seedhouse, P. and K. Richards. 2007. 'Describing and analysing institutional varieties of interaction' in H. Bowles and P. Seedhouse (eds.) *Conversation Analysis and Languages for Specific Purposes.* Bern: Peter Lang.

ISBN: 9783039114696

Pages: 17–36

Summary: This chapter attempts to conceptualise the relationship between the individual instance of interaction, the institutional sub-variety of interaction and the institutional variety of interaction, and to provide such an enabling framework.

Descriptor(s): Teacher education, Speaking, Methodology, ESP, Curriculum/syllabus

Country of research: various

Learners' background: various

Entered by: Newcastle University (School of Education, Communication and Language Sciences)

Seedhouse, P. and M. Egbert. 2006. 'The interactional organisation of the IELTS speaking test'. *IELTS Research Reports* 6: 161–206.

Summary: This report describes the interactional organisation of the IELTS Speaking test in terms of turn-taking, sequence and repair. The study is based on the analysis of transcripts of 137 audio-recorded tests using a Conversation Analysis (CA) methodology.

Descriptor(s): Assessment

Country of research: various

Learners' background: various

Associated project: The Interactional Organisation of the IELTS Speaking Test

Entered by: Newcastle University (School of Education, Communication and Language Sciences)

Sercombe, P.G., C. Raschka and C-L. Huang. 2007. 'The use of code-switching in Taiwanese EFL classrooms: Expectations and reality'. *Lingua et Linguistica* 1/2: 7–20.

Descriptor(s): Classroom interaction

Country of research: Taiwan

Entered by: Newcastle University (School of Education, Communication and Language Sciences)

Sercombe, P.G., M. Garner and C. Raschka. 2006. 'Sociolinguistic minorities, research and social relationships'. *Journal of Multilingual and Multicultural Development* 27/1: 61–78.

Entered by: Newcastle University (School of Education, Communication and Language Sciences)

Setter, J. 2005. 'Communicative patterns of intonation in L2 English teaching and learning: The impact of discourse approaches' in K. Dziubalska-Kolaczyk and J. Przedlacka (eds.) *English Pronunciation Models: A Changing Scene.* Bern: Peter Lang.

ISBN: 978-0820471730

Pages: 367–389

Summary: This chapter looks at the Discourse Intonation approach, both as a way of describing intonation in English and from a pedagogical perspective.

Descriptor(s): Pronunciation, English language

Entered by: University of Reading (Department of Applied Linguistics)

Setter, J. 2005. 'Listening to other Englishes: British listeners on Singapore speakers' in D. Deterding, A. Brown and E.L. Low (eds.) *English in Singapore: Phonetic Research on a Corpus.* Singapore: McGraw-Hill Education (Asia).

ISBN: 978-0071247276

Pages: 163–172

Summary: This chapter reports results of a study on two British listeners' opinions and understanding of Singapore English speakers.

Descriptor(s): Pronunciation, Listening, English language

Country of research: United Kingdom

Learners' background: Singapore

Institutional level: tertiary

Entered by: University of Reading (Department of Applied Linguistics)

Setter, J. 2006. 'Speech rhythm in world Englishes: The case of Hong Kong'. *TESOL Quarterly* 40/4: 763–782.

Summary: This paper compares speech rhythm in Hong Kong English in spontaneous/semi-scripted speech with that of British English.

Descriptor(s): Pronunciation, English language

Country of research: Hong Kong

Learners' background: Hong Kong

Institutional level: tertiary

Entered by: University of Reading (Department of Applied Linguistics)

Setter, J. 2008. 'Consonant clusters in Hong Kong English'. *World Englishes* 27/3-4: 502–515.

Summary: This paper looks at the make-up and occurrence of consonant clusters in spontaneous/semi-scripted speech in Hong Kong English.

Descriptor(s): Pronunciation, English language

Country of research: Hong Kong

Learners' background: Hong Kong

Institutional level: tertiary

Entered by: University of Reading (Department of Applied Linguistics)

Setter, J. 2008. 'Theories and approaches in English pronunciation' in R. Monroy and A. Sanchez (eds.) *25 Years of Applied Linguistics in Spain: Milestones and Challenges.* Murcia: Universidad de Murcia, Servicio de Publacaciaones.

Pages: 447–457

Summary: This is an overview of recent theories and approaches in English pronunciation teaching.

Descriptor(s): Pronunciation, English language

Entered by: University of Reading (Department of Applied Linguistics)

Setter, J. and J. Jenkins. 2005. 'Pronunciation'. *Language Teaching* 38: 1–17.

Summary: This is a state-of-the-art review of research and scholarship in English pronunciation teaching.

Descriptor(s): Pronunciation, English language

Country of research: United Kingdom

Entered by: University of Reading (Department of Applied Linguistics)

Shak, J. and S. Gardner. 2008. 'Young learner perspectives on four focus-on-form tasks'. *Language Teaching Research* 12/3: 387–408.

S

S

Descriptor(s): Methodology, Curriculum/syllabus

Country of research: Brunei Darussalam

Learners' background: Brunei Darussalam

Institutional level: primary

Entered by: University of Birmingham (School of Education)

Shamsudin, S. and H. Nesi. 2006. 'Computer mediated communication in English for specific purposes: A case study with computer science students at Universiti Teknologi Malaysia'. *Computer Assisted Language Learning* 19/4 & 5: 317–339.

Summary: This paper describes the design and implementation of CMC tasks as part of a programme of sustained-content language instruction. The students following this programme made significant improvements in their oral communication skills and, following the treatment, achieved higher scores than their peers in a computer science project.

Descriptor(s): Writing, Speaking, Learning technologies, ESP

Country of research: Malaysia

Learners' background: Malaysia

Institutional level: tertiary

Entered by: Coventry University

Shaw, S. 2005. 'Evaluating the impact of word processed text on writing quality and rater behaviour'. *Cambridge ESOL: Research Notes* 22: 13–19.

Summary: Stuart Shaw reviews the literature on word processed text and evaluates the impacts for the assessment of both writing quality and rater behaviour. He concludes that examiner training should ensure equity between the rating of these two formats.

www.cambridgeesol.org/rs_notes/rs_nts22.PDF

Entered by: University of Cambridge ESOL Examinations

Shaw, S. 2006. 'IELTS writing: Revising assessment criteria and scales (conclusion)'. *Cambridge ESOL: Research Notes* 24: 19–22.

Summary: Stuart Shaw considers rating scales for Writing, in his concluding article on the IELTS Writing Revision Project. He focuses on the qualitative analysis of a global survey on the revised IELTS Writing rating scale. Both raters and administrators were surveyed; the latter being a key stakeholder group rarely foregrounded in research studies.

www.cambridgeesol.org/rs_notes/rs_nts24.PDF

Entered by: University of Cambridge ESOL Examinations

Shaw, S. 2007. 'DELTA reliability: Estimating and reporting examiner performance indices for the written examination component'. *Cambridge ESOL: Research Notes* 29: 8–11.

Summary: Stuart Shaw describes a recent study to enhance the marking quality of the DELTA written examination in terms of standardisation, reliability and transparency.

www.cambridgeesol.org/rs_notes/rs_nts29.PDF

Entered by: University of Cambridge ESOL Examinations

Shaw, S. 2007. 'Modelling facets of the assessment of writing within an ESM environment'. *Cambridge ESOL: Research Notes* 27: 14–19.

Summary: Stuart Shaw describes efforts to conceptualise Cambridge ESOL's writing assessment as a workflow in terms of different facets within an Electronic Script Management (ESM) environment; he shows how this developing technology draws on databases and can benefit the assessment of writing performance.

www.cambridgeesol.org/rs_notes/rs_nts27.PDF

Entered by: University of Cambridge ESOL Examinations

Shaw, S. and C. Weir. 2007. *Studies in Language Testing Vol 26: Examining Writing: Research and Practice in Assessing Second Language Writing.* Cambridge: UCLES/CUP.

ISBN: 978052169293

Summary: This highlights the need for test developers to provide clear explanations of the ability constructs which underpin tests offered in the public domain. It shows how an understanding and analysis of a socio-cognitive validation framework in relation to specific writing tests can assist test developers to operationalise their tests more effectively in relation to different proficiency levels.

Descriptor(s): Assessment

Country of research: United Kingdom

Learners' background: various

Institutional level: adult

Entered by: University of Cambridge ESOL Examinations

Shaw, S. and C.J. Weir. 2007. *Examining Writing in a Second Language: Research and Practice in Assessing Second Language Writing, Studies in Language Testing 26.* Cambridge: Cambridge University Press and Cambridge ESOL.

ISBN: 978-0-521-69293-9

Descriptor(s): Writing, Assessment

Entered by: University of Bedfordshire (Centre for Research in English Language Learning and Assessment)

Shaw, S. and E. Galaczi. 2005. 'Skills for Life writing mark scheme trial: Validating the rating scale for entry levels 1, 2 and 3'. *Cambridge ESOL: Research Notes 20:* 8–12.

Summary: Article describes a trial of mark schemes for the forthcoming Skills for Life tests, which aimed to improve the assessment process and refine the rating scales for the writing component. This project was undertaken to ensure that assessment was standardised, ensuring a fair result for all candidates taking these modular tests designed to improve adult literacy in the UK.

www.cambridgeesol.org/rs_notes/rs_nts20.PDF

Entered by: University of Cambridge ESOL Examinations

Shiotsu, T. and C.J. Weir. 2007. 'The relative significance of syntactic knowledge and vocabulary breadth in the prediction of second language reading comprehension test performance'. *Language Testing* 24/1: 1–30.

Descriptor(s): Reading, Assessment

Entered by: University of Bedfordshire (Centre for Research in English Language Learning and Assessment)

Shoaib, A. and Z. Dörnyei. 2005. 'Affect in lifelong learning: Exploring L2 motivation as a dynamic process' in P. Benson and D. Nunan (eds.) *Learners' Stories: Difference and Diversity in Language Learning.* Cambridge: Cambridge University Press.

ISBN: 9780521614146

Pages: 22–41

Descriptor(s): Learner cognition, Learner autonomy/strategies

Entered by: University of Nottingham (School of English Studies)

Siew, C. and S. Troudi. 2006. 'An investigation into the changes in perceptions of, and attitudes towards, learning English in a Malaysian college'. *International Journal of Teaching and Learning in Higher Education* 18/2: 120–130.

Descriptor(s): Cultural issues, ESOL/EAL

Country of research: Malaysia

S

S

Learners' background: various

Institutional level: adult

Entered by: University of Exeter
(School of Education and Lifelong Learning)

Simpson, J. 2005. 'Conversational floors in synchronous text-based CMC discourse'. *Discourse Studies* 7/3: 331–367.

Entered by: University of Leeds
(School of Education)

Simpson, J. 2005. 'Language learning in a virtual world' in F. Benhamamouche (ed.) *Passerelle: Langues et Modernité. Proceedings of Foreign Languages and Modernity Conference, University of Oran, Algeria, 13–15 March 2004.* Oran, Algeria: Editions Dar El Gharb.

Pages: 51–76

Principal format: Printed

Entered by: University of Leeds
(School of Education)

Simpson, J. 2005. 'Learning electronic literacy skills in an online language learning community'. *CALL Journal* 18/4: 327–345.

Entered by: University of Leeds
(School of Education)

Simpson, J. 2005. 'Meaning-making online: Discourse and CMC in a language learning community' in A. Mendez Vilas, B. Gonzalez Pereira, J. Mesa Gonzalez and J.A. Mesa Gonzales (eds.) *Recent Research Developments in Learning Technologies. Proceedings of m-ICTE conference, Caceres, Spain, 7–10 June 2005.* Caceres, Spain: Formatex.

Pages: 175–179

Principal format: Printed

Entered by: University of Leeds
(School of Education)

Simpson, J. 2006. 'Differing expectations in the assessment of the speaking skills of ESOL learners'. *Linguistics and Education* 17/1: 40–55.

Entered by: University of Leeds
(School of Education)

Simpson, J. 2007. 'Adult ESOL in England: Policy, practice and research' in N. Faux (ed.) *Low-Educated Second Language and Literacy Acquisition (LESLLA): Research, Policy and Practice. Proceedings of 2nd Annual Forum, Commonwealth University of Virginia, September 2006.* Richmond, Virginia: Commonwealth University of Virginia.

Pages: 197–212

Principal format: Printed

Entered by: University of Leeds
(School of Education)

Simpson, J. and G. White. 2008. 'Teaching and learning listening in ESOL classes: "The rock we build the house on"'. *Language Issues* 19/2: 4–19.

Entered by: University of Leeds
(School of Education)

Simpson, J., H. Sunderland, M. Cooke and C. Wallace. 2008. 'Adult ESOL in the UK: Three perspectives on practice, policy and research' in M. Young-Scholten (ed.) *LESLLA. Proceedings of 3rd Annual Forum, University of Newcastle, September 2007.* Durham: Roundtuit Publishing.

Pages: 25–31

Principal format: Printed

Entered by: University of Leeds
(School of Education)

Simpson, J., M. Cooke and M. Baynham. 2008. *The Right Course? An Exploratory Study of Placement Practices in ESOL and Literacy.* London: NRDC.

ISBN: 978-1-905188-56-7

Summary: Available online: www.nrdc.org.uk/publications_details.asp?ID=136#

Descriptor(s): ESOL/EAL

Associated project: ESOL Placement Practices Project

Entered by: University of Leeds (School of Education)

Sinclair, B. 2006. 'Self-access language learning: Conceptualisations, practice and future directions' in D. Dixon, H. Baba, P. Cozens and M. Thomas (eds.) *Independent Learning Schemes: A Practical Approach*. Dubai: TESOL Arabia Publications.

ISBN: 9948856651

Pages: 3–18

Summary: This chapter is the leading article in a collection of papers for an international audience reporting on a range of issues for consideration when planning, implementing, operating and researching self-access, independent language learning.

Descriptor(s): Methodology, Learner autonomy/strategies

Entered by: University of Nottingham (School of Education)

Sinclair, B. 2008. 'Multiple voices: Negotiating pathways towards teacher and learner autonomy' in T. Lamb and H. Reinders (eds.) *Learner and Teacher Autonomy: Concepts, Realities and Responses*. Amsterdam: John Benjamins Publishing Company.

ISBN: 978 90 272 05179

Pages: 237–266

Summary: This chapter describes a project to develop negotiated, collaborative teaching and learning in HE as a model for continuing personal and professional development. It explores how the 'voices' of the various participants in the development of autonomy at three interacting levels informed the design and delivery of a Masters-level programme in 'Learner Autonomy' for overseas teachers of English at the University of Nottingham.

Descriptor(s): Teacher education, Cultural issues, Methodology, Learner autonomy/strategies, Curriculum/syllabus, Classroom interaction

Country of research: United Kingdom

Learners' background: various

Institutional level: tertiary

Entered by: University of Nottingham (School of Education)

Siyanova, A. and N. Schmitt. 2007. 'Native and non-native use of multi-word versus one-word verbs'. *International Review of Applied Linguistics* 45/2: 109–139.

Descriptor(s): Cultural issues, English language

Entered by: University of Nottingham (School of English Studies)

Siyanova, A. and N. Schmitt. 2008. 'L2 learner production and processing of collocation: A multi-study perspective'. *Canadian Modern Language Review* 64/3: 429–458.

Descriptor(s): Learner cognition, English language

Entered by: University of Nottingham (School of English Studies)

Skehan, P. and P. Foster. 2005. 'Pre-task and online planning: The influence of surprise information and task time on second language performance' in R. Ellis (ed.) *Planning and Task Performance in a Second Language*. Amsterdam: Benjamins.

ISBN: 90 272 1962

Pages: 193–216

Summary: This chapter reports on a study into the effects of task type and implementation conditions on learner performance, showing that the time given for a task has a strong influence on how it is performed.

S

S

Descriptor(s): Learner cognition, Classroom interaction

Country of research: United Kingdom

Learners' background: various

Institutional level: adult

Entered by: St. Mary's University College, Twickenham, London (School of Communication, Culture and Creative Arts)

Skehan, P. and P. Foster. 2007. 'Complexity, accuracy, fluency and lexis in task-based performance: A meta-analysis of the Ealing research' in S. Van Daele, A. Housen, F. Kuiken, M. Pierrard and I. Vedder (eds.) *Complexity, Accuracy and Fluency in Second Language Use, Learning and Teaching.* Brussels: VWK.

ISBN: D/2007/0455/19

Pages: 207–226

Principal format: Printed

Summary: This chapter provides a meta-analysis of the results of six studies undertaken by the authors over a number of years into L2 task design and implementation conditions.

Descriptor(s): Learner cognition, English language, Classroom interaction

Country of research: United Kingdom

Learners' background: various

Institutional level: adult

Entered by: St. Mary's University College, Twickenham, London (School of Communication, Culture and Creative Arts)

Skorczynska, H. and A. Deignan. 2006. 'Readership and purpose in the choice of economics metaphor'. *Metaphor and Symbol* 21/2: 87–104.

Entered by: University of Leeds (School of Education)

Slaght, J. and B. Howell. 2007. 'TEEP: A course-driven assessment measure'

in O. Alexander (ed.) *Proceedings of the 2005 Joint BALEAP/SATEFL Conference. New Approaches to Materials Development for Language Learning.* Oxford, Bern: Peter Lang.

ISBN: 978-3-03910-909-8

Pages: 253–263

Principal format: Printed

Descriptor(s): Assessment

Country of research: United Kingdom

Institutional level: tertiary

Entered by: University of Reading (Centre for Applied Language Studies)

Slaouti, D. 2007. 'Teacher learning about online learning: Experiences of a situated approach'. *European Journal of Teacher Education* 3/3: 285–304.

Descriptor(s): Teacher education, Learning technologies

Entered by: University of Manchester (School of Education)

Slaouti, D. and G. Motteram. 2006. 'Reconstructing practice: Language teacher education and ICT' in P. Hubbard and M. Levy (eds.) *Teacher Education in CALL.* Amsterdam: John Benjamins Publishing.

ISBN: 9027219680

Pages: 81–97

Descriptor(s): Teacher education, Learning technologies

Country of research: United Kingdom

Learners' background: various

Institutional level: tertiary

Entered by: University of Manchester (School of Education)

Smith, R.C. 2005. 'Developing professional autonomy: An action research-based MA module and its ongoing evaluation'. *Interactions* 9.

S

Summary: Case study of innovations and evaluations during 5 years of an initial teacher education MA ELT programme. A Professional Practice module was redesigned according to an action research learning model focused on developing students' ability to evaluate and continuously develop their practice for themselves. Benefits have included increased relevance to students' own practical concerns, and enhanced motivation and autonomy.

www2.warwick.ac.uk/services/ldc/resource/interactions/archive/issue26/smith

Descriptor(s): Teacher education, Curriculum/syllabus

Country of research: United Kingdom

Learners' background: various

Institutional level: tertiary

Entered by: University of Warwick (Centre for Applied Linguistics)

Smith, R.C. 2005. 'General introduction' in R.C. Smith (ed.) *Teaching English as a Foreign Language, 1936–61: Foundations of ELT, Volume 1 (of 6)*. Abingdon: Routledge.

ISBN: 0-415-29970-5

Pages: xv–cxx

Summary: Introduction to a collection of texts documenting the rise of ELT (1936–1961), showing how the British Council, the BBC and the University of London Institute of Education began to place the teaching of EFL on a firm institutional footing. Also analyses the roots and diffusion of structural-oral-situational methodology.

Descriptor(s): Cultural issues, Methodology, Materials, English language

Country of research: various

Associated project: Enhancement of the Warwick ELT Archive, with a Particular Focus on the Work of A.S. Hornby

Entered by: University of Warwick (Centre for Applied Linguistics)

Smith, R.C. 2006. 'Developing teacher-learner autonomy: constraints and opportunities in pre-service training' in L. Bobb-Wolff and J.L. Vera Batista (eds.) *Proceedings of The Canarian Conference on Developing Autonomy in the FL Classroom 2003*. La Laguna, Spain: University of La Laguna.

Principal format: CD-ROM

www2.warwick.ac.uk/fac/soc/al/staff/smith_r/developing_teacher-learner_autonomy_canaries.PDF

Descriptor(s): Teacher education, Learner autonomy/strategies

Country of research: United Kingdom

Learners' background: various

Institutional level: tertiary

Entered by: University of Warwick (Centre for Applied Linguistics)

Smith, R.C. 2007. 'The origins of ELT Journal'.

Summary: Commissioned paper for the English Language Teaching Journal (ELTJ). 'About this journal' web page describes the origins of the journal (in A.S. Hornby's work, and Hornby's and H.E. Palmer's work in Japan).

www.oxfordjournals.org/our_journals/eltj/resource/the%20origins%20of%20elt%20journal2.PDF

Descriptor(s): Cultural issues

Associated project: Enhancement of the Warwick ELT Archive, with a Particular Focus on the Work of A.S. Hornby

Entered by: University of Warwick (Centre for Applied Linguistics)

Smith, R.C. 2008. 'Commentary on "Teacher education for teacher and learner autonomy"' in M. Jiménez Raya and T.E. Lamb (eds.) *Pedagogy for Autonomy in Modern Languages Education: Theory, Practice*. Dublin: Authentik.

S

ISBN: 978-1-905275-31-1

Pages: 303–307

Summary: A commentary on teacher education initiatives for developing pedagogy for autonomy in schools. Elements of a possible 'knowledge base' are highlighted, including: parallelism between educating student-teachers and teaching (pupils) to learn; metacognitive awareness-raising; reflection on practical examples; actual engagement in a pedagogy for autonomy, especially with an action research dimension; involvement of school-based mentors; and necessary institutional adjustments.

Descriptor(s): Teacher education, Learner autonomy/strategies

Country of research: various

Learners' background: various

Institutional level: secondary

Entered by: University of Warwick (Centre for Applied Linguistics)

Smith, R.C. 2008. 'Learner autonomy (key concepts in ELT)'. *ELT Journal* 62/4: 395–397.

Summary: Clarifies the concept of learner autonomy by taking standard definitions and highlighting their practical provenance and significance. Highlights an important continuing role for teachers in promoting autonomy, while noting a tension between top-down 'training' and genuinely student-centred approaches. Concludes that learner autonomy is a cross-culturally valid educational goal, though one requiring different forms of pedagogy according to context.

Descriptor(s): Cultural issues, Methodology, Learner autonomy/strategies

Entered by: University of Warwick (Centre for Applied Linguistics)

Smith, R.C. 2008. 'The history of learner autonomy' in L. Dam (ed.) *9th Nordic Conference on Developing Learner Autonomy in Language Learning and Teaching: Status and W.* Copenhagen: CVU.

Principal format: Printed

www2.warwick.ac.uk/fac/soc/al/research/groups/llp/circal/dahla/histories/the_history_of_learner_autonomy.PDF

Descriptor(s): Management/innovation, Learner autonomy/strategies

Entered by: University of Warwick (Centre for Applied Linguistics)

Smith, R.C. and S. Erdoğan 2008. 'Teacher-learner autonomy: Programme goals and student-teacher constructs' in T. Lamb and H. Reinders (eds.) *Learner and Teacher Autonomy: Concepts, Realities and Responses.* Amsterdam: Benjamins/AILA.

ISBN: 978 90 272 0517 9

Summary: This paper clarifies dimensions of 'teacher autonomy' and argues for the goal within initial teacher education of enhancing 'teacher-learner autonomy' ('the ability to develop appropriate skills, knowledge and attitudes for oneself as a teacher, in cooperation with others'). One approach towards this goal is described, and students' personal constructs relating to the course design are investigated with repertory-grid interviews.

Descriptor(s): Teacher education, Teacher cognition, Learner cognition, Learner autonomy/strategies

Country of research: United Kingdom

Learners' background: various

Institutional level: tertiary

Entered by: University of Warwick (Centre for Applied Linguistics)

Spillett, H. 2007. 'The marking of spelling for the revised YLE tests from January 2007'. *Cambridge ESOL: Research Notes* 28: 4–7.

Summary: Helen Spillett explains the reasons for considering a change in existing policy and describes the procedures and outcomes of a consultation exercise and small-scale research study which informed the new policy implemented from 2007.

www.cambridgeesol.org/rs_notes/rs_nts28. PDF

Entered by: University of Cambridge ESOL Examinations

Spiro, J. 2007. 'Teaching poetry: Writing poetry - teaching as a writer'. *English in Education* 41/3: 78–93.

Summary: This article looks at the ways in which the skills and strategies of the creative writer can be applied to the language classroom. It shows how four specific writer strategies can be adapted for language learning, and provides examples of learner response to these. The article arrives at a notion of authenticity in writing methods.

Descriptor(s): Writing, Methodology

Country of research: United Kingdom;

Learners' background: various

Associated project: Transitions and Transformations: Exploring Creativity in Everyday and Literary Language

Entered by: Oxford Brookes University (Westminster Institute of Education)

Ssebunga-Masembe, C. and G. Thompson. 2008. 'Potential sources of comprehension difficulties in advanced secondary school science textbooks: The case of Uganda' in N. Nørgaard (ed.) *Systemic Functional Linguistics in Use (Odense Working Papers in Language and Communication Volume 29).* Odense: University of Southern Denmark.

ISBN: 978-87-90923-47-1

Pages: 749–766

Principal format: Online

Summary: Excerpts from the science textbooks used in schools in Uganda are analysed. The analyses reveal textual flaws, particularly in the way relations between propositions are constructed and signalled, that are likely to make them more difficult for students to comprehend. The paper further explores how the flaws might be rectified.

www.sdu.dk/~/media/Files/Om_SDU/Institutt er/ISK/Forskningspublikationer/OWPLC/Nr29 /Connie%20Ssebbunga%20Masembe%20%2 0%20Geoff%20Thompson.ashx

Descriptor(s): English language, ESP, Materials, Reading

Country of research: Uganda

Learners' background: Uganda

Institutional level: secondary

Entered by: University of Liverpool (School of English)

Street, J. and K. Ingham. 2007. 'Publishing vocabulary lists for BEC preliminary, PET and KET examinations'. *Cambridge ESOL: Research Notes* 27: 4–7.

Summary: Jason Street and Kate Ingham describe the process of compiling, validating, and publishing word lists for our BEC preliminary, PET and KET examinations.

www.cambridgeesol.org/rs_notes/rs_nts27. PDF

Entered by: University of Cambridge ESOL Examinations

Svalberg, A. 2005. 'Consciousness raising activities in some Lebanese English language classrooms: Teacher perceptions and learner engagement'. *Language Awareness* 14/2–3: 170–190.

Descriptor(s): Teacher cognition, Methodology, Classroom interaction

Country of research: Lebanon

Learners' background: Lebanon

Entered by: University of Leicester (English

S

T

Language Teaching and Applied Linguistics, School of Education)

Svalberg, A. 2007. 'Language Awareness: State of the art'. *Language Teaching* 40/4: 287–308.

Descriptor(s): Methodology, Learner cognition, English language

Entered by: University of Leicester (English Language Teaching and Applied Linguistics, School of Education)

T

Tavakoli, P. 2008. 'L2 performance and context of language learning: A comparative study of learners in Tehran and London'. *Journal of Teaching English Language and Literature Society of Iran* 2/5: 103–131.

Summary: The present paper examines whether language performance of learners studying English in a formal language classroom context at home (AH) is different from performance of learners who study English abroad (SA) where they would have to use English for a range of communicative purposes.

Descriptor(s): Speaking, Methodology, Learner autonomy/strategies, ESOL/EAL, Classroom interaction

Country of research: Iran

Entered by: London Metropolitan University (Faculty of Humanities, Arts, Languages and Education)

Tavakoli, P. and P. Foster. 2008. 'Task design and second language performance: The effect of narrative type on learner output'. *Language Learning* 58/2: 439–473.

Summary: This study reports on how two dimensions of narrative task design (storyline complexity and narrative structure) impact upon the accuracy, complexity and fluency of L2 performance.

Country of research: various

Learners' background: various

Institutional level: adult

Associated project: Information Foregrounding in Narrative Tasks for Second Language Classrooms

Entered by: St. Mary's University College, Twickenham, London (School of Communication, Culture and Creative Arts)

Tavakoli, P. and P. Foster. 2008. 'Task design and second language performance: The effect of narrative type on learner output'. *Language Learning* 58/2: 439–473.

Summary: This article presents a study examining how narrative structure and narrative complexity can impact the performance of second language learners. Forty learners of English in London and sixty learners in Tehran were asked to re-tell cartoon stories from picture prompts.

Descriptor(s): Speaking, Materials, Learner cognition, ESOL/EAL

Country of research: United Kingdom

Entered by: London Metropolitan University (Faculty of Humanities, Arts, Languages and Education)

Tavakoli, P. and P. Skehan. 2005. 'Strategic planning, task structure and performance testing' in R. Ellis (ed.) *Planning and task performance in a second language.* Amsterdam: John Benjamins.

ISBN: 90-272-1961-3

Pages: 239–277

Summary: Planning has proved to have positive effects on language learners' performance on tasks. This study sets out to investigate the effects of strategic planning on learners' accuracy, complexity and fluency of performance.

Descriptor(s): Speaking, ESOL/EAL, Assessment

Entered by: London Metropolitan University (Faculty of Humanities, Arts, Languages and Education)

Taylor, L. 2005. 'Closer collaboration with other Cambridge University departments'. *Cambridge ESOL: Research Notes* 19: 14.

Summary: Lynda Taylor outlines how Cambridge ESOL has forged closer links with other departments in the University of Cambridge.

www.cambridgeesol.org/rs_notes/rs_nts19. PDF

Entered by: University of Cambridge ESOL Examinations

Taylor, L. 2005. 'Defining and investigating impact: A dimension of test validation' in A. Nebel and C. Niakaris (eds.) *Best Practices in Testing: Proceedings of the 2004 EFL Testing and Evaluation Forum.* Athens: Hellenic American Union.

ISBN: n/a

Principal format: Printed

Descriptor(s): Assessment

Learners' background: various

Entered by: University of Cambridge ESOL Examinations

Taylor, L. 2005. 'Key concepts in ELT: Washback and impact'. *ELT Journal* 59/2: 154–155.

Descriptor(s): Assessment

Entered by: University of Cambridge ESOL Examinations

Taylor, L. 2005. 'Using qualitative research methods in test development and validation'. *Cambridge ESOL: Research Notes* 21: 2–4.

Summary: Lynda Taylor outlines the range of qualitative research carried out at Cambridge ESOL to support test development and monitor test quality.

www.cambridgeesol.org/rs_notes/rs_nts21. PDF

Entered by: University of Cambridge ESOL Examinations

Taylor, L. 2005. 'Washback and impact: The view from Cambridge ESOL'. *Cambridge ESOL: Research Notes* 20: 2–3.

Summary: Lynda Taylor discusses notions of washback and impact, locating them within the broader framework of consequential validity. She highlights the long tradition of consultation which we have enjoyed with our test stakeholders and the more recent role of systematic impact studies within our approach to test development and validation.

www.cambridgeesol.org/rs_notes/rs_nts20. PDF

Entered by: University of Cambridge ESOL Examinations

Taylor, L. 2006. 'The changing landscape of English: Implications for language assessment'. *English Language Teaching* 60/1: 51–60.

Descriptor(s): ESOL/EAL, English language, Assessment

Entered by: University of Cambridge ESOL Examinations

Taylor, L. 2007. 'The impact of the joint-funded research studies on the IELTS speaking module' in L. Taylor and P. Falvey (eds.) *Studies in Language Testing Vol 19: IELTS Collected Papers: Research in Speaking and Writing Assessment.* Cambridge: UCLES/CUP.

ISBN: 978052154287

Entered by: University of Cambridge ESOL Examinations

Taylor, L. 2007. 'The impact of the joint-funded research studies on the IELTS writing module' in L. Taylor and P. Falvey (eds.) *Studies in Language Testing Vol 19: IELTS Collected Papers: Research in Speaking and Writing Assessment.* Cambridge: UCLES/CUP.

T

T

ISBN: 9780521542487

Entered by: University of Cambridge ESOL Examinations

Taylor, L. and C.J. Weir. 2008. *Multilingualism and Assessment: Achieving Transparency, Assuring Quality, Sustaining Diversity, Studies in Language Testing 27.* Cambridge: Cambridge ESOL/ Cambridge University Press.

ISBN: 978-052-1-711920

Descriptor(s): Assessment

Entered by: University of Bedfordshire (Centre for Research in English Language Learning and Assessment)

Taylor, L. and F. Barker. 2008. 'Using corpora for language assessment' in N. Hornberger and E. Shohamy (eds.) *Encyclopaedia of Language and Education.* New York: Springer.

ISBN: 978-0-387-32875-1 (Print) 978-0-387-30424-3 (Online)

Pages: 241–254

Summary: In this chapter Lynda Taylor and Fiona Baker illustrate how the field of corpus linguistics has become an important and relevant source of accurate language data, which is useful for constructing tests based on scientific and empirical language documentation.

Descriptor(s): ESOL/EAL, English language, Assessment

Learners' background: various

Institutional level: tertiary

Entered by: University of Cambridge ESOL Examinations

Taylor, L. and N. Jones. 2006. 'Cambridge ESOL exams and the Common European Framework of Reference (CEFR)'. *Cambridge ESOL: Research Notes 24*: 2–5.

Summary: Lynda Taylor and Neil Jones discuss the relationship of Cambridge ESOL's exams with the Council of Europe's CEFR along four perspectives: historical, conceptual, empirical and evolutional. www.cambridgesol.org/rs_notes/rs_nts24.PDF

Entered by: University of Cambridge ESOL Examinations

Thighe, D. 2007. 'Cambridge ESOL and tests of English for specific purposes'. *Cambridge ESOL: Research Notes 27*: 2–4.

Summary: David Thighe discusses Cambridge ESOL's response to the changing assessment requirements that are resulting from globalisation and migration. He describes the growing demand for English language tests that are tailored to the needs of populations in various work-oriented contexts, outlining some of the principles that underpin the domain-related tests we offer, such as BEC, BULATS, ILEC and ICFE. www.cambridgeesol.org/rs_notes/rs_nts27. PDF

Entered by: University of Cambridge ESOL Examinations

Thompson, G. 2005. 'But me some buts: A multi-dimensional view of conjunction'. *Text 25/6*: 763–791.

Summary: Uses a Systemic Functional Linguistic approach to set out a comprehensive model of conjunction – the ways in which speakers and writers make connections between the clauses in their discourse (whether or not the connections are explicitly signalled).

Descriptor(s): English language

Entered by: University of Liverpool (School of English)

Thompson, G. 2007. 'Corpus, comparison, culture: Doing the same things differently in different languages' in W. Teubert and R. Krishnamurthy (eds.) *Corpus Linguistics: Critical Concepts in Linguistics, Volume 5.* London & New York: Routledge.

ISBN: 978-0415338950

Pages: 68–87

Summary: Focuses on the comparative analysis in classrooms of small corpora of equivalent genres in different languages. I argue for including explicit attention to language forms within CLT approaches, and for stimulating awareness-raising through cross-linguistic comparison, concentrating on exploring the 'discourse value' of lexical, structural and other choices in context.

Descriptor(s): Methodology, Learning technologies, English language

Entered by: University of Liverpool (School of English)

Timmis, I. 2005. 'Towards a framework for teaching spoken grammar'. *English Language Teaching Journal* 59/2: 117–125.

Summary: This article proposed a principled framework for the teaching of spoken grammar, taking into account sociocultural concerns about the relevance of native speaker language in an era of international English.

Descriptor(s): Speaking, Cultural issues, Methodology, English language

Country of research: United Kingdom

Learners' background: various

Entered by: Leeds Metropolitan University

Timmis, I. 2007. 'The attitudes of language learners towards varieties of the target language' in B. Tomlinson (ed.) *Language Acquisition and Development: Studies of Learners of First and Other Languages*. London: Continuum.

ISBN: 0-8264-8612-6

Pages: 122–139

Summary: This chapter discusses how learners' sense of identity might affect their attitude to varieties of the target language and how these attitudes, in turn, might affect their acquisition of the target language.

Descriptor(s): Cultural issues, English language

Entered by: Leeds Metropolitan University

Timmis, I. 2008. 'The lexical approach is dead: Long live the lexical dimension!'. *Modern English Teacher* 17/3: 5–10.

Summary: This article discusses with practical examples how a principled lexical dimension could be applied without the need to follow 'The lexical approach' as advocated by Michael Lewis (1993).

Descriptor(s): Methodology, English language

Entered by: Leeds Metropolitan University

Tonkyn, A. 2006. 'Assessing speech: What can the spoken language researcher tell the test developer?' in C. Coombe, P. Davidson and D. Lloyd (eds.) *Proceedings of the 7th and 8th Current Trends in English Language Testing Conferences*. Dubai: TESOL Arabia.

ISBN: 9948-8566-2-7

Pages: 3–22

Principal format: Printed

Summary: This paper examines research into differences in fluency, accuracy and complexity of speech at different proficiency levels. It also examines research findings concerning the reactions of raters of different kinds to features of speech. In the light of this, the revision of the high-stakes IELTS speaking test is discussed.

Descriptor(s): Speaking, English language, Assessment

Country of research: various

Learners' background: various

Institutional level: adult

Entered by: University of Reading (Department of Applied Linguistics)

T

T

Tonkyn, A. 2007. 'Short-term changes in complexity, accuracy and fluency: Developing progress-sensitive proficiency tests' in S. Van Daele, A.F. Housen, F.M. Kuiken, M. Pierrard and I. Vedder (eds.) *Fluency in Second Language Use, Learning and Teaching.* Brussels: KVAB.

ISBN: D/2007/0455/19

Pages: 263–284

Summary: This paper reports on an extended case study of the development of the oral L2 skills (grammatical/lexical complexity and accuracy, and fluency) of a group of 24 learners on a 10-week intensive university course in English for academic purposes, and how that development was perceived by trained raters.

Descriptor(s): Speaking, English language, Assessment

Country of research: United Kingdom

Learners' background: various

Institutional level: tertiary

Entered by: University of Reading (Department of Applied Linguistics)

Toogood, S. and R. Pemberton. 2006. 'Scaffolding for self-access language learning and the FTG Model' in T. Lamb and H. Reinders (eds.) *Supporting Independent Language Learning: Issues and interventions.* Frankfurt: Peter Lang.

ISBN: 3-631-54131-7

Pages: 169–199

Descriptor(s): Methodology, Learner autonomy/strategies

Country of research: Hong Kong

Learners' background: Hong Kong

Institutional level: tertiary

Entered by: University of Nottingham (School of Education)

Toogood, S. and R. Pemberton. 2007. 'Support structures for self-access learning' in A. Barfield and S. Brown (eds.) *Reconstructing Autonomy in Language Education: Inquiry and Innovation.* Basingstoke: Palgrave Macmillan.

ISBN: 978-0-230-00173-2

Pages: 180–195

Descriptor(s): Learner autonomy/strategies

Country of research: Hong Kong

Learners' background: Hong Kong

Institutional level: tertiary

Entered by: University of Nottingham (School of Education)

Trappes-Lomax, H. 2007. 'For more on X, see e.g. Y: A TESOL approach to a pedagogical grammar of citation conventions' in T. Lynch and J. Northcott (eds.) *Symposia for Language Teacher Educators.* Edinburgh: Institute for Applied Language Studies.

Principal format: CD-ROM

Descriptor(s): Writing, Teacher education, ESP

Entered by: University of Edinburgh (Institute for Applied Language Studies/Office of Lifelong Learning)

Trappes-Lomax, H. 2007. 'Vague language as a means of self-protective avoidance: Tension management in conference talks' in J. Cutting (ed.) *Vague Language Explored.* Basingstoke: Palgrave Macmillan.

ISBN: 9781403988171

Descriptor(s): Teacher education, Cultural issues, English language

Entered by: University of Edinburgh (Institute for Applied Language Studies/Office of Lifelong Learning)

Troudi, S. 2005. 'Critical content and cultural knowledge for TESOL Teachers'. *Teacher Development* 9/1: 115–129.

Descriptor(s): Teacher education, Cultural issues, ESOL/EAL

Entered by: University of Exeter (School of Education and Lifelong Learning)

Troudi, S. 2008. 'Reflecting on action research' in A. Jendli, C. Coombe and S. Troudi (eds.) *Best Practice in English Language Teaching*. Dubai: TESOL Arabia.

Pages: 433–445

Descriptor(s): Teacher education

Entered by: University of Exeter (School of Education and Lifelong Learning)

Tse, P. and K. Hyland. 2006. '"So what is the problem this book addresses?" Interactions in book reviews'. *Text and Talk* 27: 767–790.

Descriptor(s): Writing, Reading

Entered by: Institute of Education, London (Department of Learning, Curriculum and Communication)

Tse, P. and K. Hyland. 2006. 'Gender and discipline: Exploring metadiscourse variation in academic book reviews' in K. Hyland and M. Bondi (eds.) *Academic Discourse across Disciplines*. Frankfurt: Peter Lang.

ISBN: 9 783039 111831

Pages: 177–202

Descriptor(s): Writing

Entered by: Institute of Education, London (Department of Learning, Curriculum and Communication)

Tse, P. and K. Hyland. 2008. '"Robot Kung fu": Gender and the performance of a professional identity'. *Journal of Pragmatics* 40/7: 1232–1248.

Descriptor(s): Writing, ESP

Institutional level: tertiary

Entered by: Institute of Education, London (Department of Learning, Curriculum and Communication)

Tseng, W-T. and N. Schmitt. 2008. 'Towards a self-regulating model of vocabulary learning: A structural equation modelling approach'. *Language Learning* 58/2: 357–400.

Descriptor(s): Learner autonomy/strategies

Entered by: University of Nottingham (School of English Studies)

Tseng, W-T., Z. Dörnyei and N. Schmitt. 2006. 'A new approach to assessing strategic learning: The case of self-regulation in vocabulary acquisition'. *Applied Linguistics* 27/1: 78–102.

Descriptor(s): Assessment

Entered by: University of Nottingham (School of English Studies)

Tseng, W-T., Z. Dörnyei and N. Schmitt. 2008. 'A new approach to assessing strategic learning: The case of self-regulation in vocabulary acquisition'. *Applied Linguistics* 27: 78–102.

Descriptor(s): Learner autonomy/strategies

Entered by: University of Nottingham (School of English Studies)

U

Ushioda, E. 2006. 'Internal and social processes: The paradox of motivation' in Z. Kantaridou, I. Papadopoulou and I. Mahili (eds.) *Motivation in Language Learning for Specific and Academic Purposes. Proceedings of the 5th International Conference on Language Learning for Specific & Academic Purposes, University of Macedonia*. Thessaloniki: University of Macedonia Press.

Principal format: CD-ROM

U

Summary: Review of research on motivation in language learning, with implications for classroom practice and research.

Descriptor(s): Teacher education, Learner cognition, Learner autonomy/strategies, ESP

Entered by: University of Warwick (Centre for Applied Linguistics)

Ushioda, E. 2006. 'Language motivation in a reconfigured Europe: Access, identity, autonomy'. *Journal of Multilingual and Multicultural Development* 27/2: 148–161.

Summary: A critical discussion of issues of motivation, autonomy and identity in language learning and use.

Descriptor(s): Cultural issues, Learner cognition, Learner autonomy/strategies

Entered by: University of Warwick (Centre for Applied Linguistics)

Ushioda, E. 2006. 'Motivation and autonomy in language learning' in M. Kötter, O. Traxel and S. Gabel (eds.) *Investigating and Facilitating Language Learning. Papers in Honour of Lienhard Legenhausen.* Trier: Wissenschaftliger Verlag Trier.

ISBN: 978-3-88476-844-0

Pages: 283–295

Summary: Critical review of motivation and autonomy theory with reference to communicative language teaching.

Descriptor(s): Speaking, Learner cognition, Learner autonomy/strategies, Classroom interaction

Entered by: University of Warwick (Centre for Applied Linguistics)

Ushioda, E. 2007. 'Motivation, autonomy and sociocultural theory' in P. Benson (ed.) *Learner Autonomy 8: Teacher and Learner Perspectives.* Dublin: Authentik.

ISBN: 978-1-905275-00-7

Pages: 5–24

Summary: Analysis of sociocultural- theoretical perspectives on motivation and autonomy, drawing on research data from language learners and student teachers.

Descriptor(s): Learner cognition, Learner autonomy/strategies

Entered by: University of Warwick (Centre for Applied Linguistics)

Ushioda, E. 2008. 'Motivation and good language learners' in C. Griffiths (ed.) *Lessons from Good Language Learners.* Cambridge: Cambridge University Press.

ISBN: 978-0-521-88963-6

Pages: 19–34

Summary: Review of research on language motivation with implications for classroom practice.

Descriptor(s): Learner cognition, Learner autonomy/strategies

Entered by: University of Warwick (Centre for Applied Linguistics)

Ushioda, E. 2008. 'Using I-statement analysis to explore autonomy and change'.

Summary: Reports on research dimension of CUTE2 project to develop Chinese University academics' English language skills, with a focus on fostering learner autonomy.

www.echinauk.org/cases2/cute2/research.php

Descriptor(s): Learning technologies, Learner autonomy/strategies, English language

Country of research: China

Learners' background: China

Associated project: Chinese University Teacher Training in English (CUTE2)

Entered by: University of Warwick (Centre for Applied Linguistics)

Üstünel, E. and P. Seedhouse. 2005. 'Why that, in that language, right now?: Code-switching and pedagogical focus'.

International Journal of Applied Linguistics 15/3: 302–325.

Summary: The study depicts the relationship between pedagogical focus and language choice in the language teaching/learning environment of English as a Foreign Language (EFL) at a Turkish university.

http://eprints.ncl.ac.uk/deposit_details.php?deposit_id=5773

Descriptor(s): Speaking, Classroom interaction

Country of research: Turkey

Learners' background: Turkey

Institutional level: tertiary

Entered by: Newcastle University (School of Education, Communication and Language Sciences)

V

Vanderplank, R. 2008. 'The significance of first language development in five to nine year old children for second and foreign language learning'. *Applied Linguistics* 29/4: 717–722.

Summary: In this article, the language learning experiences and development of a child (the author's daughter) between the ages of five and nine are drawn on to argue that we should re-focus our comparison of first and second language acquisition away from early L1 acquisition to the early schooling period.

Descriptor(s): Learner cognition, English language

Country of research: United Kingdom

Learners' background: United Kingdom

Institutional level: primary

Entered by: University of Oxford (Language Centre)

W

V,W

Walker, C. 2008. 'Factors which influence the process of collocation' in F. Boears and S. Lindstromberg (eds.) *Cognitive Linguistic Approaches to Teaching Vocabulary and Phraseology.* Berlin: Mouton De Gruyer.

ISBN: 9783110196306

Pages: 291–308

Summary: A corpus-based investigation of the factors which influence collocation (e.g. the use of metaphor, semantic prosody etc.).

Descriptor(s): Methodology, Materials, English language

Entered by: University of Birmingham (Centre for English Language Studies and Department of English)

Walker, T. 2006. 'Linking learners to the CEFR for asset languages'. *Cambridge ESOL: Research Notes* 24: 8–10.

Summary: Tamsin Walker considers how learners taking asset exams can be said to be linked to the CEFR, describing learner-based standard-setting and suggesting a holistic approach to assessment.

www.cambridgeesol.org/rs_notes/rs_nts24.PDF

Entered by: University of Cambridge ESOL Examinations

Wall, D. 2005. *The Impact of High-Stakes Testing on Classroom Teaching: A Case Study Using Insights from Testing and Innovation Theory.* Cambridge: Cambridge ESOL and Cambridge University Press.

ISBN: 0521542499

Summary: An account of one of the earliest empirical studies of examination washback. It provides a case study of an attempt to encourage innovation in English teaching through the introductive of a new-style examination. It offers a model for investigating examination washback and for identifying the factors that may promote or inhibit innovation.

Descriptor(s): Management/Innovation, English language, Curriculum/syllabus, Classroom interaction, Assessment

Country of research: Sri Lanka

Learners' background: Sri Lanka

Institutional level: secondary

Entered by: Lancaster University (Linguistics and English Language)

Wall, D. and T. Horak. 2007. 'Using baseline studies in the investigation of test impact'. *Assessment in Education* 14/1: 99–116.

Summary: A review of the function of baseline studies in the process of educational innovation, with an illustration of the use of one such investigation in a study of the impact of the new version of TOEFL.

Descriptor(s): Management/Innovation, Assessment

Entered by: Lancaster University (Linguistics and English Language)

Wallace, C. 2005. 'Conversations around the literacy hour in a multilingual London school'. *Language and Education* 19/4: 322–338.

Summary: The study examined the literacy experiences, attitudes and repertoires of four nine-year-old bilingual children in a multilingual London primary school with reference to the way the children responded to the British National Literacy Strategy.

Descriptor(s): Reading, ESOL/EAL

Country of research: United Kingdom

Learners' background: various

Institutional level: primary

Entered by: Institute of Education, London (Department of Learning, Curriculum and Communication)

Wallace, C. 2005. 'The cultural and linguistic resources of advanced bilingual learners:

A case study of four bilingual learners in a multicultural London school'. *Prospect* 20/1: 82–94.

Summary: The study explored in-depth the linguistic and cultural resources of four bilingual learners in a London primary school. It draws implications for the curriculum and literacy teaching in multicultural contexts.

Descriptor(s): Cultural issues, Reading, ESOL/EAL, Curriculum/syllabus

Country of research: United Kingdom

Learners' background: various

Entered by: Institute of Education, London (Department of Learning, Curriculum and Communication)

Wallace, C. 2006. 'The text dead or alive: Expanding textual repertoires in the Adult ESOL classroom'. *Linguistics and Education* 17/1: 74–90.

Summary: The study looks at the use of text in the Reading Classroom in Adult ESOL classrooms. It argues that a very restricted view of text leads to a reduced literacy curriculum in which ESOL learners' resources and experiences are largely ignored.

Descriptor(s): Teacher education, Reading, ESOL/EAL, Curriculum/syllabus, Classroom interaction

Country of research: United Kingdom

Learners' background: various

Entered by: Institute of Education, London (Department of Learning, Curriculum and Communication)

Wallace, C. 2008. 'Literacy and identity: A view from the bridge in two multilingual London schools'. *Journal of Language, Identity and Education* 7/1: 61–80.

Summary: The article examines the manner in which identity impacts on literacy with reference to two nine-year-old girls and two fifteen-year-old boys in London schools who speak or have access to two or more languages.

Descriptor(s): Cultural issues, Reading, ESOL/EAL, Curriculum/syllabus

Country of research: United Kingdom

Learners' background: various

Entered by: Institute of Education, London (Department of Learning, Curriculum and Communication)

Wallace, C. 2008. 'Negotiating communication rights in multilingual classrooms: Towards the creation of critical communities of learners'. *Pedagogies* 3/3: 150–167.

Summary: The paper aims to demonstrate how classrooms can be reconfigured as critical communities. It focuses on two classrooms of adult learners in the United Kingdom to show how teachers may allow space for atypical kinds of dialogic teaching to emerge in the interests of creating critical communities of learners.

Descriptor(s): Teacher education, ESOL/EAL, Classroom interaction

Country of research: United Kingdom

Learners' background: various

Entered by: Institute of Education, London (Department of Learning, Curriculum and Communication)

Walsh, S. 2006. *Investigating Classroom Discourse.* London, New York: Routledge.

ISBN: 10: 0415364698

Summary: Investigating Classroom Discourse is based on the premise that language use and interaction is at the core of good teaching and learning.

Descriptor(s): Classroom interaction

Entered by: Queen's University, Belfast (School of Education)

Walsh, S. 2006. 'Learning to talk or talking to learn in the EFL classroom' in A. Gallagher and M. ÓLaoire (eds.) *Language Education in Ireland: Current Practice and Future Needs.* Dublin: IRAAL.

ISBN: 9780901519818

Descriptor(s): Teacher education, Learner autonomy/strategies

Entered by: Queen's University, Belfast (School of Education)

Walsh, S. 2006. 'Talking the talk of the TESOL Classroom'. *English Language Teaching Journal* 60: 133–141.

Descriptor(s): Classroom interaction

Country of research: United Kingdom

Entered by: Newcastle University (School of Education, Communication and Language Sciences)

Walsh, S. and A. O'Keeffe. 2007. 'Editorial: Raising language awareness through analysing discourse in context'. *Language Awareness* 16/3: 151–152.

Descriptor(s): Teacher education, Classroom interaction

Entered by: Newcastle University (School of Education, Communication and Language Sciences)

Walsh, S., A. O'Keeffe and M. McCarthy. 2007. '"…post-colonialism, multi-culturalism, structuralism, feminism, post-modernism and so on so forth" – vague language in academic discourse, a comparative analysis of form, function' in R. Randi and A. Adel (eds.) *Exploring Discourse through Corpora.* Amsterdam: John Benjamins.

ISBN: 978 90 272 2305 0

Descriptor(s): Teacher education, Methodology, Materials, Learner autonomy/strategies

Entered by: Queen's University, Belfast (School of Education)

Walter, C. 2007. 'First- to second-language reading comprehension: Not transfer,

W

W

but access'. *International Journal of Applied Linguistics* 17/1: 14–37.

Summary: Drawing on Gernsbacher's Structure Building Framework, I challenge the metaphor of 'transfer' of reading comprehension from L1 to L2, in favour of a description of access to an established comprehension ability. A study with a group of French learners of English confirmed the access hypothesis and made links with L2 working memory development.

Descriptor(s): Reading, Learner cognition

Country of research: France

Entered by: University of Oxford (Department of Education)

Walter, C. 2008. 'Phonology in L2 reading: Not an optional extra'. *TESOL Quarterly* 42/3: 455–474.

Summary: In the reading comprehension 'threshold', lower intermediate learners have problems comprehending texts at their level. These learners have low working memory and, notably, unreliable phonological inventories of English. This corresponds to an explanation where low-level decoding difficulties take up working memory to the detriment of higher-level comprehension activity.

Descriptor(s): Reading, Pronunciation, Learner cognition

Country of research: France

Entered by: University of Oxford (Department of Education)

Waters, A. 2005. 'Expertise in teacher education: Helping teachers to learn' in K. Johnson (ed.) *Expertise in Second Language Learning and Teaching*. Basingstoke: Palgrave Macmillan.

ISBN: 9781403920966

Pages: 210–229

Summary: Conceptualises the nature of teacher educator expertise in terms of what can be seen to be involved in attempting to facilitate teacher learning, and outlines

programme for further research in area.

Descriptor(s): Teacher education

Entered by: Lancaster University (Linguistics and English Language)

Waters, A. 2006. 'Facilitating follow-up in ELT INSET'. *Language Teaching Research* 10/1: 32–52.

Summary: Study of problems and potential in bridging 'course-based' and 'school-based' INSET in ELT.

Descriptor(s): Teacher education, Management/Innovation

Country of research: Philippines

Entered by: Lancaster University (Linguistics and English Language)

Waters, A. 2007. 'Native-speakerism in ELT: Plus ça change?'. *System* 35/3: 281–292.

Summary: Argues that 'critical theory' based attempts to counter native-speakerism in ELT are as much a cause of as a solution to the problem. The use of cultural generalisations is taken as a case in point, and, via a review of the literature on stereotyping, a less poltically-biased approach argued for.

Descriptor(s): Cultural issues

Entered by: Lancaster University (Linguistics and English Language)

Waters, A and M.L.C. Vilches. 2008. 'Factors affecting ELT reforms: The case of the Philippines basic education curriculum'. *RELC Journal* 39/1: 5–24.

Summary: Study of problems associated with implementation of ELT component of Philippines BEC, and discussion of reasons why the issues identified have occurred in both this and a wide range of other similar projects.

Descriptor(s): Teacher education, Management/Innovation, Curriculum/syllabus

Country of research: Philippines

Entered by: Lancaster University (Linguistics and English Language)

Watkins, P. 2007. 'Pre-service training and the first year of teaching' in B. Beaven (ed.) *IATEFL 2006 Harrogate Conference Selections*. Canterbury UK: IATEFL Publications.

ISBN: 1901095096

Pages: 129–130

Principal format: Printed

Entered by: University of Portsmouth (School of Languages and Area Studies)

Wedell, M. 2005. 'Cascading training down into the classroom: The need for parallel planning'. *International Journal of Educational Development* 25/6: 637–651.

Entered by: University of Leeds (School of Education)

Wedell, M. 2008. 'Developing a capacity to make "English for Everyone" worthwhile: Reconsidering outcomes and how to start achieving them'. *International Journal of Educational Development* 28/6: 628–639.

Entered by: University of Leeds (School of Education)

Weir, C. and H. Khalifa. 2008. 'A cognitive processing approach towards defining reading comprehension'. *Cambridge ESOL: Research Notes* 31: 2–10.

Summary: Cyril Weir and Hanan Khalifa describe the mental processes readers use to comprehend reading texts as a means of defining Cambridge ESOL's construct of reading that our language assessments purport to test.

www.cambridgeesol.org/rs_notes/rs_nts31.PDF

Descriptor(s): Reading, Assessment

Entered by: University of Cambridge ESOL Examinations

Weir, C. and H. Khalifa. 2008. 'Applying a cognitive processing model to Main Suite reading papers'. *Cambridge ESOL: Research Notes* 31: 11–16.

Summary: Cyril Weir and Hanan Khalifa apply this cognitive processing approach to defining reading comprehension to the Cambridge ESOL Main Suite examinations in English, focusing on two levels – the Preliminary English Test (PET) and the First Certificate in English (FCE).

www.cambridgeesol.org/rs_notes/rs_nts31.PDF

Descriptor(s): Reading, Assessment

Entered by: University of Cambridge ESOL Examinations

Weir, C. and S. Shaw. 2005. 'Establishing the validity of Cambridge ESOL writing tests: Towards the implementation of a socio-cognitive model for test validation'. *Cambridge ESOL: Research Notes* 21: 10–14.

Summary: Stuart Shaw and Cyril Weir report on ongoing research to articulate a clear theoretical and practical position for the construct of writing, which is an important component of all of our language tests. Weir's Validity framework attempts to reconfigure validity as a unitary concept, and to show how its constituent parts interact with each other.

www.cambridgeesol.org/rs_notes/rs_nts21.PDF

Entered by: University of Cambridge ESOL Examinations

Weir, C. and S. Shaw. 2006. 'Defining the constructs underpinning Main Suite writing tests: A socio-cognitive perspective'. *Cambridge ESOL: Research Notes* 26: 9–14.

Summary: Cyril Weir and Stuart Shaw summarise the constructs underpinning the Main Suite writing tests, drawing in part on corpus evidence. A clear construct definition is vital for understanding and validating language tests and this article describes the application of a socio-cognitive validity framework to the Cambridge Writing examinations.

www.cambridgeesol.org/rs_notes/rs_nts26.PDF

W

W

Entered by: University of Cambridge , ESOL Examinations

Weir, C. and S. Shaw. 2008. 'A socio-cognitive approach to writing test validation' in L. Taylor and C. Weir (eds.) *Studies in Language Testing Vol 27: Multilingualism and Assessment: Achieving Transparency, Assuring Quality, Sustaining Diversity – Proceedings of the ALTE Berlin Conference, May 2005.* Cambridge: UCLES/CUP.

ISBN: 9780521711920

Entered by: University of Cambridge ESOL Examinations

Weir, C.J. 2005. *Language Testing and Validation: An Evidence-based Approach.* Houndgrave, Hampshire: Palgrave MacMillan.

ISBN: 1-4039-1188-6/1-4039-1189-4

Descriptor(s): Writing, Speaking, Reading, Listening, Assessment

Entered by: University of Bedfordshire (Centre for Research in English Language Learning and Assessment)

Weir, C.J. 2005. 'Limitations of the Council of Europe's Framework of Reference (CEFR) in developing comparable examinations and tests'. *Language Testing* 22/3: 282–300.

Descriptor(s): Curriculum/syllabus, Assessment

Entered by: University of Bedfordshire (Centre for Research in English Language Learning and Assessment)

Weir, C.J. and H. Khalifa. 2008. 'A cognitive processing approach towards defining reading comprehension'. *Research Notes, Cambridge ESOL* 31: 2–10.

Descriptor(s): Reading, Assessment

Entered by: University of Bedfordshire (Centre for Research in English Language Learning and Assessment)

Weir, C.J. and H. Khalifa. 2008. 'Applying a cognitive processing model to Main Suite reading papers'. *Research Notes, Cambridge ESOL* 31: 11–16.

Descriptor(s): Reading, Assessment

Entered by: University of Bedfordshire (Centre for Research in English Language Learning and Assessment)

Weir, C.J. and J.R.W. Wu. 2006. 'Establishing test form and individual task comparability: A case study of a semi-direct speaking test'. *Language Testing* 23/3: 1–33.

Descriptor(s): Speaking, Assessment

Entered by: University of Bedfordshire (Centre for Research in English Language Learning and Assessment)

Weir, C.J. and S. Shaw. 2008. 'A socio-cognitive approach to writing test validation' in L. Taylor and C.J. Weir (eds.) *Multilingualism and Assessment: Achieving Transparency, Assuring Quality, Sustaining Diversity, Studies in Language Testing 27.* Cambridge: Cambridge University Press and Cambridge ESOL.

ISBN: 978-052-1-711920

Pages: 147–156

Descriptor(s): Writing, Assessment

Entered by: University of Bedfordshire (Centre for Research in English Language Learning and Assessment)

Weir, C.J., B. O'Sullivan, Y. Jin and S. Bax. 2007. 'Does the computer make a difference? Reaction of candidates to a computer-based versus a traditional hand-written form of the IELTS writing component: Effects and impact' in P. McGovern and S. Walsh (eds.) *IELTS Research Report Volume 7.* Canberra: British Council & IDP Australia.

ISBN: 987-0-9775875-2-0

Descriptor(s): Assessment

Entered by: University of Bedfordshire (Centre for Research in English Language Learning and Assessment)

Weir, C.J., B. O'Sullivan and T. Horai. 2006. 'Exploring difficulty in speaking tasks: An intra-task perspective' in P. McGovern and S. Walsh (eds.) *IELTS Research Reports Volume 6*. Canberra: British Council & IDP Australia.

ISBN: 0-9775875-0-9

Pages: 119–160

Descriptor(s): Speaking, Assessment

Entered by: University of Bedfordshire (Centre for Research in English Language Learning and Assessment)

Weir, C.J., B. O'Sullivan, Y. Jin and S. Bax. 2007. 'Does the computer make a difference? Reaction of candidates to a computer-based versus a traditional hand-written form of the IELTS writing component: Effects and impact' in P. McGovern and S. Walsh (eds.) *IELTS Research Reports Volume 7*. Canberra: British Council & IDP Australia.

ISBN: 987-0-9775875-2-0

Descriptor(s): Learning technologies, Assessment

Entered by: Canterbury Christ Church University (Department of English and Language Studies)

Wicaksono, R. 2007. 'The BBC Learning English Teacher Blogger: An early experience' in B. Beaven (ed.) *IATEFL Aberdeen Conference selections*. Canterbury, Kent: IATEFL.

ISBN: 1 901095 14 2

Principal format: Printed

Summary: An exploration of feedback on writing in an online environment.

Descriptor(s): Writing, Methodology, Learning technologies, Classroom interaction

Country of research: United Kingdom

Learners' background: Italy

Institutional level: adult

Entered by: York St John University (Languages and Linguistics)

Wicaksono, R. 2008. 'Assessing mixed nationality and mixed ability group work' in P. Kemp and R. Atfield (eds.) *Enhancing the International Learning Experience in Business Management, Hospitality, Leisure, Sport and Tourism*. Newbury: Threshold Press.

ISBN: 9781903152232

Summary: A report of a mixed methods study to explore students' attitudes to, and performance in, multilingual group work at a UK university.

Descriptor(s): Classroom interaction, Assessment

Country of research: United Kingdom

Institutional level: tertiary

Entered by: York St John University (Languages and Linguistics)

Williams, E. 2006. *Bridges and Barriers: Language in African Education and Development*. Manchester: St. Jerome.

ISBN: 1-900650-97-5

Summary: This book examines the relationship between language, education and development in Africa.

Descriptor(s): Teacher education, Cultural issues, Reading, Methodology, Materials, English language, Curriculum/syllabus, Classroom interaction, Assessment

Country of research: various

Learners' background: various

Institutional level: primary

Entered by: Bangor University (School of Linguistics and English Language)

W

W

Williams, E. 2006. 'Teaching reading: Individual and social perspectives' in E. Usó and A. Martinez (eds.) *Current Trends in the Development of the Four Language Skills in a Foreign Language.* Amsterdam: Mouton de Gruyter.

ISBN: ISBN-13 978-3-11-018968-1

Pages: 355–380

Summary: Reviews contemporary approaches to the teaching of reading comprehension in EFL/ESL.

Descriptor(s): Reading, Methodology, Materials, English language

Country of research: various

Learners' background: various

Entered by: Bangor University (School of Linguistics and English Language)

Williams, E. 2006. 'The use of ex-colonial languages in education' in K. (Gen ed.) Brown and B. (Vol ed.) Spolsky (eds.) *Encyclopedia of Language and Linguistics, Vol. 4.* Oxford: Elsevier.

ISBN: 13: 978-0-08-044299-0 10: 0-08-044299-4

Pages: 60–64

Summary: Reviews the role of language in ex-colonial countries around the world.

Descriptor(s): Cultural issues, English language

Country of research: various

Learners' background: various

Entered by: Bangor University (School of Linguistics and English Language)

Williams, E. 2007. 'Extensive reading in Malawi: Inadequate implementation or inappropriate innovation?'. *Journal of Research in Reading* 30/1: 59–79.

Summary: This article provides evidence from field research of the failure of a large-scale British aid project to effect improvement in levels of reading in Malawi.

It also provides explanations for that failure.

Descriptor(s): Reading, Methodology, Management/innovation, English language, Assessment

Country of research: Malawi

Learners' background: Malawi

Institutional level: primary

Entered by: Bangor University (School of Linguistics and English Language)

Williams, E. and A. Williams. 2007. *ESOL and EFL: An Unhelpful Distinction?* Reading, UK: CfBT Education Trust.

ISBN: 978-0-86160

Summary: This monograph provides a critical perspective on past and present policies on the teaching of English as a second/foreign language in the UK and beyond.

Descriptor(s): ESOL/EAL, English language

Country of research: various

Learners' background: various

Entered by: Bangor University (School of Linguistics and English Language)

Willis, J. 2005. 'Introduction: Aims and explorations into tasks and task-based teaching' in C. Edwards and J. Willis (eds.) *Teachers Exploring Tasks in English Language Teaching.* Basingstoke: Palgrave Macmillan.

ISBN: 1-4039-4557-8

Pages: 1–12

Entered by: Aston University (School of Languages and Social Sciences)

Willis, D. and J. Willis. 2007. *Doing Task-based Teaching.* Oxford: Oxford University Press.

ISBN: 978 0 19 442210 9

Entered by: Aston University (School of Languages and Social Sciences)

W

Wilson, J. 2005. 'Ethical issues in the testing of young learners'. *Cambridge ESOL: Research Notes* 22: 6–7.

Summary: Juliet Wilson discusses some of the ethical issues concerning testing children. She outlines Cambridge ESOL's current approach to testing this group of learners and describes how these tests were developed in the mid 1990s in terms of their design and the children's experience of taking these tests.

www.cambridgeesol.org/rs_notes/rs_nts22.PDF

Entered by: University of Cambridge ESOL Examinations

Wilson, J. 2007. 'Reviewing the Cambridge Young Learners English (YLE) tests'. *Cambridge ESOL: Research Notes* 28: 2–4.

Summary: Juliet Wilson's introductory article outlines the background to the review of the YLE tests conducted over the past 3–4 years; she goes on to consider the modifications and trialling of three different tasks and describes the research which was carried out to update the vocabulary lists.

www.cambridgeesol.org/rs_notes/rs_nts28.PDF

Entered by: University of Cambridge ESOL Examinations

Woodfield, H. 2006. 'Requests in English: ESL learners' responses to written discourse completion tasks' in *General & Theoretical Papers No. 679*. Essen: University of Duisburg-Essen.

Principal format: Printed

Entered by: University of Bristol (Graduate School of Education)

Woodfield, H. 2008. 'Interlanguage requests: A contrastive study' in M. Pütz and J. Neff-van Aertselaer (eds.) *Contrastive Pragmatics: Interlanguage and Cross-cultural Perspectives*. Berlin: Mouton de Gruyter.

ISBN: 978-3-11-019670-2

Pages: 231–264

Entered by: University of Bristol (Graduate School of Education)

Woodfield, H. 2008. 'Problematising discourse completion tasks: Voices from verbal report'. *Journal of Evaluation and Research in Education* 21/2: 43–69.

Entered by: University of Bristol (Graduate School of Education)

Wright, A. 2008. 'A corpus-informed study of specificity in Financial English: The case of ICFE reading'. *Cambridge ESOL: Research Notes* 31: 16–21.

Summary: Angela Wright investigates the specificity of Financial English reading texts compared to Business English and General English reading texts, using the new International Certificate in Financial English (ICFE) reading paper as a case study.

www.cambridgeesol.org/rs_notes/rs_nts31.PDF

Entered by: University of Cambridge ESOL Examinations

Wright, T. 2005. *Classroom Management in Language Education*. Basingstoke: Palgrave.

ISBN: 1403940894

Summary: Focuses on classroom management (CM) within the notion of classroom life. Examines the affective, spatial, temporal, discourse, cultural and institutional aspects of CM. Reviews relevant research and suggests ways of researching CM.

Descriptor(s): Teacher education, Cultural issues, Methodology, Management/innovation, Classroom interaction

X,Y

Entered by: University College Plymouth St Mark & St John (Department of International Education)

Wright, T. 2006. 'Managing classroom life' in S. Gieve and I. Miller (eds.) *Understanding the Language Classroom*. Basingstoke: Palgrave.

ISBN: 9780230206953

Pages: 64–87

Summary: Paper redefining the notion of classroom management (CM). 1. Forcesin CM: order; opportunity; care 2. Dimensions of CM: time; space; engagement; participation.

Descriptor(s): Teacher education, Methodology, Management/innovation, Classroom interaction

Entered by: University College Plymouth St Mark & St John (Department of International Education)

Wright, T. and R. Bolitho. 2007. *Trainer Development*.

Published online: Lulu.com.

ISBN: 978-1-84753-232-9

Summary: This book is a personal view of the process of working in teacher and trainer development programmes. It discusses affective, social and cognitive issues among others.

Descriptor(s): Teacher education

Entered by: University College Plymouth St Mark & St John (Department of International Education)

X

Xing, P. and G. Fulcher. 2007. 'Reliability assessment for two versions of the Vocabulary Levels Test'. *System* 35/2: 182–191.

Descriptor(s): Assessment

Entered by: University of Leicester (English Language Teaching and Applied Linguistics, School of Education)

Y

Yanagawa, K. and A.B. Green. 2008. 'To show or not to show: The effects of item stems and answer options on performance on a multiple-choice listening comprehension test'. *System* 36/1: 107–122.

Descriptor(s): Listening, Learner cognition, Learner autonomy/strategies, Assessment

Country of research: Japan

Learners' background: Japan

Institutional level: secondary

Entered by: University of Bedfordshire (Centre for Research in English Language Learning and Assessment)

Yang, M., R.G. Badger and Z. Yu. 2006. 'A comparative study of peer and teacher feedback in a Chinese EFL writing class'. *Journal of Second Language Learning* 15/3: 179–200.

Entered by: University of Leeds (School of Education)

Yazigi, R. and P. Seedhouse. 2005. '"Sharing Time" with young learners'. *Teaching English as a Second Language Electronic Journal (TESL-EJ)* 9/3: A–1.

http://eprints.ncl.ac.uk/deposit_details.php?deposit_id=1118

Descriptor(s): Speaking, Classroom interaction

Country of research: United Arab Emirates

Learners' background: various

Institutional level: primary

Entered by: Newcastle University (School of Education, Communication and Language Sciences)

Young-Scholten, M. and C. Ijuin. 2006. 'How can we best measure adult ESL student progress?'. *TESOL Adult Education Interest Section Newsletter, September* 4/2: n/a.

Summary: Application of the stages of Organic Grammar to intermediate-level ESOL adults on a US program.

Descriptor(s): Assessment

Country of research: United States of America

Institutional level: adult

Entered by: Newcastle University (School of Education, Communication and Language Sciences)

Yu, G. 2007. 'Students' voices in the evaluation of their written summaries: Empowerment and democracy for test takers?'. *Language Testing* 24/4: 539–572.

Summary: This paper analysed the students' attitudes and perceptions towards the use of two scoring templates (the expert and the popular) and its differential statistical effects on the judgment of the summarisation performance of these students. The implications of the findings are discussed with specific reference to the value of involving test-takers in assessment criteria development.

Descriptor(s): Writing, Reading, English language, Assessment

Country of research: China

Learners' background: China

Institutional level: tertiary

Entered by: University of Bristol (Graduate School of Education)

Yu, G. 2008. 'Reading to summarize in English and Chinese: A tale of two languages?'. *Language Testing* 25/4: 521–551.

Summary: This paper reports on the significant differential effects of the use of English and Chinese on the processes and products of summarisation as a measure of reading comprehension, drawing upon data from students' actual test performances, as well as their perceptions of such effects. The findings have implications for the design of summarisation and other integrated reading/writing tasks.

Descriptor(s): Writing, Reading, English language, Assessment

Country of research: China

Learners' background: China

Institutional level: tertiary

Entered by: University of Bristol (Graduate School of Education)

Z

Zegerac, V. 2005. 'Four conceptions of language' in K. Brown (ed.) *Encyclopaedia of Language and Linguistics (2nd edition) vol.6.* Amsterdam: Elsevier.

ISBN: 0-08-044299-4

Pages: 340–344

Entered by: University of Bedfordshire (Centre for Research in English Language Learning and Assessment)

Zegerac, V. 2006. 'Believing in: A pragmatic account'. *Lingua* 116: 1703–1721.

Entered by: University of Bedfordshire (Centre for Research in English Language Learning and Assessment)

Zegerac, V. 2007. 'A cognitive pragmatic perspective on communication and culture' in H. Kotthoff and H. Spencer-Oatey (eds.) *Handbook of Intercultural Communication (Handbooks of Applied Linguistics 7).* Berlin: Mouton de Gruyter.

ISBN: 978-3-11-018471-6

Z

Descriptor(s): Cultural issues

Entered by: University of Bedfordshire
(Centre for Research in English Language
Learning and Assessment)

Zegerac, V. 2008. 'Culture and
communication' in H. Spencer-Oatey (ed.)
*Culturally Speaking: Managing Rapport across
Cultures [2nd edition]*. London: Continuum.

ISBN: 978-0-826-493101/978-0-826-493095

Descriptor(s): Cultural issues

Entered by: University of Bedfordshire
(Centre for Research in English Language
Learning and Assessment)

Zeronis, R. 2007. 'The DELTA revision
project – Progress update'. *Cambridge
ESOL: Research Notes* 29: 4–8.

Summary: Ron Zeronis provides a progress
update on the current DELTA revision
project, which includes the development
of a modular syllabus.

www.cambridgeesol.org/rs_notes/rs_nts29.
PDF

Entered by: University of Cambridge
ESOL Examinations

Zimmerman, C. and N. Schmitt. 2005.
'Lexical questions to guide the teaching
and learning of words'. *CATESOL Journal*
17/1: 1–7.

Descriptor(s): Teacher education, Learner
cognition, Learner autonomy/strategies

Entered by: University of Nottingham
(School of English Studies)

DOCTORAL THESES SUPERVISED AND COMPLETED

Doctoral (PhD or EdD) theses supervised and completed within UK universities are listed below by institution. It should be noted that not all universities where doctoral work is supervised were able to supply details in this category, and so the list is not a fully comprehensive one. Regarding availability, doctoral theses completed within UK institutions are gradually being digitised by the British Library's Electronic Theses Online Service (EThOS), and their website (http://ethos.bl.uk/Home.do) would therefore be an appropriate first port of call for users of this directory who are interested in consulting a particular thesis.

Aston University (School of Languages and Social Sciences)

Morris-Adams, M. 2008. *Coherence and Understanding in Informal Conversation between Native and Non-native Speakers of English.*

Supervisor(s): Sue Garton

Awarding institution: Aston University

Summary: The study investigates informal conversations between native English speakers and international students living in the UK, with a focus on topic management strategies. The research suggests that the conversations flowed freely and coherently and were marked by a relative scarcity of the communicative difficulties often associated with NS–NNS interactions.

Descriptor(s): Speaking, Cultural issues

Bangor University (School of Linguistics and English Language)

Al-Musali, A. 2008. *Note Taking in English Lectures: A Study of Omani EFL University Students.*

Supervisor(s): Eddie Williams

Awarding institution: Bangor University, Wales

Summary: An experimental investigation into the effect of a skills programme on the note taking ability in English of Omani university students.

Descriptor(s): Methodology, Learner cognition, Learner autonomy/strategies, English language, Curriculum/syllabus

Country of research: Oman

Learners' background: Oman

Institutional level: tertiary

Sappapan, P. 2007. *Reading Strategies of Thai University Students in English.*

Supervisor(s): Eddie Williams

Awarding institution: Bangor University

Summary: An experimental investigation of reading strategies of Thai university students in English.

Descriptor(s): Methodology, Management/innovation, Learner autonomy/strategies, English language, Classroom interaction

Country of research: Thailand

Learners' background: Thailand

Institutional level: tertiary

Canterbury Christ Church University (Department of English and Language Studies)

Aboshiha, P. 2008. *Identity and Dilemma: The "Native Speaker" English Language Teacher in a Globalizing World.*

Supervisor(s): Adrian Holliday

Awarding institution: University of Kent

Summary: British teachers' attitudes towards theory and professionalism within the context of the changing ownership of English and globalisation.

Descriptor(s): Teacher education, Cultural issues, English language

Institutional level: adult

Brooks, K. 2007. *The Significance of Culture in Language Learning: Working with Adult EFL Learners in Mexico.*

Supervisor(s): John Kullman and Martin Hyde

Awarding institution: University of Kent

Descriptor(s): Cultural issues, Methodology, Curriculum/syllabus

Country of research: Mexico

Institutional level: tertiary

Carlson, A. 2007. *Computers, Literacy and the Bilingual/Bicultural Child.*

Supervisor(s): Stephen Bax

Awarding institution: University of Kent

Summary: A study of children from Japanese and English language homes using specially created Internet sites.

Descriptor(s): Cultural issues, Learning technologies, Curriculum/syllabus

---

Crawford, T. 2008. *ESL Writing in the University of Guanajuato: The Struggle to Enter a Discourse Community.*

Supervisor(s): Christopher Anderson and Alan Cunningsworth

Awarding institution: University of Kent

Summary: A study of classroom discourses surrounding the transitions between Mexican Spanish and English.

Descriptor(s): Writing, Cultural issues, Curriculum/syllabus

Country of research: Mexico

Institutional level: tertiary

Delikurt, P. 2006. *Revolution or Evolution in Educational Change: The Intended Policy–Actual Policy–Policy in Use Continuum Revisited. A Case Study in the English Language Teaching and Learning Context.*

Supervisor(s): Adrian Holliday

Awarding institution: University of Kent

Descriptor(s): English language, Curriculum/syllabus

Country of research: Cyprus

Institutional level: secondary

Duan, Y. 2007. *The Influence of the Chinese University Entrance Exam (English).*

Supervisor(s): Adrian Holliday

Awarding institution: University of Kent

Summary: Investigation of the discourses of Chinese secondary school students in their response to the national university entrance examination – the Gau Kao. A yin-yang theory of discourse.

Descriptor(s): Cultural issues, Assessment

Country of research: China

Institutional level: secondary

Gallagher, K. 2007. *An Exploration within a Sociocultural Approach to Language Education: A Reflexive Case Study.*

+system!

Supervisor(s): Adrian Holliday and Richard Cullen

Awarding institution: University of Kent

Summary: A study of Emirati women trainee teachers in a college of higher technology in the UAE.

Descriptor(s): Teacher education, Cultural issues, Curriculum/syllabus

Country of research: United Arab Emirates

Institutional level: tertiary

Grounds, P. 2008. *Discovering Dynamic Durability: Beyond Sustainability in an English Language Curriculum Project.*

Supervisor(s): Adrian Holliday and Richard Cullen

Awarding institution: University of Kent

Summary: Looking at curriculum issues around the setting up of self-access centres in Mexico.

Descriptor(s): Cultural issues, Management/innovation, Learner autonomy/strategies, Curriculum/syllabus

Country of research: Mexico

Institutional level: tertiary

Lengeling, M. 2007. *Becoming an English Teacher: Participants' Voices and Identities in an In-service Teacher Training Course in Central Mexico.*

Supervisor(s): Stephen Bax and Richard Cullen

Awarding institution: University of Kent

Summary: Student teachers doing the COTE.

Descriptor(s): Teacher education, Cultural issues

Country of research: Mexico

Institutional level: tertiary

Muñoz de Cote, L.M. 2008. *Monologues and Dialogues in the Language Classroom: A Study of Students' Experience in Trying to Learn English as a Compulsory Component at a Mexican University.*

Supervisor(s): John Kullman

Awarding institution: University of Kent

Descriptor(s): Learner autonomy/strategies, Curriculum/syllabus

Country of research: Mexico

Institutional level: tertiary

Narvaez, O.M. 2007. *An Exploration into Student Early Leaving at a University Language Department in Mexico: Voicing Students' Critical Insights on Institutional Practices.*

Supervisor(s): John Kullman

Awarding institution: University of Kent

Descriptor(s): Curriculum/syllabus

Country of research: Mexico

Institutional level: tertiary

Cardiff University (School of English, Communication and Philosophy)

Akbar, R. 2007. *Bilingualism among Kuwaiti Children.*

Supervisor(s): Nikolas Coupland

Awarding institution: Cardiff University

Descriptor(s): ESOL/EAL

Country of research: Kuwait

Learners' background: Kuwait

Institutional level: primary

Emery, H. 2005. *An Investigation into the Nature and Causes of Reading and Spelling Errors Made by Arab ESL Learners.*

Supervisor(s): Alison Wray

Awarding institution: Cardiff University

Descriptor(s): Writing, Learner autonomy/strategies, English language

Country of research: United Arab Emirates

Learners' background: United Kingdom

Institutional level: tertiary

McGee, I. 2006. *Formulaic Language and Second Language Learning/Teaching.*

Supervisor(s): Alison Wray

Awarding institution: Cardiff University

Descriptor(s): Learner cognition

Country of research: Saudi Arabia

Learners' background: Saudi Arabia

Institutional level: tertiary

Munyandamutsa, J-B. 2005. *A Phonological Interlanguage Study of Rwandan Learners of English.*

Supervisor(s): Paul Tench

Awarding institution: Cardiff University

Descriptor(s): Speaking

Country of research: Rwanda

Learners' background: Rwanda

Namba, K. 2008. *English–Japanese Bilingual Children's Code-Switching: A Structural Approach with Emphasis on Formulaic Language.*

Supervisor(s): Alison Wray

Awarding institution: Cardiff University

Descriptor(s): ESOL/EAL

Country of research: Japan

Learners' background: Japan

Institutional level: primary

Su, Y-L. 2008. *Overcoming Barriers to Reach Nativelikeness in Adult Second Language Acquisition.*

Supervisor(s): Alison Wray

Awarding institution: Cardiff University

Descriptor(s): Speaking, Learner autonomy/strategies

Country of research: United Kingdom

Learners' background: United Kingdom

Institutional level: tertiary

Zhao, S-F. 2005. *A Consideration of the Washback Effect of English as a Foreign Language Oral Examinations at Tertiary Level in China: Teaching, Testing, and Syllabus Change.*

Supervisor(s): Christine Pegg

Awarding institution: Cardiff University

Descriptor(s): Speaking, Curriculum/syllabus, Assessment

Country of research: China

Learners' background: China

Institutional level: tertiary

Institute of Education, London (Department of Learning, Curriculum and Communication)

Adjoe, C. 2006. *Language Policy and Planning in Ghana: A Monolingual Ideology, Ethoses and Discourse in a Multilingual Society.*

Supervisor(s): Catherine Wallace

Awarding institution: Institute of Education, University of London

Summary: The study aims to establish how far a multilingual ideology can be established as the basis for language policy in Ghana.

Descriptor(s): Teacher education, Cultural issues, English language

Country of research: Ghana

Learners' background: Ghana

Annous, S. 2006. *"Nativespeakerism" and the Status of Non-native Teachers of English (NNTE) in Lebanon.*

Supervisor(s): Amos Paran

Awarding institution: University of London

Summary: The study, involving teachers, administrators and students, found ELT perceived as a semi-profession, because NNTE were part-timers with different qualifications. The discourse of NNTE created a third space between those of NS and NNS teachers. The NNTE life cycle follows a pattern of honeymoon, maturity and retirement.

Country of research: Lebanon

Institutional level: tertiary

Gray, J. 2007. *Cultural Content in the British ELT Global Coursebook: A Cultural Studies Approach.*

Supervisor(s): David Block

Awarding institution: Institute of Education, University of London

Descriptor(s): Cultural issues, Materials

Joo, M-J. 2007. *Korean University Students' Attitudes to, and Performances on, a Face-to-Face Interview (FTFI) and a Computer Administered Oral Test (CAOT).*

Supervisor(s): Catherine Walter

Awarding institution: Institute of Education, University of London

Summary: This study explores Korean university students' attitudes to, and performance on, a Face-To-Face interview (FTFI) and a Computer Administered Oral Test (CAOT), and finally the effects of attitudes on performance in a Korean university context. Conclusions pointed to the desirability of a CAOT in situations where FTFIs were impractical.

Descriptor(s): Speaking, Learning technologies, Assessment

Country of research: Korea, Republic of (South Korea)

Mehmedbegovic, D. 2008. *"Miss, Who Needs the Languages of Immigrants?": A Study in Attitudes and Values Attached to Bilingualism in England and Wales.*

Supervisor(s): Catherine Wallace

Awarding institution: Institute of Education, University of London

Summary: The study explores the values and attitudes attached to bilingualism on the part of key policy makers and lead professionals in education in England and Wales.

Descriptor(s): Teacher education, Cultural issues, Management/innovation, ESOL/EAL, English language, Curriculum/syllabus

Country of research: United Kingdom

Mugford, G. 2005. *Solidarity, Supportiveness and Creative Language Use in Second Language Interpersonal Talk.*

Supervisor(s): Catherine Wallace

Awarding institution: Institute of Education, University of London

Summary: The study analyses the problematic nature of L2 interpersonal language by examining data collected on second language users who are engaged in L2–L2 small talk in a target-language context.

Descriptor(s): Speaking, Cultural issues, English language

Country of research: Mexico

Learners' background: Mexico

Ng, C. S. N. 2006. *The Effects of Direct Instruction in Phonological Skills on L2 Reading Performance of Chinese Learners of English.*

Supervisor(s): Amos Paran

Awarding institution: University of London

Summary: Three studies were conducted, including two training studies. Results indicate that phonological skills training can be effective in promoting L2 reading skills, but only if provided at primary level. A similar intervention at secondary level was not effective.

Descriptor(s): Reading

Country of research: Hong Kong

Learners' background: Hong Kong

Institutional level: primary

O'Regan, J. 2006. *The Text as a Critical Object: On Theorising Exegetic Procedures in Classroom-based Critical Discourse Analysis.*

Supervisor(s): Catherine Wallace

Awarding institution: Institute of Education, University of London

Summary: The study explores ways in which critical discourse analysis can be translated into classroom practice.

Descriptor(s): Speaking, Cultural issues, Reading, Materials, Classroom interaction

Country of research: United Kingdom

Learners' background: United Kingdom

Yoo, I-Y. 2008. *English for Korean Postgraduate Engineering Students in the Global Academic Community: Perceptions of the Importance of English, Skills-based Needs and Sociocultural Behaviours.*

Supervisor(s): Catherine Wallace

Awarding institution: Institute of Education, University of London

Summary: The study offers a needs analysis of tertiary-level ESP education in Korea and the UK, by comparing two EAP settings: a Korean Institute of Engineering in Korea and a comparable institutional setting in London.

Descriptor(s): Writing, Speaking, Cultural issues, Reading, Listening, ESP

Country of research: Korea, Republic of (South Korea)

Learners' background: Korea, Republic of (South Korea)

King's College London (Department of Education and Professional Studies)

Andon, N. 2008. *What Roles Do Theory and Research Play in Language Teaching? A Case Study on the Task-based Approach in Language Teaching.*

Supervisor(s): Constant Leung and Brian Street

Awarding institution: King's College London

Summary: Task-based language teaching as an approach to English language teaching and learning is explored in this thesis in the form of a case study, in order to examine the ways that language teachers make use of theory and research presented to them in the professional literature and on training courses.

Descriptor(s): Teacher education, Teacher cognition, Methodology, Curriculum/syllabus

Country of research: United Kingdom

Learners' background: various

Institutional level: adult

Cogo, A. 2007. *Intercultural Communication in English as a Lingua Franca. A Case Study.*

Supervisor(s): Jennifer Jenkins and Constant Leung

Awarding institution: King's College London

Dewey, M. 2007. *English as a Lingua Franca: An Empirical Study of Innovation in Lexis and Grammar.*

Supervisor(s): J. Jenkins and C. Leung

Awarding institution: University of London

Summary: This thesis deals with international spread of English. It provides analysis of a corpus of spoken interactions in English as lingua franca settings, the primary aim of which is systematic and detailed descriptions of innovative lexicogrammatical features occurring in ELF communication. The discussion also considers the likely pedagogical implications of these findings.

Descriptor(s): Teacher education, Methodology, Materials, English language

Country of research: United Kingdom

Lancaster University (Linguistics and English Language)

Al-Zadjali, R. 2008. *The Integrated Assessment of Reading and Writing: Investigating Test Products and Processes in an EFL Context.*

Supervisor(s): J.C. Alderson

Awarding institution: Lancaster University

Descriptor(s): Writing, Reading, English language, Assessment

Cheng, X. 2006. *Investigating Chinese Students' Academic Reading Practices in a UK University.*

Supervisor(s): A. Waters

Awarding institution: Lancaster University

Summary: This study used a 'new literacies' and 'activity theory' framework to investigate factors affecting Chinese students approaches to reading academic texts in their subject areas (Management Studies and Educational Research).

Descriptor(s): ESP, Cultural issues, Reading

Country of research: United Kingdom

Learners' background: China

Institutional level: tertiary

Cutrim-Schmid, E. 2005. *An Investigation of the Use of of Interactive Whiteboard Technology in the Language Classroom.*

Supervisor(s): A. Waters

Awarding institution: Lancaster University

Summary: Study of effects on learning of interactive whiteboard (including the ACTIVote component), in conjunction with mixed-nationality groups of summer EAP programme students, and using a 'critical theory of technology framework'.

Descriptor(s): Methodology, Materials, Learning technologies, Classroom interaction

Country of research: United Kingdom

Glover, P. 2006. *Examination Influences on How Teachers Teach: A Study of Teacher Talk.*

Supervisor(s): D. Wall

Awarding institution: Lancaster University

Descriptor(s): Methodology, English language, Classroom interaction, Assessment

Country of research: Hungary

Learners' background: Hungary

Institutional level: secondary

Green, W. 2008. *The Cognitions and Practices of Tertiary-Level Japanese Teachers of EFL.*

Supervisor(s): A. Waters

Awarding institution: Lancaster University

Summary: Study of teaching methods of several Japanese teachers of EFL in a

college setting in Japan, in terms of rationales for and influence on them of a number of factors. Uses and extends Borg's model of teacher cognition.

Descriptor(s): Teacher cognition

Country of research: Japan

Learners' background: Japan

Institutional level: tertiary

Keranen, N. 2008. *A Multi-Theoretical Approach to Investigating Research Engagement by University ELT Staff.*

Supervisor(s): A. Waters

Awarding institution: Lancaster University

Summary: Uses Ajzen's 'Theory of Planned Behaviour' and the concept of the 'Matthew effect' to throw light on why some among the sample of tertiary level language teachers in Mexico who were studied were research active while others were not.

Descriptor(s): Writing, Teacher education, Teacher cognition

Country of research: Mexico

Institutional level: tertiary

Lee, K.W. 2007. *ESL Teacher Development and Curriculum Innovation: The Case of the Malaysian SMART School Project.*

Supervisor(s): A. Waters

Awarding institution: Lancaster University

Summary: Investigation into implementation problems associated with the Malaysian SMART school curriculum, especially its teacher development component, informed by Hall and Hord's 'Levels of Implementation' and Adey's 'professional development' models.

Descriptor(s): Teacher education, Management/Innovation, Curriculum/syllabus

Country of research: Malaysia

Institutional level: secondary

Mercer, S. 2008. *Investigating Learner Self-Concept.*

Supervisor(s): A. Waters

Awarding institution: Lancaster University

Summary: Using data generated by a number of groups of BA TEFL students at an Austrian university, a case is made for paying a good deal more attention to the notion of self-concept in applied linguistics/ELT, and a new, more organic and less hierarchical model for the investigation of language learner self-concept is proposed.

Descriptor(s): Learner cognition, Learner autonomy/strategies

Country of research: Austria

Learners' background: Austria

Institutional level: tertiary

Oak, H. 2008. *Exploring EFL Reading Instruction in High School Classrooms in Korea: The Pedagogic Life of the Grammar Translation Method.*

Supervisor(s): J.C. Alderson

Awarding institution: Lancaster University

Descriptor(s): Methodology, Reading, English language

Papageorgiou, S. 2007. *Setting Standards in Europe: The Judges' Contribution to Relating Language Examinations to the Common European Framework of Reference.*

Supervisor(s): J.C. Alderson

Awarding institution: Lancaster University

Descriptor(s): Assessment

Tsagari, C. 2006. *Investigating the Washback Effect of a High-Stakes EFL Exam in the Greek Context: Participants' Perceptions, Material Design and Classroom Applications.*

Supervisor(s): J.C. Alderson

Awarding institution: Lancaster University

Descriptor(s): English language, Assessment

Van Moere, A. 2007. *Group Oral Tests: How Does Task Affect Candidate Performance and Test Scores?*

Supervisor(s): J.C. Alderson

Awarding institution: Lancaster University

Descriptor(s): Speaking, Assessment

Leeds Metropolitan University

Van Ginkel, A. 2007. *Towards a Methodology for Transfer Reading.*

Supervisor(s): I. Timmis

Awarding institution: Leeds Metropolitan University

Summary: This thesis proposed a framework for transferring reading from the language of wider communication to the mother tongue based on the author's research with the Sabaot people in Kenya.

Descriptor(s): Cultural issues, Reading, Methodology

Newcastle University (School of Education, Communication and Language Sciences)

Al-Nouh, N. 2008. *Primary English in Kuwait.*

Supervisor(s): M. Young-Scholten and F. Myles

Awarding institution: Newcastle University

Descriptor(s): Curriculum/syllabus

Institutional level: primary

Queen's University, Belfast (School of Education)

Li, L. 2008. *EFL Teachers' Beliefs about ICT Integration in Chinese Secondary Schools.*

Supervisor(s): Tony Gallagher

Awarding institution: Queen's University, Belfast

Descriptor(s): Teacher education, Learner autonomy/strategies

University of Bath (Department of Education)

Spiro, J. 2008. *How I have Arrived at a Notion of Knowledge Transformation, through Understanding the Story of Myself as Creative Writer, Educator, Manager, and Educational Researcher.*

Supervisor(s): Jack Whitehead

Awarding institution: University of Bath

Summary: The thesis explores the meaning and practice of 'creativity' across a number of roles, including the creative writer, and the English language educator. It considers the way these roles can inform one another, and offers case studies of 'creative' learning in practice: including its role in materials development and assessment.

www.actionresearch.net/living/janespirophd.s
html

Descriptor(s): Writing, Reading, Materials, English language, Assessment

Country of research: various; Learners' background: various; Institutional level: adult

University of Birmingham (Centre for English Language Studies and Department of English)

Brauer, H. 2008. *Evaluation of a Short Study Abroad Language Programme.*

Supervisor(s): Chris Kennedy

Awarding institution: Centre for English Language Studies, University of Birmingham

Descriptor(s): Curriculum/syllabus, Assessment

Country of research: Japan

Learners' background: Japan

Institutional level: secondary

Connerty, M. 2008. *Variation in Academic Writing among Generation 1.5 Learners, Native Speaker Learners and ESL Learners.*

Supervisor(s): Susan Hunston

Awarding institution:
University of Birmingham

Summary: The thesis is a corpus study of three cohorts of students. Its aim is to characterise the writing of generation 1.5 students in the US.

Descriptor(s): Writing, ESOL/EAL

Country of research: United States of America

Learners' background: various

Institutional level: tertiary

Groom, N. 2007. *Phraseology and Epistemology in Humanities Writing.*

Supervisor(s): Susan Hunston

Awarding institution:
University of Birmingham

Summary: The thesis uses identification of statistically salient grammar words as the focus for an investigation of recurrent phraseology in two humanities disciplines (English Literature and History).

Descriptor(s): Writing, ESP

Guo, X-T. 2006. *Verbs in the Written English of Chinese Learners: A Corpus-based Comparison Between Non-native Speakers and Native Speakers.*

Supervisor(s): Susan Hunston

Awarding institution:
University of Birmingham

Summary: The thesis is a study of verb use, comparing a corpus of English essays written by Chinese learners and a corpus of essays written by native speakers.

Descriptor(s): Writing

Country of research: China

Learners' background: China

Institutional level: tertiary

Hayes, D. 2006. *An Exploration of the Lives and Careers of Teachers.*

Supervisor(s): Chris Kennedy

159

Awarding institution: Centre for English Language Studies, University of Birmingham

Descriptor(s): Teacher education

Country of research: Sri Lanka

Kindt, D. 2005. *A Systemic View of Emergent Course Design.*

Supervisor(s): Chris Kennedy

Awarding institution: Centre for English Language Studies, University of Birmingham

Summary: An evaluation of the effects of an innovative methodology on Japanese university students.

Descriptor(s): Methodology, Materials, Learner autonomy/strategies, Curriculum/syllabus

Country of research: Japan

Learners' background: Japan

Institutional level: tertiary

Kojima, H. 2007. *Autonomy, Collaboration and Reflection in EFL Teacher Education in Japan: To What Extent Can Collaboration and Reflection Serve as Strategies to Develop EFL Teacher Trainees' Autonomy in Japan.*

Supervisor(s): Jeannette Littlemore

Awarding institution: University of Birmingham

Summary: This thesis explored the role of teacher autonomy in teacher training contexts in Japan.

Descriptor(s): Teacher education, Teacher cognition, Curriculum/syllabus

Country of research: Japan

Learners' background: Japan

Institutional level: tertiary

Stark, P. 2007. *Social Cohesion in Workplace Meetings.*

Supervisor(s): Chris Kennedy

Awarding institution: Centre for English Language Studies, University of Birmingham

Descriptor(s): English language, Curriculum/syllabus

Suganthi Priscilla, J. 2005. *The Writing Process and Writer Identity: Investigating the Influence of Revision on Linguistic and Textual Features of Writer Identity in Dissertations.*

Supervisor(s): Susan Hunston

Awarding institution: University of Birmingham

Summary: The thesis is a study of the changes made during re-drafting of MA theses and the effect of these changes on the construal of writer identity in the theses.

Descriptor(s): Writing, ESP

Country of research: United Kingdom

Learners' background: various

Institutional level: tertiary

University of Birmingham (School of Education)

Abdullah, S.S. 2005. *Constructing Understanding around Text: Investigating Reading as a Social Practice.*

Supervisor(s): D. Martin

Awarding institution: University of Birmingham

Al-Etani, S.Y. 2006. *Investigating Students' Motivation to Learn English as a Foreign Language in a Vocational College in Saudi Arabia.*

Supervisor(s): D. Martin

Awarding institution: University of Birmingham

Bhaowises, C. 2005. *Exploring the Implementation of Educational Change at Classroom Level.*

Supervisor(s): A. Blackledge

Awarding institution: University of Birmingham

Chiu, Y.Y. 2008. *Helping and Hindering? How Educational Leaders Affect the Overseas Student Learning Experience.*

Supervisor(s): Christopher Rhodes

Awarding institution: University of Birmingham

Copland, F. 2007. *Feedback in Pre-service English Language Teacher Training: Discourses of Process and Power.*

Supervisor(s): A. Creese

Awarding institution: University of Birmingham

Country of research: United Kingdom

Learners' background: United Kingdom

English, M. 2005. *A Study of the Relationship Between the form of Pedagogic Practice and the Acquisition of Communicative Competence on the Part of Junior Schoolchildren.*

Supervisor(s): Harry Daniels

Awarding institution: University of Birmingham

Farrugia, M. 2006. *Medium and Message: The Use and Development of an English Mathematics Register in Two Maltese Primary Classrooms.*

Supervisor(s): David Hewitt

Awarding institution: University of Birmingham

Majer, B. 2006. *The Shaping of the Learner Identity of Bilingual Adults During Curriculum Study at an English Further Education College.*

Supervisor(s): A. Creese

Awarding institution: University of Birmingham

Country of research: United Kingdom

Learners' background: United Kingdom

Institutional level: adult

Mariou, E. 2008. *Symbolic Bilingualism and Identity in Pontian Greek Adolescent Girls.*

Supervisor(s): D. Martin

Awarding institution: University of Birmingham

Country of research: Greece

Learners' background: Greece

Institutional level: secondary

Sousa de las Heras, L. 2006. *Discursive Practices and the Construction of Identity of Spanish/English Adolescents in a Spanish/English School in the UK: An Ethnographic Approach.*

Supervisor(s): D. Martin

Awarding institution: University of Birmingham

Institutional level: secondary

University of Bristol (Graduate School of Education)

Afitska, O. 2008. *A Formative Perspective on Language Teaching and Assessment: Supporting Ethnic Minority Children in English Primary Classrooms.*

Supervisor(s): P. Rea-Dickins

Awarding institution: University of Bristol

Alexander, C. 2006. *Teachers Online: A Case Study of English Language Teaching Using the Internet.*

Supervisor(s): R. Kiely

Awarding institution: University of Bristol

Azahar, Z. 2008. *Mediation in Second Language Learning in an Asynchronous Computer-mediated Communication Environment: A Case Study of ESL Learners' and Teachers' perceptions.*

Supervisor(s): P. Rea-Dickins

Awarding institution: University of Bristol

Barati, H. 2005. *Test-taking Strategies and the Assessment of Reading Skills: An Approach to Construct Validation.*
Supervisor(s): P. Rea-Dickins
Awarding institution: University of Bristol

Cohen, I. 2007. *Classroom Interaction that Promotes EFL Vocabulary Acquisition of Pupils with Specific Learning Difficulties.*
Supervisor(s): P. Rea-Dickins
Awarding institution: University of Bristol

Haines, K. 2008. *The Situated Language Learning of International Students Taking Degree Programmes Taught Through English in the Netherlands.*
Supervisor(s): P. Rea-Dickins
Awarding institution: University of Bristol

Hung, S-M. 2008. *A Case Study on Learners' "Skills of Discovery and Interaction" in Instant Messenger-mediated Intercultural Dialogue between University Students in Taiwan and in UK.*
Supervisor(s): P. Rea-Dickins
Awarding institution: University of Bristol

Knowles, T. 2008. *An Interpretative Study of the Motivation of Language Teachers in a Japanese University.*
Supervisor(s): P. Rea-Dickins
Awarding institution: University of Bristol

Md-Yunus, M. 2008. *Factors Affecting the Use of Information and Communication Technologies (ICT) in Teaching English as a Second language (ESL) in Malaysia as Perceived by ESL Teachers.*
Supervisor(s): Sally Barnes and Pauline Rea-Dickins

Mohamad, M. 2008. *The Malaysian ESL Syllabus Document: A Case Study of its Specifications and Implementation in the Classrooms.*
Supervisor(s): P. Rea-Dickins

and H. Woodfield
Awarding institution: University of Bristol

Scott, C. 2005. *Washback in the UK Primary Context with EAL Learners: Exploratory Case Studies.*
Supervisor(s): P. Rea-Dickins
Awarding institution: University of Bristol

Sheehan, S. 2007. *Self-assessment and the Common European Framework of References for Languages: Learning, Teaching, Assessment. A Case Study of the Implementation of Self-Assessment with Adult Learners of English.*
Supervisor(s): P. Rea-Dickins
Awarding institution: University of Bristol

Sundrarajun, C. 2007. *From Interaction to Presentation: Oral English Skills Development in the Thai University Context.*
Supervisor(s): R. Kiely
Awarding institution: University of Bristol

Woodfield, H. 2005. *Requests in English: ESL Learners and Native Speakers' Responses to Discourse Completion Tasks.*
Supervisor(s): S. Gardner
Awarding institution: University of Bristol

Yin, M. 2005. *A Progressively Focussed Qualitative Study of Teachers' Thinking in English for Academic Purposes (EAP) Classroom Language Assessments.*
Supervisor(s): P. Rea-Dickins
Awarding institution: University of Bristol

Yu, G. 2005. *Towards a Model of Using Summarization Tasks as a Measure of Reading Comprehension.*
Supervisor(s): P. Rea-Dickins
Awarding institution: University of Bristol

Zhao, B. 2008. *Corrective Feedback and Learner Uptake: Focus-on-Form Instruction in Primary School EFL Classrooms in China.*

Supervisor(s): R. Kiely and G. Yu

Awarding institution: University of Bristol

Zhao, H. 2008. *Who Takes the Floor: Peer Assessment and Teacher Assessment? A Longitudinal Comparative Study of Peer- and Teacher-Assessment in a Chinese University EFL Writing Class.*

Supervisor(s): P. Rea-Dickins

Awarding institution: University of Bristol

Country of research: China

Zou, B. 2008. *How Computers are Being Used to Develop Listening and Speaking Skills in TESOL.*

Supervisor(s): Sally Barnes and Pauline Rea-Dickins

Awarding institution: University of Bristol

University of Cambridge ESOL Examinations

Ashton, K. 2008. *Comparing Proficiency Levels in an Assessment Context: The Construct of Reading for Secondary School Learners of German, Japanese and Urdu in England.*

Supervisor(s): E. Esch and N. Jones

Awarding institution: Cambridge University

Descriptor(s): Cultural issues, Reading, Learner cognition, Learner autonomy/ strategies, Curriculum/syllabus, Assessment

Country of research: United Kingdom

Learners' background: various

University of Edinburgh (Institute for Applied Language Studies/Office of Lifelong Learning)

Abadikhah, S. 2008. *The Effect of Collaborative Output Activities on the Learning of English Relative Clauses: An Empirical Study of Mechanical and Meaningful Output.*

Supervisor(s): Tony Lynch and Cathy Benson

Awarding institution: University of Edinburgh

Summary: A study comparing the learning benefits for Iranian learners of English receiving instruction in different types of classroom activity.

Descriptor(s): Methodology, Learner cognition

Irvine, A. 2006. *Extensive Reading and L2 Development: A Study of Hong Kong Secondary Learners of English.*

Supervisor(s): Tony Lynch and Alan Davies

Awarding institution: University of Edinburgh

Descriptor(s): Reading

Moriyama, A. 2007. *A Noticing-promotion Approach and L2 Development: A Study of English Interrogative Acquisition in the Classroom.*

Supervisor(s): Tony Lynch and Cathy Benson

Awarding institution: University of Edinburgh

Summary: A classroom-based study of Japanese learners of English engaged in paired communication tasks.

Descriptor(s): Speaking, Methodology, Learner cognition

Sudajit-apa, M. 2008. *Systematising EAP Materials Development: Design, Evaluation and Revision in a Thai Undergraduate Reading Course.*

Supervisor(s): Tony Lynch and Eric Glendinning

Awarding institution: University of Edinburgh

Summary: A study of two cycles of materials development, piloting and revision, using learners' and teachers' perceptions of materials use and value to inform the process of revision.

Descriptor(s): Reading, Methodology, Materials

University of Essex (Department of Language and Linguistics)

Angouri, J. 2007. *Language in the Workplace. A Multimethod Study of Communicative Activity in Seven Multinational Companies Situated in Europe.*

Supervisor(s): Nigel Harwood

Awarding institution: University of Essex

Descriptor(s): Writing, Speaking, Cultural issues, ESP, English language

Country of research: various

Lee, D.J. 2007. *Corpora and the Classroom: A Computer-aided Error Analysis of Korean Students' Writing and the Design and Evaluation of Data-driven Learning Materials.*

Supervisor(s): Nigel Harwood

Awarding institution: University of Essex

Descriptor(s): Writing, Materials, Learning technologies, English language, Curriculum/syllabus

Country of research: Korea, Republic of (South Korea);

Institutional level: secondary

University of Leicester (English Language Teaching and Applied Linguistics, School of Education)

Akhras, C.A. 2005. *Simulating Job Interviews: A Pedagogic Process in the Eyes of the Students, Interviewer and Educator.*

Supervisor(s): A. Svalberg

Awarding institution: University of Leicester

Descriptor(s): Methodology

Country of research: Lebanon

Learners' background: Lebanon

Institutional level: tertiary

Al-Mutairi, N. 2007. *The Influence of Educational and Sociocultural Factors on the Learning Styles and Strategies of Female Students in Saudi Arabia.*

Supervisor(s): R.D. Davies

Awarding institution: University of Leicester

Descriptor(s): Learner autonomy/strategies

Country of research: Saudi Arabia

Learners' background: Saudi Arabia

Carmel, R. 2007. *The Trend for English for Young Learners (EYL) in Grades 1 and 2 in Israel: A Critical Discourse Analysis.*

Supervisor(s): S. Gieve

Awarding institution: University of Leicester

Descriptor(s): Curriculum/syllabus

Country of research: Israel

Learners' background: Israel

Institutional level: primary

Chia. S.C.C. 2006. *Learner Autonomy: A Case Study on People's Republic of China (PRC) Scholars Studying in a University in Singapore.*

Supervisor(s): S. Gieve

Awarding institution: University of Leicester

Descriptor(s): Learner cognition, Learner autonomy/strategies

Country of research: Singapore

Learners' background: China

Institutional level: tertiary

Chinniah, Y.A. 2006. *Attitudes and Perceptions of Three Secondary Singaporean Students toward the Varieties of Spoken English in Singapore.*

Supervisor(s): S. Gieve

Awarding institution: University of Leicester

Descriptor(s): Learner cognition

Country of research: Singapore

Learners' background: Singapore

Institutional level: secondary

Fujimoto-Adamson, N. 2008. *Team-Teaching: Redefining Partnership in a Japanese Junior High School.*

Supervisor(s): K. Armstrong

Awarding institution: University of Leicester

Descriptor(s): Methodology

Country of research: Japan

Learners' background: Japan

Institutional level: secondary

Horne, B.J. 2008. *Reconciling Individual Communication Desires with Society's Communicative Norms: A Qualitive Study of How Japanese University Students Carry Out Discussions in English.*

Supervisor(s): K. Armstrong

Awarding institution: University of Leicester

Descriptor(s): Classroom interaction

Country of research: Japan

Learners' background: Japan

Institutional level: tertiary

Jebejian, A. 2007. *Changing Ideologies and Extralinguistic Determinants in Language Maintenance and Shift Among Ethnic Diaspora Armenians in Beirut.*

Supervisor(s): A. Svalberg

Awarding institution: University of Leicester

Descriptor(s): Cultural issues

Country of research: Lebanon

Learners' background: Armenia

Keung, M-L.M. 2006. *Re-expressing Cultural Identity: University Students' Perceptions About and Use of Putonghua in Hong Kong.*

Supervisor(s): K. Armstrong

Awarding institution: University of Leicester

Descriptor(s): Cultural issues

Country of research: Hong Kong

Learners' background: Hong Kong

Institutional level: tertiary

Lee, H-H.C 2006. *Cultural Teaching and Learning in EFL: With Specific Reference to Taiwanese Senior High School Class.*

Supervisor(s): R.D. Davies

Awarding institution: University of Leicester

Descriptor(s): Cultural issues

Country of research: Taiwan

Learners' background: Taiwan

Institutional level: secondary

Lee. H.H., 2008. *Information and Communication Technology in Teaching: The Teachers' Perspective.*

Supervisor(s): S. Gieve

Awarding institution: University of Leicester

Descriptor(s): Teacher cognition

Country of research: Singapore

Institutional level: tertiary

Lee, S.L.C. 2005. *History and Current Tends of Teaching Cantonese as a Foreign Language: Investigating Approaches to Teaching and Learning Cantonese.*

Supervisor(s): P.M. Rogerson-Revell

Awarding institution: University of Leicester

Mosbah, G.A. 2008. *Treatment of Classroom Oral Error: A Comparative Study between Native and Non-native Speaking Teachers .*

Supervisor(s): Svalberg A.

Awarding institution: University of Leicester

Descriptor(s): Classroom interaction

Country of research: Lebanon

Nomnian, S.K 2008. *Investigating Identity, Agency and Classroom Engagement of Thai Postgraduate Students in a British University: A Discourse Approach.*

Supervisor(s): J. Norton

Awarding institution: University of Leicester

Descriptor(s): Learner cognition

Country of research: United Kingdom

Learners' background: Thailand

Institutional level: tertiary

Robinson, F.N. 2005. *An Investigation of the Needs of the Providers, the Students and the*

Business Community Regarding Business English Courses.

Supervisor(s): P. Rogerson-Revell

Awarding institution: University of Leicester

Descriptor(s): Curriculum/syllabus

Said Al-Ramahi, A.S.M. 2006. *English for Industrial Security Programs (EIS); A Potential ESP Model for Organisation Employees' Purposes: Implications for the Teaching of English in Saudi ARAMCO.*

Supervisor(s): A. Svalberg

Awarding institution: University of Leicester

Descriptor(s): Curriculum/syllabus

Country of research: Saudi Arabia

Learners' background: Saudi Arabia

Sinno, Z. 2008. *The Impact on Language Learning of Lebanese Students' Attitude towards English in the Context of Globalization and Anti-Americanism.*

Supervisor(s): A. Svalberg

Awarding institution: University of Leicester

Descriptor(s): Learner cognition

Country of research: Lebanon

Learners' background: Lebanon

Institutional level: tertiary

Wang, D. 2006. *Learning Environments and the Use of Vocabulary Learning Strategies: A Case Study of Chinese Learners.*

Supervisor(s): S. Gieve

Awarding institution: University of Leicester

Descriptor(s): Learner autonomy/strategies

Country of research: Singapore

Learners' background: China

Institutional level: secondary

University of Liverpool (School of English)

Kim, C-K. 2006. *Writer–Reader Interaction in Science Popularisations: A Corpus Based*

Cross-cultural Study of Writers' Management of Textual Interaction with Readers in English and Korean Science Popularisation.

Supervisor(s): Geoff Thompson and Carol Marley

Awarding institution: University of Liverpool

Summary: A cross-cultural comparison of discourse choices in science popularisation texts from British and Korean newspapers. The focus is on resources for involving the reader, and on the links between differences in the use of these resources and wider socio-cultural factors.

Descriptor(s): Cultural issues, ESP

Country of research: Korea, Republic of (South Korea)

McLaughlin, S.A. 2006. *Each One of Us Owns a Story. Childhood in the Second Intifada: A Linguistic Analysis of Conflict and Hope.*

Supervisor(s): Geoff Thompson and Sue Thompson

Awarding institution: University of Liverpool

Summary: A linguistic exploration of the ways in which a group of schoolchildren from the West Bank construe their experiences living under Israeli military occupation, and their resulting ideologies. The study analyses the evaluative choices in 160 texts, written and spoken in English by Palestinian males and females, aged 12–18.

Descriptor(s): Cultural issues

Country of research: Israel

Learners' background: Palestinian Territories

Institutional level: secondary

University of Manchester (School of Education)

Andreou, A. 2008. *Teacher Professional Development in an Online Learning Environment: An Action Research Project.*

Supervisor(s): Gary Motteram

Awarding institution:
University of Manchester

Summary: A study into the use of a teacher-created online learning environment for delivering CPD for adult learners in Cyprus.

Descriptor(s): Teacher education, Learning technologies, Curriculum/syllabus

Country of research: Cyprus

Learners' background: Cyprus

Institutional level: adult

Etherington, M.S. 2005. *Student Perceptions of Grammar and its Role Within the UK University English for Academic Purposes Context.*

Supervisor(s): Teresa O'Brien

Awarding institution:
University of Manchester

Descriptor(s): Materials, Learner cognition, Learner autonomy/strategies, ESP, Curriculum/syllabus

Country of research: United Kingdom

Learners' background: various

Institutional level: tertiary

Fritz, T. 2006. *The Acquisition of Stress by Adult Learners of English.*

Supervisor(s): Michael Beaumont

Awarding institution:
University of Manchester

Summary: A study of the acquisition of stress patterns in adult learners of English.

Descriptor(s): Speaking, Pronunciation

Country of research: Austria

Learners' background: various

Institutional level: adult

Kazantzis, I. 2006. *Fundamental Considerations and Strategies in the Process of Designing, Delivering and Evaluating Courses for English for Specific Purposes: The ESPecialists' Perspective.*

Supervisor(s): Richard West

Awarding institution:
University of Manchester

Descriptor(s): ESP, Curriculum/syllabus

Khadrah, S. 2007. *NNS/NNS Interaction During Task-based Synchronous Computer-mediated Communication.*

Supervisor(s): Diane Slaouti and Juup Stelma

Awarding institution:
University of Manchester

Summary: A descriptive study of NNS-NNS interaction in a SCMC environment in a private language centre in Syria. Aims included (a) to explore different aspects of NNS–NNS interaction in task-based SCMC, and (b) to investigate how these aspects were influenced by the characteristics of the SCMC technology employed.

Descriptor(s): Methodology, Learning technologies, Classroom interaction

Country of research: Syria

Learners' background: Syria

Institutional level: adult

Motteram, G. 2007. *Crossing Material Boundaries: A Cultural–Historical Case Study of E-learning Materials Development in China.*

Supervisor(s): Julian Williams

Awarding institution:
University of Manchester

Summary: A study into the informal learning of a community of e-learning practitioners as a part of a large international materials development project for online learning.

Descriptor(s): Teacher education, Cultural issues, Management/innovation, Learning technologies, Curriculum/syllabus

Country of research: China

Learners' background: China

Institutional level: tertiary

Song, J. 2007. *Measuring Korean EFL Learners' Proficiency: A Comparative Analysis of the Spoken and Written English of Korean and British Students.*

Supervisor(s): Steve Jones

Awarding institution:
University of Manchester

Summary: A comparison of the distribution of linguistic features in the spoken and written English of Korean and British university students.

Descriptor(s): Writing, Speaking, English language

Country of research: United Kingdom

Learners' background: various

Institutional level: tertiary

Toledo, G. 2005. *Factors that Influence Implementation of Information and Communication Technology for English as a Foreign Language in a Mexican Educational Context.*

Supervisor(s): Diane Slaouti

Awarding institution:
University of Manchester

Descriptor(s): Materials, Learning technologies, Curriculum/syllabus

Country of research: Mexico

Learners' background: Mexico

Torres, S. 2006. *Towards an Understanding of the Relationship Between Teachers' Beliefs and Their Thinking about the use of Generic Tools in Language Education: Three Case Studies in a Colombian Context.*

Supervisor(s): Diane Slaouti

Awarding institution:
University of Manchester

Descriptor(s): Teacher education, Teacher cognition, Methodology

Country of research: Colombia

Learners' background: Colombia

University of Nottingham (School of Education)

Abdul Rahim, F. 2007. *Expanding the Capacity to Learn Through the ECAM Model of Mediation: Teaching and Learning English and Mathematics as a Second Language in a Malaysian Primary School.*

Supervisor(s): Do Coyle and Philip Hood

Awarding institution:
University of Nottingham

Descriptor(s): Teacher education, Methodology, ESOL/EAL, ESP, Classroom interaction

Country of research: Malaysia

Learners' background: Malaysia

Institutional level: primary

Estradas, M.S. 2007. *Perspectives on Teacher Autonomy: An Investigation into Teacher Autonomy and its Relationship with the Development of Learner Autonomy.*

Supervisor(s): Barbara Sinclair

Awarding institution:
University of Nottingham

Descriptor(s): Learner autonomy/strategies

Country of research: India

Learners' background: various

Institutional level: secondary

Hsu, W-C. 2005. *Representations, Constructs and Practice of Autonomy Via a Learner Training Programme in Taiwan.*

Supervisor(s): Barbara Sinclair

Awarding institution:
University of Nottingham

Descriptor(s): Learner autonomy/strategies

Country of research: Taiwan

Learners' background: Taiwan

Institutional level: secondary

Kao, S-H. 2007. *The Development of Learner Autonomy in Taiwanese Primary School*

Learners of English: A Theoretical Model, Framework and Practice.

Supervisor(s): Barbara Sinclair

Awarding institution:
University of Nottingham

Descriptor(s): Learner autonomy/strategies

Country of research: Taiwan

Learners' background: Taiwan

Institutional level: primary

Savvidou, C.J. 2007. *Developing Storytelling as a Tool for Teacher Learning.*

Supervisor(s): Do Coyle

Awarding institution:
University of Nottingham

Descriptor(s): Teacher education, Teacher cognition, Learning technologies

Country of research: Cyprus

Learners' background: various

Institutional level: tertiary

Wang, T. 2007. *A Learner Support Model for Tertiary Web-based English Language Education in China: Dialogues Between Learner Support System Design, Utilisation and Learning Ecologies.*

Supervisor(s): Charles Crook

Awarding institution:
University of Nottingham

Descriptor(s): Learning technologies

Country of research: China

Learners' background: China

Institutional level: adult

University of Nottingham (School of English Studies)

Ainy, S. 2007. *Use of Literature in Developing Learners' Speaking Skills in Bangladeshi EFL Contexts.*

Supervisor(s): Ronald Carter

Awarding institution:

University of Nottingham

Al-Abbasi, J-A. 2007. *Beliefs and Vocabulary Learning Strategies in Saudi Arabia.*

Supervisor(s): Norbert Schmitt

Descriptor(s): Cultural issues, Learner autonomy/strategies

Learners' background: Saudi Arabia

Al-Homoud, F-A. 2008. *Vocabulary Acquisition via Extensive Input.*

Supervisor(s): Norbert Schmitt

Awarding institution:
University of Nottingham

Descriptor(s): Learner autonomy/strategies

Cheng, H-F. 2006. *Motivational Teaching Practice of Taiwanese English Teachers.*

Supervisor(s): Zoltan Dörnyei

Awarding institution:
University of Nottingham

Descriptor(s): Teacher education, Teacher cognition, Classroom interaction

Learners' background: Taiwan

Dawson, E. 2007. *Emotion Tracking Pedagogy (ETP): A Creative Pedagogy For The Teaching of World Englishes Literature.*

Supervisor(s): John McCrae and Peter Stockwell

Awarding institution:
University of Nottingham

Descriptor(s): Learner cognition, English language

Ding, P. 2008. *The Nature and Impact of Teacher Enthusiasm in Second Language Acquisition.*

Supervisor(s): Zoltan Dörnyei

Descriptor(s): Teacher education, Classroom interaction

Edwards, P. 2006. *Willingness to Communicate among Korean Learners of English.*

Supervisor(s): Zoltan Dörnyei

Awarding institution:
University of Nottingham

Learners' background: Korea, Republic of (South Korea)

Evison, J. 2008. *Turn-openers in Academic Talk: An Exploration of Discourse Responsibility.*

Supervisor(s): Michael McCarthy

Awarding institution:
University of Nottingham

Descriptor(s): Speaking, ESP, English language

Ghenghesh, P. 2005. *The Motivation of Learners of English and Arabic at an International School in Tripoli, Libya.*

Supervisor(s): Zoltan Dörnyei

Awarding institution:
University of Nottingham

Learners' background: Libya

Institutional level: secondary

Gilmore, A. 2008. *Getting Real in the Language Classroom: Developing Japanese Students' Communicative Competence with Authentic Materials.*

Supervisor(s): Ronald Carter and Zoltan Dörnyei

Awarding institution:
University of Nottingham

Descriptor(s): Learner autonomy/strategies, Classroom interaction

Learners' background: Japan

Guilloteaux, M.J. 2007. *Motivating Language Learners: A Classroom-oriented Investigation of Teachers' Motivational Practices and Students' Motivation.*

Supervisor(s): Zoltan Dörnyei

Awarding institution:
University of Nottingham

Descriptor(s): Learner autonomy/strategies, Classroom interaction

Learners' background: Korea, Republic of (South Korea)

Handford, M.J.A. 2007. *The Genre of the Business Meeting: A Corpus-based Study.*

Supervisor(s): Svenja Adolph and Michael McCarthy

Awarding institution:
University of Nottingham

Descriptor(s): ESP, English language

Kubanyiova, M. 2007. *Teacher Development in Action: An Empirically-based Model of Promoting Conceptual Change in In-service Language Teachers in Slovakia.*

Supervisor(s): Zoltan Dörnyei

Awarding institution:
University of Nottingham

Descriptor(s): Teacher education, Teacher cognition

Learners' background: Slovakia

Lumala, P. 2007. *Towards The Reader – Text Interactive Approach to Teaching Imaginative Texts: The Case for the Integrated English Curriculum in Kenya.*

Supervisor(s): Ronald Carter and John McCrae

Awarding institution:
University of Nottingham

Descriptor(s): Reading, Learner cognition, Learner autonomy/strategies

Learners' background: Kenya

Mansor, N. 2006. *Collaborative Learning via Email Discussion: Analyzing the Impact of Students' Interactions and Knowledge Construction on ESL Writing Performance.*

Supervisor(s): Ronald Carter

Awarding institution:
University of Nottingham

Descriptor(s): Writing, Learning technologies, Learner autonomy/strategies

Roberts, P. 2005. *Spoken English as a World Language: International and Intranational Settings.*

Supervisor(s): Ronald Carter and Michael McCarthy

Ryan, S. 2008. *The Ideal L2 Selves of Japanese Learners of English.*

Supervisor(s): Zoltan Dörnyei

Awarding institution:
University of Nottingham

Descriptor(s): Cultural issues, Learner cognition

Learners' background: Japan

Schauer, G. 2005. *Interlanguage Pragmatic Development of German Learners of English: A Longitudinal Multimedia Investigation.*

Supervisor(s): Zoltan Dörnyei and Svenja Adolphs

Awarding institution:
University of Nottingham

Learners' background: Germany

Sheen, Y. 2006. *Corrective Feedback, Individual Differences and the Acquisition of English Articles by Second Language Learners.*

Supervisor(s): Zoltan Dörnyei

Awarding institution:
University of Nottingham

Descriptor(s): Learner autonomy/strategies

Suyansah, S. 2007. *Promoting Critical Reading Practises: An Investigation in English as a Second (ESL) Classroom.*

Supervisor(s): Ronald Carter

Awarding institution:

University of Nottingham

Than, S. 2005. *Teaching Language-based Approaches to Literature in Thailand: An Experimental Study of the Effectiveness of 'Elementary' Stylistic Analysis and Language-based Approaches to Teaching Literature.*

Supervisor(s): Ronald Carter

Tseng, W-T. 2006. *Towards a Self-regulating Model of Vocabulary Learning Motivation: A Structural Equation Modelling Approach.*

Supervisor(s): Norbert Schmitt

Awarding institution:
University of Nottingham

Descriptor(s): Learner autonomy/strategies, English language

Walters, J-M. 2006. *Beyond Exhortation: Teaching ESL/EFL Students to Infer Meaning from Context.*

Supervisor(s): Ronald Carter

Awarding institution:
University of Nottingham

Descriptor(s): Learner cognition, Learner autonomy/strategies

Xu, X-L. 2007. *Construction and Validation of a Vocabulary Learning Strategy Inventory and its Application to Chinese EFL Tertiary Learners.*

Supervisor(s): Norbert Schmitt

Awarding institution:
University of Nottingham

Yasmin, F. 2005. *Predictors of Language Learning Success in Bangladeshi Secondary Educational Institutions.*

Supervisor(s): Zoltan Dörnyei

Awarding institution:
University of Nottingham

Learners' background: Bangladesh

Institutional level: secondary

Yen, A-C. 2007. *Resistance and Reality – A Study of Reactions to Representational Materials in English Teaching in Taiwan.*

Supervisor(s): Ronald Carter and John McCrae

Awarding institution: University of Nottingham

Learners' background: Taiwan

Zahran, K. 2005. *Contact, Acculturation and Fluency: The Case of International Students in the University of Nottingham.*

Supervisor(s): Zoltan Dörnyei

Awarding institution: University of Nottingham

Country of research: United Kingdom

Learners' background: various

Institutional level: tertiary

University of Sheffield (School of English)

Hobbs, V. 2007. *Examining Short-term ELT Teacher Education: An Ethnographic Case Study of Trainees' Experiences.*

Supervisor(s): Gibson Ferguson

Awarding institution: University of Sheffield

Summary: This thesis investigates the beliefs, experiences, behavior, and attitudes of course participants on a Trinity College London TESOL Certificate course. Results demonstrated that the length of the course necessitates a prioritization of practice over theory and a focus on behavioral change at the expense of examination/critique of participants' pre-existing beliefs.

Descriptor(s): Teacher education, Teacher cognition

Country of research: United Kingdom

Institutional level: adult

Lin, H-Y. 2007. *The Cultural Politics of English as a Global Language in Taiwan.*

Supervisor(s): Gibson Ferguson

Awarding institution: University of Sheffield

Descriptor(s): English language

Country of research: Taiwan

Makdid, L. 2007. *An Investigation into the Appropriacy and Feasibility of Communicative Grammar Teaching in the Syrian University Context.*

Supervisor(s): Gibson Ferguson

Awarding institution: University of Sheffield

Descriptor(s): Curriculum/syllabus, Classroom interaction

Papathanasiou, E, 2006. *The Effects of Semantic Clustering in L2 Word Learning.*

Supervisor(s): Gibson Ferguson

Awarding institution: University of Sheffield

Descriptor(s): Curriculum/syllabus

Country of research: Greece

University of Southampton (Modern Languages, School of Humanities)

Du, J. 2008. *Content-based Instruction in Further Education in China.*

Supervisor(s): George Blue

Awarding institution: University of Southampton

Summary: This was an action research study of the introduction of content based English language instruction in an advanced vocational setting in China (legal education)

Descriptor(s): Methodology, Management/Innovation, ESP

Country of research: China

Learners' background: China

Institutional level: tertiary

Kaowiwattanakul, S. 2008. *Deveopment of Critical Thinking in the L2 Literature Classroom in Thai Higher Education :*

Conceptions and Pedagogical Practices.

Supervisor(s): Ros Mitchell

Awarding institution: University of Southampton

Summary: This project was an observational study of English literature education in a Thai university setting, with a focus on the extent and nature of students' criticality development in English-medium education

Descriptor(s): Writing, Teacher cognition, Cultural issues, Methodology, Learner cognition, Classroom interaction, Assessment

Country of research: Thailand

Learners' background: Thailand

Institutional level: tertiary

Kongsak, S. 2008. *World Literature in English as a Means of Cultural Enrichment for Thai University Students.*

Supervisor(s): Christopher Brumfit and Ros Mitchell

Awarding institution: University of Southampton

Summary: This project involved design of a world literature curriculum to be taught through English, appropriate to the needs of English majors in a Thai university setting

Descriptor(s): Cultural issues, Methodology, Curriculum/syllabus

Country of research: Thailand

Learners' background: Thailand

Institutional level: tertiary

Lee, C.N. 2005. *Supporting English Learning in the Family: An Ethnographic Case Study of a Young Korean-English Learner.*

Supervisor(s): Ros Mitchell

Awarding institution: University of Southampton

Summary: This was a longitudinal case study of a Korean L1 child learning English over several months' residence in England.

Interaction with family and peers was analysed using a sociocultural framework.

Descriptor(s): Speaking, Cultural issues, Reading, Listening, ESOL/EAL

Country of research: United Kingdom

Learners' background: Korea, Republic of (South Korea)

Institutional level: primary

Wisniewska, I. 2006. *Parallel Process in Language Teacher Education.*

Supervisor(s): Christopher Brumfit and Michael Grenfell

Awarding institution: University of Southampton

Summary: This thesis was a case study of an ESL teacher education programme in a North American setting which explored the contribution of trainer modelling of instructional processes to trainee development.

Descriptor(s): Teacher education, Methodology, ESOL/EAL

Country of research: United States of America

Learners' background: United States of America

Institutional level: tertiary

Zhao, T. 2007. *An Ethnographic Study of the Intercultural Adaptation Process between Chinese Students and Their British Lecturers and Fellow Students in the UK.*

Supervisor(s): Christopher Brumfit and Michael Grenfell

Awarding institution: University of Southampton

Summary: This was a study of the adaptation of Chinese students to a UK higher education setting, in the context of a postgraduate management programme.

Descriptor(s): Cultural issues, ESP

Country of research: United Kingdom

Learners' background: China

Institutional level: tertiary

University of Warwick (Centre for Applied Linguistics)

Chang, Y.H. 2006. *Group Influences on Individual Learners' Motivation: A Study of Group Dynamics in EFL Classrooms.*

Supervisor(s): Ema Ushioda and Judith Kennedy

Awarding institution: University of Warwick

Summary: A study of group dynamics and its influences on individual learner motivation, using questionnaires and interviews.

Descriptor(s): Learner autonomy/strategies, Learner cognition

Country of research: Taiwan

Learners' background: Taiwan

Institutional level: tertiary

Chuang, F-Y. 2005. *Addressing the Grammar Needs of Chinese EAP Students: An Account of a CALL Materials Development Project.*

Supervisor(s): Hilary Nesi

Awarding institution: University of Warwick

Descriptor(s): Writing, Materials, Learning technologies

Country of research: United Kingdom

Learners' background: China

Institutional level: tertiary

Chung, I-F. 2006. *A Study of English Learning Attitudes and Perceptions among Senior High School Students in Taiwan.*

Supervisor(s): Judith Kennedy and Ema Ushioda

Awarding institution: University of Warwick

Summary: Analyses Taiwanese senior high school students' perceptions of

communicative language teaching, using focus group and questionnaire data.

Descriptor(s): Curriculum/syllabus, Learner cognition, Materials, Methodology

Country of research: Taiwan

Learners' background: Taiwan

Institutional level: secondary

Erdoğan, S. 2005. *Experienced EFL Teachers' Personal Theories of Good Teaching: A PCT-based Investigation.*

Supervisor(s): Judith Kennedy and Julia Khan

Awarding institution: University of Warwick

Descriptor(s): Teacher education, Teacher cognition, Cultural issues, Methodology

Country of research: Turkey

Learners' background: Turkey

Institutional level: secondary

Geary, M.P. 2008. *Constructing Conceptualizations of English Academic Writing within an EFL context: Streams of Influence at a Taiwan University.*

Supervisor(s): Hilary Nesi and Keith Richards

Awarding institution: University of Warwick

Guerra, L. 2005. *Teaching and Learning English as an International Language in Portugal: Policy, Practice and Perceptions.*

Supervisor(s): Julia Khan and Richard Smith

Awarding institution: University of Warwick

Descriptor(s): Cultural issues, English language, Curriculum/syllabus

Country of research: Portugal

Learners' background: Portugal

Institutional level: secondary

Haoucha, M. 2005. *The Effects of a Feedback-based Instruction Programme on Developing EFL Writing and Revision Skills of First Year Moroccan University Students.*

Supervisor(s): Tricia Hedge and Ema Ushioda

Awarding institution: University of Warwick

Summary: Practitioner research on using feedback in a process writing approach in a Moroccan university context.

Descriptor(s): Writing, Methodology

Country of research: Morocco

Learners' background: Morocco

Institutional level: tertiary

Hussin, H. 2006. *Dimensions of Questioning: A Qualitative Study of Current Classroom Practice in Malaysia.*

Supervisor(s): Richard Smith and Sheena Gardner

Awarding institution: University of Warwick

Icmez, S. 2005. *Impact of a Critical Reading Course on High School Students in Turkey.*

Supervisor(s): Sheena Gardner

Awarding institution: University of Warwick

Descriptor(s): Cultural issues, Reading, Curriculum/syllabus

Country of research: Turkey

Learners' background: Turkey

Institutional level: secondary

Jiang, X. 2008. *Constructing Concepts of Learner Autonomy in Language Education in the Chinese Context: A Narrative-based Inquiry into University Students' Conceptions of Successful English Language Learning.*

Supervisor(s): Richard Smith and Shelagh Rixon

Awarding institution: University of Warwick

Khasandi-Telewa, V. 2007. *"English is Must to Us": Languages and Education in Kakuma Refugee Camp.*

Supervisor(s): Sheena Gardner and

Julia Khan

Awarding institution: University of Warwick

Lai, H-Y. 2008. *Learning English as an International Language or Not? A Study of Taiwanese Students' Motivation and Perceptions.*

Supervisor(s): Ema Ushioda and Annamaria Pinter

Awarding institution: University of Warwick

Summary: A survey of Taiwanese university students' motivation for learning English and perceptions of English as an international language, using questionnaire and interviews, including interviews with teachers.

Descriptor(s): English language, Learner cognition

Country of research: Taiwan

Learners' background: Taiwan

Institutional level: tertiary

Li, N. 2007. *Practitioner Research on Task Motivation in a Chinese University Context: Integrating Macro and Micro Perspectives.*

Supervisor(s): Ema Ushioda and Judith Kennedy

Awarding institution: University of Warwick

Summary: A qualitative study of task motivation among Chinese university learners, using an exploratory practice framework.

Descriptor(s): Teacher cognition, Reading, Methodology, Learner cognition, Learner autonomy/strategies

Country of research: China

Learners' background: China

Institutional level: tertiary

Nitta, R. 2007. *The Focus-on-form Effects of Strategic and Online Planning: An Analysis of Japanese Oral Performance and Verbal Protocols.*

Supervisor(s): Sheena Gardner

Awarding institution: University of Warwick

Papioannou, V. 2008. *Teachers' Experiences in a UK International School: The Challenges of Adaptation.*

Supervisor(s): Keith Richards

Awarding institution: University of Warwick

Pramoolsook, I. 2008. *Genre Transfer from Dissertations to Research Articles among Thai Scientists.*

Supervisor(s): Sheena Gardner

Awarding institution: University of Warwick

Raktham, C. 2008. *Cultures and Learner Behaviours: A Qualitative Investigation of a Thai Classroom.*

Supervisor(s): Ema Ushioda and Richard Smith

Awarding institution: University of Warwick

Summary: A qualitative analysis of Thai university students' classroom behaviours in relation, particularly to 'large' versus 'small' culture frameworks.

Descriptor(s): Classroom interaction, Learner cognition, Cultural issues

Country of research: Thailand

Learners' background: Thailand

Institutional level: tertiary

Shamsudin, S. 2008. *English for Specific Purposes. Task-based Synchronous Computer-mediated Communication: Effectiveness in Meeting the Communicative Needs of Computer Science Students.*

Supervisor(s): Hilary Nesi

Sherazi, S.N. 2007. *A Study of Methods of Evaluating CALL Multimedia Materials for Language Learning.*

Supervisor(s): Hilary Nesi and Julia Khan

Awarding institution: University of Warwick

Tante, C.A.A. 2007. *Investigating the Nature of Young Learner Classroom Assessment in an ESL Context: The Case of Cameroon.*

Supervisor(s): Shelagh Rixon and Richard Smith

Awarding institution: University of Warwick

Wang, Q. 2007. *Primary EFL in China: Teachers' Perceptions and Practices with Regard to Learner-Centredness.*

Supervisor(s): Shelagh Rixon and Richard Smith

Awarding institution: University of Warwick

Descriptor(s): Methodology, Management/ innovation, Classroom interaction

Country of research: China

Learners' background: China

Institutional level: primary

Wu, P-C. 2008. *Social Networks, Language Learning and Language School Student Sojourners: A Qualitative Study.*

Supervisor(s): Richard Smith and Ema Ushioda

Awarding institution: University of Warwick

Summary: A qualitative study of language school student sojourners' out-of-class experiences and social interactions, and their impact on language learning behaviours.

Descriptor(s): Cultural issues, Learner cognition, Learner autonomy/strategies

Country of research: United Kingdom

Learners' background: various

Institutional level: adult

Yaacob, A. 2006. *Malaysian Literacy Practices in English: "Big Books", CD-ROMs and the Year 1 Literacy Hour.*

Supervisor(s): Sheena Gardner

Awarding institution: University of Warwick

Descriptor(s): Materials,
Classroom interaction

Yakovchuk, N. 2007. *Plagiarism and
International Students: An Investigation
in the British Higher Education Context.*

Supervisor(s): Richard Smith and Hilary Nesi

Awarding institution: University of Warwick

EXTERNALLY FUNDED PROJECTS

Externally funded projects are ordered below by starting date (to qualify for the directory a project had to have a start date or an end date within the 2005–2008 time frame, hence the presence of some projects which started earlier than 2005). As with other types of entry in the directory, when details of a particular research project were submitted by more than one institution (for example, due to research collaborators being based at different UK institutions), each separate submission has been included since the specific details entered tend to be different. Aside from being externally funded and starting or ending within the 2005-2008 time frame, a further criterion for a project to be included was that details should be provided of a publicly accessible further source of information about the project – for example, a report or article relating to the project and/or a project website. URLs have been checked and are correct at the time of publication of this PDF/paper version of the directory.

2002

H. Nesi and P. Thompson.
April 2002–March 2005. 'Enhancement of the British Academic Spoken English Corpus'

Funding body: Arts and Humanities Research Board (AHRB) RE/AN6806/APN13545

Summary: The BASE corpus consists of 160 lectures and 39 seminars recorded in a variety of university departments. It contains 1,644,942 tokens in total (lectures and seminars). Holdings are distributed equally across four broad disciplinary groups: Arts and Humanities, Life Sciences, Physical Sciences and Social Science.

www.coventry.ac.uk/base

Descriptor(s): Teacher education, Speaking, Listening, ESP, Classroom interaction

Country of research: United Kingdom

Learners' background: various

Institutional level: tertiary

Entered by: Coventry University

Hilary Nesi and Paul Thompson.
2002–2005. 'Enhancement of the British Academic Spoken English Corpus'

Funding body: Arts and Humanities Research Board (AHRB)

Summary: This project (RE/AN6806/APN13545) aimed to develop the BASE corpus of academic speech (with video recordings and transcripts of lectures and seminars across disciplines). The corpus consists of 160 lectures and 40 seminars recorded in a variety of departments at the universities of Warwick and Reading.

www2.warwick.ac.uk/fac/soc/al/research/collect/base

Descriptor(s): Speaking, Listening, ESP

Country of research: United Kingdom

Learners' background: various

Institutional level: tertiary

Entered by: University of Warwick (Centre for Applied Linguistics)

2003

J.C. Alderson. 2003–2005. 'ENLTA: European Network for Language Testing and Assessment'

Funding body: European Commission

Summary: The purpose of this project was to create a network of individual language testers in Europe. The major outcome was the establishment of the European Association for Language Testing and Assessment (EALTA).

www.ling.lancs.ac.uk/groups/ltrg/oldprojects/enlta.htm

Descriptor(s): Teacher education, Assessment

Country of research: various

Entered by: Lancaster University (Linguistics and English Language)

J.C. Alderson. 2003–2007. 'The Dutch CEFR Construct Project'

Funding body: Dutch Ministry of Education

Summary: The aim of this project was to determine whether the Common European Framework of Reference (CEFR) provided adequate guidance for designing language tests. A major outcome was an internet-based grid to ehlp test analysts to examine the relationship between tests of reading and listening and the CEFR.

www.ling.lancs.ac.uk/cefgrid

Descriptor(s): Assessment

Entered by: Lancaster University (Linguistics and English Language)

M. Baynham, C. Roberts, M. Cooke and J. Simpson. 2003–2006. 'ESOL Effective Practice Project'

Funding body: NRDC/ESF

Summary: Project report available online: www.nrdc.org.uk/publications_details.asp?ID=89#

www.personal.leeds.ac.uk/~edujsi/research_projects.htm

Descriptor(s): ESOL/EAL

Entered by: University of Leeds (School of Education)

Joan Cutting. January 2003–January 2006. 'ELSY: Devising a Multimedia Airport Syllabus for Young People who are Unemployed and Under-qualified'

Funding body: European Commission Leonardo Language Competences

Summary: A survey of the language used by unskilled airport workers – security guard, bus driver, fast food worker and ground handler – was used as a basis for designing English Language Teaching materials on CD.

http://ec.europa.eu/education/programmes/socrates/lingua/community/community5.PDF

Descriptor(s): Materials, Learning technologies, ESP, English language

Institutional level: adult

Entered by: University of Edinburgh (School of Education)

Gordon Joyes, Sheena Banks and Trevor Grimshaw. September 2003–December 2008. 'V-ResORT: Virtual Resources for Online Research Training'

Funding body: HEFCE

Summary: The V-ResORT (Virtual Resources for Online Research Training) project team have worked with the higher education research training community to develop online resources for training in research methodology and methods for use by scholars at Masters level, Doctoral level and beyond. The core materials are a set of video interviews in which researchers describe and discuss projects they have conducted.

www.V-resort.ac.uk

Descriptor(s): Teacher education,

Teacher cognition, Learning technologies,
Learner autonomy/strategies

Country of research: United Kingdom

Learners' background: various

Institutional level: tertiary

Entered by: University of Bath
(Department of Education)

2004

D. Wall and T. Horák. September 2004–
March 2006. 'The Impact of Changes in the
TOEFL Examination on Teaching and
Learning in Central and Eastern Europe.
Phase 2, Coping with Change'

Funding body: Educational Testing Service

Summary: The second of a four-phase
investigation of the effect of changes in the
TOEFL examination on classroom practices.
This phase investigated how teachers and
their institutions reacted to news about
changes in the examination, and how this
affected their planning of new preparation
courses.

www.ets.org/portal/site/ets/menuite

Descriptor(s): Management/Innovation,
English language, Curriculum/syllabus,
Assessment

Country of research: various

Learners' background: various

Institutional level: secondary

Entered by: Lancaster University
(Linguistics and English Language)

**H. Nesi, S. Gardner, P. Thompson and
P. Wickens.** 2004–2007. 'An Investigation
of Genres of Assessed Writing in British
Higher Education'

Funding body: Economic and
Social Research Council (ESRC, UK)

Summary: ESRC Project no. 000-23-0800.
See, for example, Gardner, S.F. 2008.
'Mapping Ideational Meaning in a Corpus

of Student Writing' in Jones, C. & Ventola,
E. (eds.) *New Developments in the Study
of Ideational Meaning: From Language
to Multimodality.*

London: Equinox Publishing. For other
publications arising from the project, see:
www.coventry.ac.uk/researchnet/d/536

Descriptor(s): Writing, English language

Country of research: United Kingdom

Learners' background: various

Institutional level: tertiary

Entered by: University of Birmingham
(School of Education)

**H. Nesi, S. Gardner, P. Thompson and
P. Wickens.** November 2004–December
2007. 'An Investigation of Genres of
Assessed Writing in British Higher Education'

Funding body: Economic and Social
Research Council (ESRC) RES-000-23-0800

Summary: The corpus contains 2,761
proficient student assignments (2,897 texts,
6,506,995 words) produced and assessed
as part of university degree coursework,
fairly evenly distributed across 35 university
disciplines and four levels of study. Each text
is placed into one of thirteen genre families,
according to its components and social
purpose.

www.coventry.ac.uk/bawe

Descriptor(s): Writing, ESP,
English language, Assessment

Country of research: United Kingdom

Learners' background: various

Institutional level: tertiary

Entered by: Coventry University

**Hilary Nesi, Sheena Gardner, Paul
Thompson and Paul Wickens.** 2004–2007.
'An Investigation of Genres of Assessed
Writing in British Higher Education'

Funding body: Economic and Social
Research Council (ESRC)

Summary: This project (RES-000-23-0800) was a collaboration between the universities of Warwick, Reading and Oxford Brookes. The project aimed to develop the British Academic Written English (BAWE) corpus and describe the linguistic features of genres of assessed student writing in different disciplines.

www2.warwick.ac.uk/fac/soc/al/research/coll
ect/bawe/

Descriptor(s): Writing, ESP, English language, Assessment

Country of research: United Kingdom

Learners' background: various

Institutional level: tertiary

Entered by: University of Warwick (Centre for Applied Linguistics)

Hilary Nesi, Sheena Gardner, Paul Thompson and Paul Wickens. 2004–2007. 'An Investigation of Genres of Assessed Writing in British Higher Education'

Funding body: Economic and Social Research Council.

Summary: The project created the British Academic Written English corpus as a collaboration between Warwick, Reading and Oxford Brookes universities. The corpus contains 3000 good-standard student assignments (6,506,995 words) across four broad disciplinary areas and at undergraduate and postgraduate levels. The project investigated the characteristics and range of genres across disciplines.

http://www.coventry.ac.uk/researchnet/d/911

Descriptor(s): Writing, ESP, English language

Country of research: United Kingdom

Learners' background: various

Institutional level: tertiary

Entered by: Oxford Brookes University (Westminster Institute of Education)

C. Davison, L. Hamp-Lyons, R. Tang and S. Andrews. September 2004–August 2006. 'School-based Assessment in Secondary English in Hong Kong'

Funding body: Hong Kong Research Grants Council Central Earmarked Research Grant (CERG)
http://sba.edu.hku.hk/new_sba/projects.html

Descriptor(s): Assessment

Entered by: University of Bedfordshire (Centre for Research in English Language Learning and Assessment)

Fei-Yu Chuang. October 2004–October 2005. 'The Effectiveness of Computer-based Materials as a Means of Teaching the English Article System'

Funding body: TIRF (TESOL International Research Foundation) Doctoral Dissertation Grant

Summary: This study aimed to investigate the effect of electronic self-access grammar materials on Chinese undergraduates' mastery of the English article system.

www.tirfonline.org/Chuangproposal.PDF

Descriptor(s): Writing, Materials, ESOL/EAL

Country of research: United Kingdom

Learners' background: China

Institutional level: tertiary

Entered by: University of Warwick (Centre for Applied Linguistics)

2005

Richard Smith. 2005–2007. 'Enhancement of the Warwick ELT Archive, with a Particular Focus on the Work of A.S. Hornby'

Funding body: A.S. Hornby Educational Trust

Summary: Specific outcomes: A comprehensive bibliography of published writings by A.S. Hornby, including many works published in Japan; A unique and comprehensive collection of writings by A.S. Hornby, available in one place for consultation by interested researchers and Hornby scholars or alumni; A secure collection of archival materials relating to A.S. Hornby; A collection of audio recordings by A.S. Hornby (gramophone records, tapes of lectures).

www2.warwick.ac.uk/fac/soc/al/research/coll ect/elt_archive/research_projects/

Descriptor(s): Methodology, English language

Entered by: University of Warwick (Centre for Applied Linguistics)

Gary Motteram. January 2005–June 2007. 'Language Learning with Certified Live Online Trainers'

Funding body: European Commission

Summary: This project involved a total of 23 European partners in 6 countries between 2005 and 2007. The purpose was to develop a training course for experienced language teaching professionals wishing to make use of desktop video and other synchronous and asynchronous tools to teach languages online.

http://lancelotschool.com/index.php?option= com_content&view=article&id=49&Itemid=2

Descriptor(s): Teacher education, Methodology, Learning technologies, Curriculum/syllabus

Country of research: various

Learners' background: various

Institutional level: tertiary

Entered by: University of Manchester (School of Education)

P. Seedhouse and M. Egbert. January 2005–December 2006. 'The Interactional Organisation of the IELTS Speaking Test'

Funding body: British Council IELTS Research Programme

Summary: Describes the interactional organisation of the IELTS Speaking Test in terms of turn-taking, sequence and repair. The study is based on the analysis of transcripts of 137 audio-recorded tests using a Conversation Analysis (CA) methodology. Report of this project available: www.ielts.org/researchers/research/volumes /volume_6.aspx

Descriptor(s): Assessment

Country of research: various

Learners' background: various

Entered by: Newcastle University (School of Education, Communication and Language Sciences)

L. Hamp-Lyons and C. Davison. January 2005–January 2007. 'Longitudinal Study on the School-based Assessment Component of the 2007 HKCE English Language Examination'

Funding body: HKEAA/EMB Hong Kong http://sba.edu.hku.hk/new_sba/projects.html

Descriptor(s): Assessment

Entered by: University of Bedfordshire (Centre for Research in English Language Learning and Assessment)

M. Baynham, C. Roberts, M. Cooke, J. Simpson, K. Ananiadou, J. Callaghan, J. Mcgoldrick and C. Wallace. January 2005–January 2007. 'Effective Teaching and Learning'

Funding body: National Research and Development Centre

Summary: The project investigated the manner in which Adult ESOL classrooms interpreted ways of teaching ESOL in UK classrooms, through a series of in-depth studies of classroom interaction.

www.nrdc.org.uk/publications_details.asp?ID =89

Descriptor(s): ESOL/EAL, English language,

Curriculum/syllabus, Classroom interaction, Assessment

Country of research: United Kingdom

Learners' background: various

Entered by: Institute of Education, London (Department of Learning, Curriculum and Communication)

Pauline Foster and Parvaneh Tavakoli. April 2005–April 2006. 'Effects of Information Grounding and Task Design on Native and Non-native Performance'

Funding body: ESRC (Grant no. RES-000-22-1155)

Summary: This project investigated the effects that different task characteristics could have on native and non-native speakers' performance on oral narrative tasks.

www.esrcsocietytoday.ac.uk/ESRCInfoCentre/ Plain_English_Summaries/knowledge_comm unication_learning/communication_informati on/index91.aspx

Descriptor(s): Speaking, Materials, ESOL/EAL

Country of research: United Kingdom

Learners' background: various

Institutional level: tertiary

Entered by: London Metropolitan University (Faculty of Humanities, Arts, Languages and Education)

Keith Johnson and Sarah Jackson. April 2005–March 2006. 'Exploring the Procedures Used in Non-linguistic Skill Teaching and Assessing their Relevance for Language Teaching'

Funding body: AHRB

Summary: Looks at the teaching procedures used by teachers of skill subjects other than languages, and considers their potential applications within language teaching. See Johnson, K. and Jackson, S. 2006.

'Comparing language teaching and other-skill teaching: has the language teacher anything to learn?'. *System* 34: 532–546.

Descriptor(s): Teacher education, Teacher cognition, Methodology, Materials, Curriculum/syllabus

Country of research: United Kingdom

Learners' background: United Kingdom

Institutional level: tertiary

Entered by: Lancaster University (Linguistics and English Language)

Pauline Foster and Parvaneh Tavakoli. April 2005–March 2006. 'Information Foregrounding in Narrative Tasks for Second Language Classrooms'

Funding body: ESRC

Summary: This study investigated the effect of narrative structure on L1 and L2 performance, finding that complexity of narrative line increased syntactic complexity in both groups, and also that L2 learners in London had a significantly more native-like vocabulary, though they did not have greater syntactic ability.

www.esrcsocietytoday.ac.uk/ESRCInfoCentre/ Plain_English_Summaries/knowledge_comm unication_learning/communication_informati on/index91.aspx

Descriptor(s): Learner cognition, Assessment

Country of research: United Kingdom

Learners' background: various

Institutional level: adult

Entered by: St. Mary's University College, Twickenham, London (School of Communication, Culture and Creative Arts)

Hilary Nesi, Tim Kelly and Ema Ushioda. October 2005–July 2007. 'Chinese University Teacher Training in English (CUTE2)'

Funding body: HEFCE

Summary: e-China UK project with Cambridge, Tsinghua and Warwick universities to help Chinese university academics develop English language skills for purposes of teaching, academic exchange and professional development.

www.echinauk.org/cases2/cute2/research.php

Descriptor(s): Learning technologies, Learner autonomy/strategies, English language

Country of research: China

Learners' background: China

Entered by: University of Warwick (Centre for Applied Linguistics)

L. Hamp-Lyons and C. Davison. November 2005–October 2009. 'Development of Materials for Professional Development Courses for Teachers in Preparation for School-based Assessment Workshops'

Funding body: Hong Kong Examinations and Assessment Authority/Hong Kong Education Bureau

http://sba.edu.hku.hk/new_sba/projects.html

Descriptor(s): Teacher education, Materials, Assessment

Entered by: University of Bedfordshire (Centre for Research in English Language Learning and Assessment)

2006

J. Slaght, S. Brewer, C. Roche, M. Calderwood and D. Schmitt. 2006– .'"Can Do" Project'

Funding body: BALEAP

Summary: The aim of the 'Can Do' project is to compile a list of 'can do' statements, validated by subject teachers and EAP teachers, which can be used for, among other things, final assessment of students at the end of their EAP studies at British universities, prior to beginning academic courses.

www.baleap.org.uk/bids/index.aspx

Descriptor(s): Writing, Speaking, Reading, Pronunciation, Listening, Learner cognition, ESP, English language, Assessment

Country of research: United Kingdom

Institutional level: tertiary

Entered by: University of Reading (Centre for Applied Language Studies)

James Simpson, Melanie Cooke and Mike Baynham. 2006–2007. 'ESOL Placement Practices Project'

Funding body: NRDC/ESF

www.personal.leeds.ac.uk/~edujsi/research_projects.htm

Descriptor(s): ESOL/EAL

Entered by: University of Leeds (School of Education)

R. Kiely, P. Rea-Dickins and J. Clegg. January 2006–December 2009. 'PRO-CLIL: Providing Guidelines for CLIL Implementation in Primary and Pre-primary Education – Evaluation Component'

Funding body: COMENIUS 2.1 Action of the SOCRATES Programme

Summary: This project is an evaluation of the PRO-CLIL project, implemented in four European countries. PRO-CLIL aims to increase young children's exposure to foreign languages and to improve the quality of teaching in CLIL classrooms and schools. See: Kiely, R. 2009. Assessment in CLIL.

www.northwestacademy.net/european_projects.php

www.bris.ac.uk/education/research/centres/creole/projects/#proclil

Descriptor(s): Curriculum/syllabus

Country of research: Cyprus

Institutional level: primary

Entered by: University of Bristol (Graduate School of Education)

Alison Wray and Christine Pegg. January 2006–December 2006. 'The Effect of Memorized Learning on the Writing Scores of Chinese IELTS Test-takers'

Funding body: IELTS

Summary: Addressed the assessment of performance in IELTS Academic Writing task 2 when candidates may have reproduced lengthy memorised chunks of text that potentially disguise their true proficiency. Demonstrated a simple technique to assess the impact of memorised material without assuming it is necessarily wrong to memorise. A report is published in *IELTS Reports*, Volume 9 (2009): 191–216, www.ielts.org/researchers/research/volumes. aspx

Descriptor(s): Writing, Learner autonomy/strategies, Assessment

Country of research: United Kingdom

Learners' background: China

Institutional level: tertiary

Entered by: Cardiff University (School of English, Communication and Philosophy)

R. Kiely. January 2006–March 2008. 'SAIL: Socialisation and Identity in Learning in Applied Linguistics'

Funding body: LTSN, HEFCE/HEA (LLAS)

Summary: A study of learning processes within a one-year masters programme in a UK university, focussing on English language and academic literacy skills, and drawing on socialisation and identity theory.

www.bris.ac.uk/education/research/centres/ creole/projects/#sail

Descriptor(s): Writing, Cultural issues, Materials, ESP

Country of research: United Kingdom

Learners' background: various

Institutional level: tertiary

Entered by: University of Bristol (Graduate School of Education)

John Field. January 2006–December 2006. 'The Cognitive Validity of the Lecture-based Question in the IELTS Listening Test'

Funding body: The British Council

Summary: Investigation of extent to which the cognitive processes elicited by the IELTS listening test correspond to the processes employed in a real-life lecture listening situation. See Field, J. 2009. 'A cognitive validation of the lecture-listening component of the IELTS listening paper'. *IELTS Research Reports* Vol. 9.

www.ielts.org/researchers/research/volumes. aspx

Descriptor(s): Listening

Country of research: United Kingdom

Learners' background: various

Institutional level: tertiary

Entered by: University of Reading (Department of Applied Linguistics)

C. Davison, L. Hamp-Lyons, C. Leung and S. Andrews. January 2006–January 2008. 'The Use of Summative Oral School-based Assessment for Formative Purposes in Secondary ESL in Hong Kong'

Funding body: Hong Kong Research Grants Council Central Earmarked Research Grant (CERG)

http://sba.edu.hku.hk/new_sba/projects.html

Descriptor(s): Speaking, Assessment

Entered by: University of Bedfordshire (Centre for Research in English Language Learning and Assessment)

A. Creese, T. Barac, A. Bhatt, A.J. Blackledge, S. Hamid, V. Lytra, P. Martin, W.L. Wei and G. Yagcioglu-Ali. March 2006–August 2007. 'Multilingualism in Complementary Schools in Four Linguistic Communities'

Funding body: ESRC

Summary: ESRC project number RES-000-23-1180

www.education.bham.ac.uk/research/project s1/esrc5/index.shtml

Entered by: University of Birmingham (School of Education)

D. Wall and T. Horák. March 2006–March 2008. 'The Impact of Changes in the TOEFL Examination on Teaching and Learning in Central and Eastern Europe. Phase 3, The Role of the Coursebook, and Phase 4, Describing Change'

Funding body: Educational Testing Service

Summary: Third and fourth phases of an investigation into the effects of changes in the TOEFL examination on classroom teaching. The third phase analysed TOEFL preparation coursebooks and their influence on teachers. The fourth phase investigated how TOEFL classrooms were managed in the period following the introduction of the new examination. Report in press.

www.ling.lancs.ac.uk/groups/ltrg/oldprojects/ toeflimpact2.htm

Descriptor(s): Management/Innovation, English language, Curriculum/syllabus, Assessment

Country of research: various

Learners' background: various

Institutional level: adult

Entered by: Lancaster University (Linguistics and English Language)

S. Andrews, C. Davison and L. Hamp-Lyons. August 2006–July 2008.

'Aligning Assessment with Curriculum Reform in Junior Secondary English Language Teaching'

Funding body: Hong Kong Quality Education Fund

http://sba.edu.hku.hk/new_sba/projects.html

Descriptor(s): Curriculum/syllabus, Assessment

Entered by: University of Bedfordshire (Centre for Research in English Language Learning and Assessment)

Trevor Grimshaw. September 2006–December 2007. 'Chinese Learners' Perceptions and Constructions of British Academic Culture'

Funding body: British Academy

Summary: This project was designed to explore Chinese-speaking students' experiences of life at a British university, focusing on their views of the host academic culture and the extent to which their expectations were met. See: Grimshaw, T. 2007. 'Problematizing the construct of "the Chinese Learner": insights from ethnographic research'. *Educational Studies* 33/3: 299–311.

Descriptor(s): Cultural issues, ESP, English language

Country of research: United Kingdom

Learners' background: China

Institutional level: tertiary

Entered by: University of Bath (Department of Education)

Michael Hoey, Michaela Mahlberg and Mike Scott. September 2006–August 2008. 'The Textual Priming of Hard News Stories'

Funding body: AHRC

Summary: A study of the way lexical choices correlate with text beginnings and paragraph boundaries, as predicted by lexical priming theory. It was found that there was a strong correlation between the use of certain words and clusters and certain structuring choices. This has implications for the way paragraphing ought to be taught.

www.ahrc.ac.uk/FundedResearch/Pages/Res earchDetail.aspx?id=119390

Descriptor(s): Writing, English language

Country of research: United Kingdom

Institutional level: adult

Entered by: University of Liverpool (School of English)

S. Andrews, L. Hamp-Lyons, L-Y. Cheng and C. Davison. September 2006–August 2009. 'An Impact Study of a High-stakes ESL Assessment Innovation in Hong Kong Secondary Schools'

Funding body: Hong Kong Research Grants Council Central Earmarked Research Grant (CERG)

http://sba.edu.hku.hk/new_sba/projects.html

Descriptor(s): Assessment

Entered by: University of Bedfordshire (Centre for Research in English Language Learning and Assessment)

J.C. Alderson, R. Al-Zadjali, J. Banerjee, T. Horák, S. Papageorgiou and A. Van Moere. 2006 - 2007. 'ELPACS - The Validation of a Test of English for Air Traffic Controllers'

Funding body: Eurocontrol

Summary: This project was commissioned by Eurocontrol to provide an external evaluation of their new test of English Language Proficiency for Aeronautical Communication (ELPAC)

http://elpac.info/index.php?option=com_con tent&task=view&id=50&Itemid=42

Descriptor(s): Speaking, Listening, ESP, Assessment

2007

Melinda Whong and Judith Hanks. January 2007–January 2008. 'An Active Awareness Approach to In-sessional English Teaching'

Funding body: Languages, Linguistics and Area Studies in Higher Education

Summary: This project developed an In-sessional English programme based on existing theories of language learning and linguistics. Active awareness develops the intuition underlying Focus on Form through the discovery of constructions appropriate for academic writing in a course called Reading for Writing.

www.llas.ac.uk/resourcedownloads/2631/Wh ong.PDF

Descriptor(s): Writing, Reading, Materials, Learner autonomy/strategies, English language, Curriculum/syllabus

Country of research: United Kingdom

Learners' background: various

Institutional level: tertiary

Entered by: University of Leeds (Department of Linguistics and Phonetics)

Marina Orsini-Jones, David Jones and Christine Sinclair (Strathclyde). January 2007–April 2008. 'Grammar: Researching Activities for Student Progress'

Funding body: Subject Centre for Languages, Linguistics and Area Studies (LLAS)

Summary: A team formed by language lecturers, instructional designers and a lecturer in linguistics aimed at identifying the grammar 'stumbling blocks' encountered by students when engaging with learning to learn languages and design a task that would help students overcome them.

www.llas.ac.uk/resourcedownloads/2631/orsi nijones.PDF

Descriptor(s): Learning technologies, Learner autonomy/strategies, English language, Curriculum/syllabus, Assessment

Country of research: United Kingdom

Learners' background: various

Institutional level: tertiary

Entered by: Coventry University

Diane Slaouti, Gary Motteram and Zeynep Onat-Stelma. January 2007–January 2009. 'A Worldwide Investigation of EFL Teacher Use of Technology for Adult Language Learning'

Funding body: Cambridge University Press

http://edtechandtesol.info/wp/?page_id=92

Descriptor(s): Methodology, Learning technologies, Curriculum/syllabus

Country of research: various

Learners' background: various

Institutional level: adult

Entered by: University of Manchester (School of Education)

R.A. Hawkey and C.J. Weir. January 2007–January 2008. 'Language, Study Skill and Related Issues Facing International Students in the First Year of their MPhil/PhD Studies: Relevance to Institutional Language, Academic and Other Support Services'

Funding body: Pedagogical Research Fund for Languages, Linguistics and Area Studies

www.llas.ac.uk/resourcedownloads/2631/hawkey.PDF

Descriptor(s): Learner autonomy/strategies

Entered by: University of Bedfordshire (Centre for Research in English Language Learning and Assessment)

A.B. Green, R.A. Hawkey and C.J. Weir. January 2007–January 2008. 'Discourse Level Functional Progression at the C Level of the CEFR'

Funding body: the English Profile Project

Summary: A review of the place of language functions in English language learning and their use in materials for English language teaching and assessment.

www.cambridgeesol.org/rs_notes/offprints/pdfs/RN33p19-25.PDF

Descriptor(s): English language

Entered by: University of Bedfordshire (Centre for Research in English Language Learning and Assessment)

A.B. Green, A. Unaldi and C.J. Weir. January 2007–January 2008. 'The Cognitive Processes of Second Language Academic Readers'

Funding body: Pedagogical Research Fund for Languages, Linguistics and Area Studies in Higher Education

www.llas.ac.uk/resourcedownloads/2631/weir.PDF

Descriptor(s): Reading, Assessment

Entered by: University of Bedfordshire (Centre for Research in English Language Learning and Assessment)

J. Kormos. January 2007–Jannuary 2010. 'Equal Rights in Foreign Language Learning'

Funding body: Nemzeti Kutatási és Technológiai Hivatal (National Bureau for Research and Development) Hungary

Summary: The research project investigated the learning processes of dyslexic and Deaf students and surveyed the teaching methods that prove to be useful in helping these learners successfully acquire a foreign language.

http://esely.elte.hu

Country of research: Hungary

Learners' background: Hungary

Entered by: Lancaster University (Linguistics and English Language)

Martha Young-Scholten. February 2007–July 2009. 'Setting Language Acquisition Research to Music'

Funding body: Aimhigher Tyne and Wear

Summary: Development of two pieces of choral music to illustrate how children perceive English during their first year of life and how they develop oral production.

www.ncl.ac.uk/elll/news/item?young-ears-young-tongues-concert-at-the-sage-copy

Descriptor(s): English language

Country of research: United Kingdom

Institutional level: pre-primary

Entered by: Newcastle University (School of Education, Communication and Language Sciences)

Joan Swann, Ronald Carter and Rob Pope. March 2007–September 2007. 'Transitions and Transformations: Exploring Creativity in Everyday and Literary Language'

Funding body: AHRC

Summary: This project brought together researchers, teachers and writers to explore the meaning and practice of creativity in literary and non-literary texts. Themes included: Creativities (texts in context, genres in practice); Creativity across modes (media and technologies); Creative interpretations (audience responses, reading and rewriting).

http://creet.open.ac.uk/seminars/transitions-and-transformations/index.cfm

Descriptor(s): Writing, Cultural issues, Reading, English language

Country of research: United Kingdom

Institutional level: tertiary

Entered by: Oxford Brookes University (Westminster Institute of Education)

P. Rea-Dickins and G. Yu. June 2007–December 2010. 'SPINE: Student Performance in National Examinations – the Dynamics of Language Factor'

Funding body: ESRC/DfID

Summary: This three-year project investigates the impact of the language of examinations and media of instruction in secondary schools on examination performance. The research is taking place in Zanzibar where, as in many schools in sub-Saharan Africa, learners are acquiring subject knowledge and understanding through a language that is not their first language. See: Rea-Dickins, P., G. Yu and O Afitska. 2009. 'The consequences of examining through an unfamiliar language of instruction and its impact for school-age learners in sub-Saharan African school systems' in L. Taylor and C. Weir (eds.) *Language Testing Matters: the social and educational impact of language assessment.* Cambridge: Cambridge University Press.

www.bristol.ac.uk/spine

Descriptor(s): Methodology, ESOL/EAL, Classroom interaction, Assessment

Country of research: Tanzania

Learners' background: Tanzania

Institutional level: secondary

Entered by: University of Bristol (Graduate School of Education)

North West Academy of English (UK), IAL Piemonte (Italy), Tampere College (Finland), ROC MB College (Netherlands) June 2007–February 2009. 'Developing Expertise in the EU'

Funding body: Leonardo da Vinci (EU)

Summary: The project focused on the topic of Migrant Integration. The main objective was to support improvements in quality and innovation in education/training systems. The aim was to compare examples of good practices implemented in Northern Ireland, Italy, Finland and the Netherlands.

www.northwestacademy.net/european_projects.php

Descriptor(s): Cultural issues, English language

Country of research: various

Learners' background: various

Entered by: North West Academy of English

Sally Mitchell and James Taylor. September 2007–December 2008. 'Cross-institutional Implementation and Evaluation of Digital Dialogue Games for Inclusive and Personalised Learning (INTERLOC)'

Funding body: JISC

Summary: The project, with the Learning Technology Research Institute (LTRI) at London Metropolitan, developed, implemented and evaluated 'state-of-the-art' software (interloc) and related infrastructure (Openfire, Jabber) to support highly interactive and collaborative learning through synchronous digital dialogue games. It was led by Dr Andrew Ravenscroft of LTRI.

www.interloc.org/funding.htm#deliverables

Descriptor(s): Methodology, Learning technologies, Classroom interaction

Country of research: United Kingdom

Learners' background: various

Institutional level: adult

Entered by: Queen Mary, University of London (Language and Learning Unit)

L. Hamp-Lyons and C. Davison. September 2007–September 2009. 'Continuation of the Longitudinal Study on the School-based Assessment Component of the 2007 HKCE English Language Examination'

Funding body: HKEAA/EMB Hong Kong

http://sba.edu.hku.hk/new_sba/projects.html

Descriptor(s): Assessment

Entered by: University of Bedfordshire (Centre for Research in English Language Learning and Assessment)

James Simpson. October 2007–October 2009. 'Identities Online Project'

Funding body: British Academy

www.personal.leeds.ac.uk/~edujsi/research_projects.htm

Descriptor(s): ESOL/EAL

Entered by: University of Leeds (School of Education)

Janet Enever, Carmen Munoz, Magdalena Szpotowicz, Lucilla Lopriore, Eva Lindgren, Resi Damhuis, Jelena Mihaljevic Djigunovic. December 2007–November 2010. 'Early Language Learning in Europe (ELLiE)'

Funding body: European Commission, Lifelong Learning Programme

Summary: The research aims to clarify what can realistically be achieved through making an early start to foreign/second language learning in state schools where relatively limited amounts of class time are available for foreign language learning. See website for further details.

www.ellieresearch.eu

Descriptor(s): Teacher education, Speaking, Cultural issues, Reading, Pronunciation, Methodology, Materials, Management/innovation, Listening, Learning technologies, Learner cognition, Learner autonomy/strategies, Curriculum/syllabus, Classroom interaction, Assessment

Country of research: various

Learners' background: various

Institutional level: primary

Entered by: London Metropolitan University (Faculty of Humanities, Arts, Languages and Education)

2008

R. Kiely and M. Davis. January 2008–January 2010. 'InSITE: Integrating Systematic Investigation into Teaching of English'

Funding body: CfBT

Summary: This project is examining the impact on teaching skills of professional development activity based on training in analysis aspects of research skills and episodes from the teachers' own classrooms. In exploring innovative strategies in Continuing Professional Development (CPD), InSITE addresses a policy issue in language teaching, and a theoretical issue in teacher learning: the contribution of research skills and a research perspective to teaching effectiveness.

www.bris.ac.uk/education/research/centres/creole/projects/#insite

Descriptor(s): Teacher education, Methodology, Management/innovation, ESOL/EAL

Country of research: United Kingdom

Learners' background: United Kingdom

Institutional level: adult

Entered by: University of Bristol (Graduate School of Education)

A.B. Green, C.J. Weir and R.A. Hawkey. January 2008–July 2009. 'Testing the English Language Skills of International Students at the Foundation Level'

Funding body: English Language Testing

Summary: Development of a placement test intended for use with English language improvement courses preparatory to academic study through the medium of English.

www.englishlanguagetesting.co.uk/render.aspx?siteID=1&navIDs=1,168

Descriptor(s): Assessment

Entered by: University of Bedfordshire (Centre for Research in English Language Learning and Assessment)

H. Nesi, S. Astley, B. Brick, A. Buick, N. Endacott, S. Harrison, E. Moreton. March 2008–March 2010. 'A Study of Lecturing Styles in Malaysia and the UK'

Funding body: British Council

Summary: The project aims to identify and describe typical lecture discourse features, compare English-medium lecturing styles in Malaysia and the UK, and explore the current role of English-medium instruction in Malaysian HE. This entails developing a small corpus of engineering lectures for use in staff development, lecturer training and EAP instruction.

www.coventry.ac.uk/elc

Descriptor(s): Teacher education, Cultural issues, Listening, ESOL/EAL, ESP, Classroom interaction

Institutional level: tertiary

Entered by: Coventry University

M. Young-Scholten. April 2008–July 2009. 'How do Uneducated L2 Adults Become Readers?'

Funding body: British Academy

Summary: Short-term longitudinal study of the phonological awareness, linguistic competence and reading skills of immigrant adults enrolled in ESOL classes.

www.leslla.org/files/resources/BA2008projectblurbyoung-scholten.PDF

Descriptor(s): Reading

Country of research: United Kingdom

Institutional level: adult

Entered by: Newcastle University (School of Education, Communication and Language Sciences)

G. Yu, P. Rea-Dickins and R. Kiely.
June 2008–December 2009. 'Cog-Pro:
The Cognitive Processes of Taking IELTS
Academic Writing Task One'

Funding body: IELTS and the British Council

Summary: This new research project,
supported by a grant from the British
Council and IELTS Research Fund. The
research aims to understand candidates'
cognitive processes in taking IELTS
Academic Writing Task One (AWT1)
which uses graphs as test input.

www.bris.ac.uk/education/research/centres/
creole/projects/#cogpro

Descriptor(s): Writing, Learner cognition,
Assessment

Country of research: China

Learners' background: China

Institutional level: tertiary

Entered by: University of Bristol
(Graduate School of Education)

Trevor Grimshaw and John Lowe.
October 2008–December 2009.
'Rethinking the Needs of International
Students: Critical Perspectives on the
Internationalisation of UK HE Institutions'

Funding body: ESRC

Summary: This seminar series aims
to challenge cultural stereotypes of
'the international student'; explore the
intercultural experiences of international
students in UK HE; develop new theoretical
understandings of factors impacting
on international students' experiences;
and contribute to the development of UK
HE provision to meet the needs and
challenges of international students.

www.education.bham.ac.uk/research/semina
rs1/esrc/isss.shtml

Descriptor(s): Cultural issues,
Management/innovation, English language

Country of research: United Kingdom

Learners' background: various

Institutional level: tertiary

Entered by: University of Bath
(Department of Education)

Pauline Foster. October 2008–September
2009. 'Native-like Selection in Second
Language Acquisition: The Effects of Age,
Aptitude and Socialisation'

Funding body: ESRC

Summary: The study explores the
development of native-like lexical
intuitions in English by Polish immigrants
to the UK, and by English L2 users in
Poland, comparing these with native
speaker baseline data. The aim is to
illuminate why such intuitions might
fail to develop.

www.smuc.ac.uk/ccca/staff/pauline-foster-
research.htm

Descriptor(s): Learner cognition

Country of research: United Kingdom

Learners' background: Poland

Entered by: St. Mary's University College,
Twickenham, London (School of
Communication, Culture and Creative Arts)

**Helen Casey, Richard Andrews,
Dina Mehmedbegovic, Catherine Wallace
and David Mallows.** October 2008–
September 2010. 'Building a Strategy
for English as an Additional Language
(EAL) for the Teaching Workforce'

Funding body: Training and Development
Agency

Summary: The project aims to work with
TDA to build a coherent and sustainable
strategy for EAL in England. We have
conducted a research review, case studies,
expert interviews and a national survey
as the foundation for the strategy, which

is now out for consultation (May 2009).

www.teachingeal.org.uk/

Descriptor(s): Writing, Teacher education, Cultural issues, Reading, ESOL/EAL, English language, Curriculum/syllabus

Country of research: United Kingdom

Learners' background: various

Entered by: Institute of Education, London (Department of Learning, Curriculum and Communication)

CONTRIBUTING INSTITUTIONS

The following institutions have contributed entries to the directory. All names of departments etc., URLs and contact email addresses are as supplied by the institutions in question. Their accuracy has, wherever possible, been verified at the time of publication of this PDF/paper form of the directory, but there can unfortunately be no guarantee that all details will remain correct, even in the short-term. There can be no guarantee, either, that a particular researcher will continue to be affiliated with the institution named at the foot of each of his/her entries in this directory. However, an online search for name of researcher plus name of institution can often reveal direct and correct contact details when needed.

**Aston University
(School of Languages
and Social Sciences)**
www.aston.ac.uk/lss
Contact: s.garton@aston.ac.uk

**Bangor University
(School of Linguistics
and English Language)**
www.bangor.ac.uk/linguistics
Contact: cah@bangor.ac.uk

**Canterbury Christ Church University
(Department of English
and Language Studies)**
www.canterbury.ac.uk/arts-
humanities/english-language-studies
Contact: language.studies@canterbury.ac.uk

**Cardiff University
(School of English, Communication
and Philosophy)**
www.cardiff.ac.uk/encap
Contact: encap-res@cardiff.ac.uk

Coventry University
www.coventry.ac.uk/elphe
Contact: ELTresearch.bes@coventry.ac.uk

Durham University (Language Centre)
www.dur.ac.uk/lang.centre
Contact: p.b.nathan@durham.ac.uk

**Heriot-Watt University (School of
Management and Languages)**
www.sml.hw.ac.uk/
Contact: enquiries@hw.ac.uk

**Institute of Education, London
(Department of Learning, Curriculum
and Communication)**
www.ioe.ac.uk/study/departments/361.html
Contact: FCP.Enquiries@ioe.ac.uk

**King's College London (Department
of Education and Professional Studies)**
http://kcl.ac.uk/schools/sspp/education
Contact: ldc@kcl.ac.uk

**Lancaster University
(Linguistics and English Language)**
www.ling.lancs.ac.uk
Contact: a.waters@lancaster.ac.uk

Leeds Metropolitan University
www.leedsmet.ac.uk/international/english
Contact:
internationalfacultyresearch@leedsmet.ac.uk

**London Metropolitan University
(Faculty of Humanities, Arts,
Languages and Education)**
www.londonmet.ac.uk/depts/faculty-of-
humanities-arts-languages-and-
education.cfm
Contact: p.tavakoli@londonmet.ac.uk

Middlesex University
(English Language and Learning Support)
www.lr.mdx.ac.uk/ells/index.htm
Contact: ells@mdx.ac.uk

Newcastle University
(School of Education, Communication
and Language Sciences)
www.ncl.ac.uk/ecls
Contact: peter.sercombe@ncl.ac.uk

North West Academy of English
www.northwestacademy.net
Contact: info@northwestacademy.net

Nottingham Trent University
(School of Arts and Humanities)
www.ntu.ac.uk/hum/centres/nlc/index.html
Contact: nlc@ntu.ac.uk

The Open University
(Faculty of Education and Languages)
www.open.ac.uk/education-and-
languages/index.php
Contact: c.l.johns-mackenzie@open.ac.uk

Oxford Brookes University (Westminster
Institute of Education)
www.brookes.ac.uk/wie/about/
Contact: jspiro@brookes.ac.uk

Queen Mary, University of London
(Language and Learning Unit)
www.languageandlearning.qmul.ac.uk
Contact: s.perrin@qmul.ac.uk

Queen's University, Belfast
(School of Education)
www.qub.ac.uk/schools/SchoolofEducation
Contact: c.linse@qub.ac.uk

St. Mary's University College, Twickenham,
London (School of Communication,
Culture and Creative Arts)
www.smuc.ac.uk
Contact: fosterp@smuc.ac.uk

Swansea University
(Department of Applied Linguistics)
www.swan.ac.uk/arts/AppliedLinguistics
Contact: AppliedLinguistics@swansea.ac.uk

University College Plymouth
St Mark & St John (Department
of International Education)
www.marjon.ac.uk/courses/international
Contact: inted@marjon.ac.uk

University of Bath
(Department of Education)
www.bath.ac.uk/education
Contact: education@bath.ac.uk

University of Bedfordshire
(Centre for Research in English
Language Learning and Assessment)
www.beds.ac.uk/research/bmri/crella
Contact: tony.green@beds.ac.uk

University of Birmingham
(Centre for English Language Studies
and Department of English)
www.english.bham.ac.uk
www.cels.bham.ac.uk
Contact: cels@bham.ac.uk

University of Birmingham
(School of Education)
www.education.bham.ac.uk/index.shtml
Contact: education@bham.ac.uk

University of Brighton
(School of Humanities)
http://arts.brighton.ac.uk//
Contact: a.pickering@bton.ac.uk

University of Bristol
(Graduate School of Education)
www.bris.ac.uk/education/research/centres/
creole
Contact: R.Kiely@bris.ac.uk

University of Cambridge
ESOL Examinations
www.cambridgeesol.org/what-we-do
Contact: validation@cambridgeesol.org

University of East London
(Cass School of Education)
www.uel.ac.uk/education
Contact: j.gray@uel.ac.uk

University of Edinburgh
(Institute for Applied Language
Studies/Office of Lifelong Learning)
www.ials.ed.ac.uk
Contact: ials.enquiries@ed.ac.uk

University of Edinburgh
(School of Education)
www.education.ed.ac.uk
Contact: joan.cutting@ed.ac.uk

University of Essex (Department of
Language and Linguistics)
www.essex.ac.uk/linguistics/
Contact: nharwood@essex.ac.uk

University of Exeter
(School of Education
and Lifelong Learning)
http://education.exeter.ac.uk
Contact: d.a.myhill@ex.ac.uk

University of Glasgow
(Language and Literature,
Faculty of Education)
www.gla.ac.uk/departments/curriculumstudie
s/subjectareas/languageandliterature
Contact: c.rodgers@educ.gla.ac.uk

University of Leeds
(Department of Linguistics and Phonetics)
www.leeds.ac.uk/linguistics
Contact: linguistics@leeds.ac.uk

University of Leeds (School of Education)
www.education.leeds.ac.uk
Contact: not supplied

University of Leeds
(The Language Centre)
www.leeds.ac.uk/languages/lc_home.html
Contact: langc@leeds.ac.uk

University of Leicester
(English Language Teaching and Applied
Linguistics, School of Education)
www.le.ac.uk/se/
Contact: soed@le.ac.uk

University of Liverpool (School of English)
www.liv.ac.uk/english
Contact: english@liv.ac.uk

University of Manchester
(School of Education)
www.education.manchester.ac.uk
Contact: Juup.Stelma@manchester.ac.uk

University of Northumbria
(Department of Humanities,
School of Arts and Social Sciences)
www.northumbria.ac.uk/sd/academic/sass/
about/humanities/englishhome/
Contact: az.dasc@northumbria.ac.uk

University of Nottingham
(School of Education)
www.nottingham.ac.uk/education
Contact:
education.enquiries@nottingham.ac.uk

University of Nottingham
(School of English Studies)
www.nottingham.ac.uk/english/research/cral
Contact: Svenja.Adolphs@nottingham.ac.uk)

University of Oxford
(Department of Education)
www.education.ox.ac.uk
Contact:
general.enquiries@education.ox.ac.uk

University of Oxford
(Language Centre)
www.lang.ox.ac.uk
Contact: admin@lang.ox.ac.uk

University of Portsmouth
(School of Languages and Area Studies)
www.port.ac.uk/departments/academic/slas
Contact: Tricia.Coverdale-Jones@port.ac.uk

University of Reading
(Centre for Applied Language Studies)
www.cals.rdg.ac.uk/index.asp
Contact: eap.cals@reading.ac.uk

University of Reading
(Department of Applied Linguistics)
www.reading.ac.uk/app_ling
Contact: app_ling@reading.ac.uk

University of Salford
(School of Languages)
www.languages.salford.ac.uk
Contact: h.a.jarvis@salford.ac.uk

University of Sheffield
(School of English)
www.shef.ac.uk/english/
Contact: g.r.ferguson@sheffield.ac.uk

University of Southampton
(Modern Languages,
School of Humanities)
www.soton.ac.uk/ml
Contact: j.jenkins@soton.ac.uk

University of Sussex
(The Sussex Language Institute)
www.sussex.ac.uk/languages
Contact: efl@sussex.ac.uk

University of Warwick
(Centre for Applied Linguistics)
www.warwick.ac.uk/al
Contact: appling@warwick.ac.uk

University of West of England
(School of Humanities,
Languages and Social Sciences)
www.uwe.ac.uk/hlss
Contact: Michael.Daller@uwe.ac.uk

University of Westminster
(Centre for English Learning
and Teaching)
www.wmin.ac.uk/sshl/page-3635
Contact: patersk@westminster.ac.uk

University of York
(Department of Educational Studies)
www.york.ac.uk/depts/educ
Contact: educ15@york.ac.uk

York St John University
(Languages and Linguistics)
http://w3.yorksj.ac.uk/Default.aspx
Contact: linglang@yorksj.ac.uk